D1604151

COMPUTATIONAL GEOMETRY—
Curve and Surface Modeling

COMPUTATIONAL GEOMETRY— Curve and Surface Modeling

Su Bu-qing
Liu Ding-yuan

Fudan University
Shanghai
China

Translated by
Chang Geng-zhe
University of Science and Technology of China
He Fei Province
China

ACADEMIC PRESS, INC.

Harcourt Brace Jovanovich, Publishers

Boston San Diego New York
Berkeley London Sydney
Tokyo Toronto

Copyright © 1989 by Academic Press, Inc. and
Shanghai Scientific and Technical Publishers.

All rights reserved.
No part of this publication may be reproduced or
transmitted in any form or by any means, electronic
or mechanical, including photocopy, recording, or
any information storage and retrieval system, without
permission in writing from the publisher.

ACADEMIC PRESS, INC.
1250 Sixth Avenue, San Diego, CA 92101

United Kingdom Edition published by
ACADEMIC PRESS INC. (LONDON) LTD.
24–28 Oval Road, London NW1 7DX

Library of Congress Cataloging-in-Publication Data

Su, Pu-ch'ing, Date—
Computational geometry—curve and surface
modeling.

Translation of: Chi suan chi ho.
Bibliography: p.
Includes index.
1. Geometry—Data processing.
I. Liu, Ting-yüan.
II. Title.
QA447.S813 1989 516 88-3465
ISBN 0-12-675610-4

Alkaline paper

Printed in the United States of America
89 90 91 92 9 8 7 6 5 4 3 2 1

Contents

Preface to the English Edition

CAD/CAM (Computer Aided Design and Manufacture) and computer graphics have undergone rapid and striking development in the last 20 years. Geometric modeling is one of the most important basic tools in these fields.

According to the definition given by Forrest, computational geometry is concerned with computer-based representation, analysis and synthesis of shape information. This subject is also called Computer Aided Geometric Design (CAGD) by many other authors. The study of free-form curve and surface modeling is the main aspect in geometric modeling.

Basic theories, geometric properties, and numerical algorithms of curves and surfaces widely used in CAGD, as well as their applications to CAD/CAM are presented in this book from a geometric point of view.

The authors discovered the geometric properties of parametric polynomial curves by using the theory of affine invariants for algebraic curves. Among other things, we would particularly like to mention the affine classification according to the number of inflection points and singularities of planar cubic Bézier curves.

Besides an introduction to the fundamental methods of curve and surface modeling in CAGD, including parametric splines, Coons patches, Bézier and B-spline techniques, our own practical experience in developing CAD/CAM systems at ship building factories in Shanghai has also been involved in this book. Such an experience stimulated the authors to study the fairness of curves and networks, and nonlinear spline curves, and to prove the equivalence of a certain class of spline curves. All these results have been applied to CAD techniques in car, ship, plane and mechanical industries, as well as architecture in China.

It is desirable that readers of this book have a good background in analytical geometry, calculus and linear algebra.

The Chinese version of the present book was finished in 1979. Since then CAGD has been greatly improved. New results are so tremendous that there is quite enough for another book. Approximately 170 papers published after 1979—considered among the most important results in this field—have been added to this edition's reference section.

The authors are glad to see the English version of this book published, allowing us an academic exchange with readers all over the world.

Sincere thanks go to Professor Chang Geng-zhe for his translation. We are also indebted to the editors at Academic Press and Shanghai Scientific and Technical Publishers for their efforts in the preparation of the English edition.

Su Bu-qing
Liu Ding-yuan

Institute of Mathematics
Fudan University
Shanghai, China

CHAPTER I

Introduction

1 What Is Computational Geometry?

Problems of geometric designs often arise in the ship-building, aircraft and car industries. For instance, when the fitting and fairing of a ship form are to be designed, the designer must draw a curve to fit approximately several points given in a plane. In the car industry, a clay model is made by hand, and the surface of the model is divided into patches whose boundaries, forming a network of curves, should then be designed. The term computational geometry was initially used by Minsky and Papert (1969) as a substitute for model recognition. A formal definition for the term was given by Forrest in 1971 as "computer-based representation, analysis, synthesis (design) and computer-controlled manufacture of two- and three-dimensional shapes." By geometric information we mean data points or characteristic polygons that determine certain geometric objects, such as curves on a plane or surfaces in space. In mathematical lofting for ship bodies, derivatives specified at the end-points of the spline curve represent information for the curve. By representation we mean to form the mathematical model (e.g., the equation of the curve) and then to find adequate information about the curve (e.g., to evaluate the points on the curve) by using computers, based on the mathematical model. To investigate whether or not there are loops, cusps or unwanted inflection-points on the curve is referred to as analysis and synthesis. Computational geometry is concerned with all these aspects. Consequently it is closely related to

"Computer Aided Geometric Design." Computational geometry is a flowering discipline formulated from approximation theory of functions, differential geometry, algebraic geometry, computational mathematics and especially numerical control.

2 Fitting and Fairing in Curves and Surfaces

The objects studied in computational geometry are curves and surfaces. In geometric design, a surface is generally divided into several patches such that each boundary shared by two adjacent patches is a plane curve and such that the projection of four boundaries of each patch into the xy-plane forms a rectangle. Hence, except for the study of smooth matching of patches along common boundaries and around corners, the fundamental objects of our research are the fitting and fairing of plane curves.

Techniques of interpolation and approximation are frequently applied to curves and surfaces. Suppose that a set of data points is given in a Cartesian coordinate system of the xy-plane. Interpolation requires that we find the equation of a curve passing exactly through each data point. The equation enables us to compute points other than data points on the curve. There is another way to solve the problem: Draw a curve which need not pass through each data point exactly but should make the sum of the squares of the differences between the ordinates of each data point and the corresponding point on the curve as small as possible. This is known as least-square approximation. Of course, there are other methods of approximation.

Properties of geometric shapes are different from those of functions, and ordinary techniques for interpolation and approximation of functions may not be suitable for geometric shapes. For instance, shape is independent of choice of coordinate system, i.e., in whatever coordinate system we choose, the geometric shape (such as bend, singularities, inflection points, etc. of a curve) always remains unchanged. However the function which represents the curve, $y=f(x)$ in the xy-plane, does depend on the coordinate system. Equations of the same curve or surface vary with coordinate systems. Moreover, some technique of approximation may not be good enough for computation of the ordinate y of a point on the curve in a chosen coordinate system. The desirable technique for fitting and approximation is to use a simple function, such as a polynomial in x of degree n, instead of the general one. A curve C_n is then plotted by a pen plotter. This is the geometric shape we want. Sometimes, a special shape is given, say a circular arc. In this case convenient techniques for fitting may be used. In general, a fitting or approximation with certain tolerance, which takes over basic properties of the curve or surface and is fair or smooth, is acceptable. "Smoothness" of a curve refers to the continuity of direction of its tangent, more precisely to the continuity of its curvature, while "fairness" indicates that the curve should not have too many inflection points.

Analysis and synthesis of fitting and fairing curves with small deflection will be done at first as follows. By "curve with small deflection" we mean that the curve has at each point a slope (i.e., the tangent of the angle formed by the x-axis and the tangent line of the curve) whose absolute value is less than 1. In this case, the radius of curvature $R(x)$ of the curve $y=f(x)$ at the point (x, y) can be replaced approximately by $1/y''(x)$. This fact is the foundation of the theory of spline functions. For many years, long thin strips of wood or plastic much like the French curve (and called splines) have been used by designers to fair in a smooth curve between specificed points. By attaching lead weights, called "ducks," at points along the spline, the spline can be made to pass through the specified points. If we regard the designer's spline as a thin beam, then the Bernoulli–Euler law

$$M(x)=EI\left[\frac{1}{R(x)}\right]$$

is satisfied. Here $M(x)$ is the bending moment; E is Young's modulus; I is the geometric moment of inertia, and $R(x)$ is the radius of curvature of the elastica (i.e., the curve assumed by the deformed axis of the beam). For small deflection, we have

$$y''(x)=\left(\frac{1}{EI}\right)M(x).$$

Since the ducks act effectively as simple supports, the variation of $M(x)$ between duck positions is linear. Hence a cubic segment C_3 will be obtained between each pair of adjacent data points. Joining these n cubics in such a way that two adjacent segments have equal slope and curvature at junctions where two segments meet, a curve consisting of n cubics is obtained and called the cubic spline. This method is different from that of the least-square approximation; note that the cubic spline passes through each data point exactly.

3 Fitting and Fairing in Curves with Large Deflection

The technique described in the previous section is not suitable for curves with large deflection. If we use cubic splines to fit those curves, then we have to adopt a coordinate system for each curve segment. Hence a coordinate system has to be transformed into that of the next segment. It is very complicated to do so. In this case, so-called "simple" spline curves discussed in the last section should be replaced by the parametric spline curves. The equation for its segment is expressed by cubic polynomials in t:

$$\begin{aligned} x &= a_0 + a_1 t + \frac{1}{2!} a_2 t^2 + \frac{1}{3!} a_3 t^3, \\ y &= b_0 + b_1 t + \frac{1}{2!} b_2 t^2 + \frac{1}{3!} b_3 t^3, \end{aligned} \qquad (E_3)$$

where, without loss of generality, we assume that $0 \leqslant t \leqslant 1$. Otherwise the transformation of parameter will do the work:

$$t \to \frac{t - t_1}{t_2 - t_1},$$

in which t_1 and t_2 $(t_1 < t_2)$ are parametric values corresponding to the end-points of the segment.

It is easy to see that to determine coefficients a_i, b_i $(i = 0, 1, 2, 3)$ it suffices to know $x(0)$, $x'(0)$, $x(1)$, $x'(1)$ and the corresponding values of y. Incidentally, note that when the directions of the tangent lines have been specified at the end-points of curve (E_3), the following transformations,

$$\begin{aligned} &x'(0) \to \lambda x'(0), \\ &y'(0) \to \lambda y'(0), \end{aligned} \quad (\lambda > 0) \qquad \begin{aligned} &x'(1) \to \mu x'(1), \\ &y'(1) \to \mu y'(1), \end{aligned} \quad (\mu > 0) \qquad (T)$$

are permitted in choosing $x'(j)$ and $y'(j)$, $j = 0, 1$.

Parametric equations (E_3) represent a cubic algebraic curve, as it intersects the straight line $ax + by + c = 0$ at three points (including imaginary points). It is characterized by the fact that the curve has a singularity (a loop or a cusp). We should check whether or not the singularity occurs on the curve segment in which we are interested. If it does, we have to adjust the parametric pair (λ, μ) in the transformation (T) until the loop or cusp does not occur for $0 \leqslant t \leqslant 1$. This process is equivalent to adjusting the magnitudes of the tangent vectors at the end-points. On the other hand, we should also examine whether or not inflection points occur on the curve segment. First, no restrictions are put on the parameter t in equation (E_3), i.e., we consider the whole curve rather than any segment. We then examine each segment of the interpolatory curve. In fact, the equation for inflection points on the curve is

$$pt^2 - 2qt + 2r = 0,$$

where $(p, q, r) = (a_1, a_2, a_3) \times (b_1, b_2, b_3)$.

Obviously the equation is invariant under affine transformations. However, p, q and r are not invariants under the linear transformation of parameter t,

$$t = c\bar{t} + f \qquad (c \neq 0).$$

If $p = 0$, then the curve (E_3) becomes a "simple" spline curve. Under the assumption $p \neq 0$, it follows that the quantity

$$I = \left(\frac{q}{p}\right)^2 - 2\frac{r}{p}$$

is a relative invariant of weight (-2). Its importance is indicated by the following facts:

1. If $I > 0$, then (E_3) has two real inflection-points.
2. If $I = 0$, then there is a cusp on (E_3).
3. If $I < 0$, then there is a loop on (E_3).

Let us consider the first case, in which $I > 0$. There are two real inflection points on the whole curve. However, they do not necessarily occur on the segment we discussed. There will be two possibilities. First, if the curvature of the curve has opposite signs at the end-points, then an inflection point will inevitably occur on the segment. Secondly, if the curvature of the curve has the same sign at the end-points and p, q and r satisfy certain conditions, two real inflection-points will appear in the segment. These inflection points are called "unwanted."

For the purpose of fairness, we have to find an interpolation which can eliminate the unwanted inflection points. We can do this by changing the magnitudes of the tangent vectors at the end-points while keeping their directions fixed. We shall show that in the first quadrant of the $\lambda\mu$-plane, there exists a rectangular region R called the *normal region*, such that if $(\lambda, \mu) \in R$ then the corresponding parametric cubic segment contains neither unwanted inflection points nor cusps nor loops.

4 The Bézier Curve and Its Extensions

Theories of curve and surface synthesis developed by Coons, Hosaka and others have been applied in practice. But it is very complicated to specify all conditions for connection in synthesis. In 1968 Bézier worked out a technique in which the whole curve or surface is represented by a single formula, which is very convenient for shape control.

Let $\boldsymbol{P}_0, \boldsymbol{P}_1, \ldots, \boldsymbol{P}_n$ be $n+1$ ordered points in the space and consider the (open) polygon $\boldsymbol{P}_0\boldsymbol{P}_1 \cdots \boldsymbol{P}_n$ formed by joining successive points, which is called the *characteristic polygon.* The Bézier curve is a curve tangential at its end-points to the first and last side of the polygonal line and represented by a sum of weighted vectors of the vertices of the polygon. It is known that the Bézier curve is the Bernstein approximation

$$B_n(\boldsymbol{P}_0, \boldsymbol{P}_1, \ldots, \boldsymbol{P}_n) = \sum_{v=0}^{n} \boldsymbol{P}_v \phi_v(s), \qquad 0 \leqslant s \leqslant 1,$$

in which

$$\phi_v(s) = \binom{n}{v} s^v (1-s)^{n-v}, \qquad v = 0, 1, \ldots, n,$$

are, for fixed s, the discrete binomial probability density functions for a fixed probability. The Bézier curve is a weighted mean of sample points $\boldsymbol{P}_0, \boldsymbol{P}_1, \ldots, \boldsymbol{P}_n$, with weights $\phi_v(s)$.

An elegant technique has been developed by Bézier at Regie Renault, a car company in France. Data from a small clay model, or a hand-sketched curve, is plotted, full size, on a drafting machine. The stylist estimates graphically the parameters of an approximating curve which is then drawn by the machine. Three-dimensional curves are approximated in two plane projections. An acceptable approximation is usually achieved in a few iterations by adjusting the curve parameters.

Generalizations of the Bézier curve, i.e., interactive interpolation and approximation by Bézier polynomials, have been obtained by Forrest (1972) and Gordon and Riesenfeld (1974). Hosaka and Korota (1976) improved Bézier curves by using a piecewise approximation method and showed the connections between the Bézier curve and B-splines.

5 Bicubic Spline Functions and Their Applications to Surface Fairing

Surface patches are widely used nowadays in computer aided geometric design for surface descriptions. A surface patch generally has four boundaries, which are defined by piecewise parametric equations of the parameter u or w. The four points at which the boundaries meet are called *corners* of the patch. The patch is generated by blending shapes of the boundaries with suitable "blending functions." A surface is formed by different patches, and adjacent patches have a certain continuity along their common boundary. The theory of patches and blending functions was first developed by S. A. Coons (1964, 1967) who observed that the so-called bicubic patches, defined in terms of four blending functions, are adequate for practical surface descriptions.

The first successful extension of cubic splines in one variable to bicubic spline functions is due to Carl deBoor (1962). Bicubic splines are defined on rectangular grids of a rectangular domain. Bicubic spline functions were applied later by J. G. Hayes and J. Halliday (1974) to the fitting of arbitrary data.

It is necessary to specify boundary conditions if we use bicubic spline functions for practical surface fitting. In 1977, Xin Yuanlong developed an algorithm in which boundary conditions are replaced by fairness conditions. A scheme for surface fairing was also presented by him. Such schemes have been successfully applied to mathematical lofting of ship bodies.

6 Intrinsic Affine Invariants of Parametric Curves in Affine Hyperspace

We noted in Section 3 that the important affine invariant I of a cubic-parametric curve enables us to determine whether or not there are real inflection-points or singularities on the curve. In 1977, Su Buchin generalized the result to quintic parametric curves. In general, the plane parametric curve of degree n is expressed by

$$x=\sum_{i=0}^{n}\frac{1}{i!}a_it^i,\qquad y=\sum_{i=0}^{n}\frac{1}{i!}b_it^i. \tag{E_n}$$

From the fact that it intersects a straight line $\lambda x+\mu y+v=0$ usually in n points, we conclude that the curve is an algebraic curve C_n of degree n. Its genus,

$$p=\tfrac{1}{2}(n-1)(n-2)-d-r,$$

is equal to zero, where d and r denote the number of loops and cusps on C_n, respectively. Generally, C_n has $2(n-2)$ inflection points (including imaginary ones).

Set

$$p_{i,j}=a_ib_j-a_jb_i \qquad (i<j;\ i,j=1,2,\ldots,n).$$

When $n = 5$, the quintic algebraic curve C_5 represented by the equation (E_5) has six inflection points and six singularities. This is not good for fairness of the curve. To reduce the number of inflection points to the minimum and to ensure that the curve does not become a simple quintic curve, we assume that

$$p_{35} = 0, \qquad p_{45} = 0, \qquad p_{25} \neq 0.$$

Under these assumptions, three relative[1] affine invariants a, b and g have been found. If $a \neq 0$, we have two intrinsic[1] affine invariants $b/(a)^2$ and $g/(a)^4$. The number of real singularities has been computed according to the following eight cases: $g \leqslant 0, b \gtreqqless 0$; $g > 0, b > 2\sqrt{g}$ and $g > 0, b < -2\sqrt{g}$.

The result can be extended to the plane parametric curve of degree n satisfying h conditions,

$$p_{r,n} = 0 \qquad (r = n - h, n - h + 1, \ldots, n - 1),$$

$$p_{n-h-1,n} \neq 0,$$

in which $0 \leqslant h \leqslant n - 3$. We obtain $2n - h - 4$ or $2n - 5$ relative affine invariants for $n > 3$, $h > 0$ and $n \geqslant 3$, $h = 0$ respectively.

In higher-dimensional affines spaces, more general results have been obtained by Su Buchin and Xin Yuanlong in 1980: a parametric curve of degree n in m-dimensional affine spaces, with $n > m > 2$, usually has $m(n - m) - 2$ intrinsic affine invariants.

[1] See Chapter 8 for a definition and discussion of the terms "relative" and intrinsic."

CHAPTER II

Spline Functions

1 Cubic Spline Functions

Developments in the theory and application of spline functions began with cubic spline functions, which have been studied in detail and have the earliest application to computational geometry. Reasons for this are the following:

(1) The cubic spline is the spline of the lowest degree with C^2 continuity, and C^2 continuity meets the needs of most problems arising from engineering and mathematical physics. Spline functions of lower degrees are numerically simple and stable.
(2) Since it is the linear approximation of the mathematical model of the draftman's spline, in the case of small deflection, the cubic spline is very close to the curve drawn by the material spline and satisfies the conventional requirement of fairness.
(3) Because of its strong convergence in the mathematical sense, it has been widely used in numerical solutions of differential and integral equations, as well as in numerical differentiation and integration.

Along with the development of computational geometry, geometric and nonlinear splines have flourished both in theory and practice. Nevertheless, cubic spline functions still remain a fundamental and introductory tool.

Curves that are often used in computational geometry, such as parametric cubic spline curves, cubic B-spline curves, spline curves in tension and geometric spline curves, etc., could be regarded as certain varieties of the cubic spline functions.

The problem of interpolation, often arises in engineering and mathematics. Given a set of ordered and discrete points in the plane, a smooth curve is going to be drawn which passes through all these points. For many years, long thin elastic strips of wood or some other material have been used by draftsmen to form a smooth curve passing through these specified points. These strips or splines are anchored in place by attaching lead weights called "ducks" at points along the spline.

If we regard the draftsman's spline as a thin beam and the ducks as concentrated loads on the beam, the deformed curve of the beam satisfies the differential equation

$$EIk(x) = M(x) \tag{1.1}$$

by the Bernoulli–Euler law of material mechanics, if the beam is placed on a certain Cartesian coordinate system. Here EI represents the coefficient of rigidity which is a constant for the uniform wooden spline. Since there is no outside force acting on the beam between any two adjacent ducks, the bending moment $M(x)$ is a linear function of x. The deformed curve $y = y(x)$ has the curvature $k(x) = y''/(1+y'^2)^{3/2}$. Being a nonlinear ordinary differential equation, the solution of (1.1) cannot be represented in terms of elementary functions. Its exact solution will be discussed in Chapter VI. In the case of the "small deflection" for the beam, i.e., $|y'| \ll 1$, y' is negligible and then (1.1) can be approximated by the linear equation $EIy'' = M(x)$, i.e., $y^{(4)} = 0$. We see that the deformed curve $y = y(x)$ is a piecewise cubic which is continuous and has both a continuous first derivative and a continuous second derivative at each duck. Normally, however, there is a jump discontinuity in its third derivative at the ducks. This is the mechanical background of the cubic spline. Now we are ready to study and represent the cubic spline mathematically.

1.1 Interpolatory Cubic Spline Functions

Definition 1 In an interval $[a, b]$, a partition

$$\Delta: a = x_0 < x_1 < x_1 < \cdots < x_n = b$$

is given. A function $s(x)$ is called a cubic spline function if the following conditions are satisfied:

(1) $s(x)$ is cubic in each subinterval $[x_{i-1}, x_i]$, $(i = 1, 2, \ldots, n)$;

(2) $s(x)$ is continuous together with its first and second derivatives on $[a, b]$, i.e.,

$$s^{(k)}(x_i-0)=s^{(k)}(x_i+0), \qquad k=0,1,2; \qquad i=1,2,\ldots,n-1.$$

Each point x_i $(i=0,1,\ldots,n)$ is called a knot of $s(x)$.

In addition, if an associated set of ordered values y_i $(i=0,1,\ldots,n)$ is prescribed and $s(x)$ satisfies

(3) $s(x_i)=y_i$ $(i=0,1,\ldots,n)$,

$s(x)$ is said to be an interpolatory cubic spline function.

1° Representation and Continuity Equations

(1) Representation and M-continuity equations determined by values of the function and the second derivatives.

Denote

$$\begin{aligned} &s(x_i)=y_i, \qquad s'(x_i)=m_i, \\ &s''(x_i)=M_i \qquad (i=0,1,\ldots,n). \end{aligned} \tag{1.2}$$

Since the second derivative of $s(x)$ is linear in the subinterval $[x_{i-1}, x_i]$, we have

$$s''(x)=M_{i-1}\frac{x_i-x}{h_i}+M_i\frac{x-x_{i-1}}{h_i} \qquad (x_{i-1}\leqslant x\leqslant x_i), \tag{1.3}$$

where $h_i=x_i-x_{i-1}$ is the length of the subinterval. If we integrate twice and evaluate the constants of integration by (1.2), we obtain the equations

$$\begin{aligned} s'(x)=&-M_{i-1}\frac{(x_i-x)^2}{2h_i}+M_i\frac{(x-x_{i-1})^2}{2h_i}+\frac{y_i-y_{i-1}}{h_i} \\ &-\frac{h_i(M_i-M_{i-1})}{6} \qquad (x_{i-1}\leqslant x\leqslant x_i), \end{aligned} \tag{1.4}$$

$$\begin{aligned} s(x)=&M_{i-1}\frac{(x_i-x)^3}{6h_i}+M_i\frac{(x-x_{i-1})^3}{6h_i}+\left(\frac{y_{i-1}}{h_i}-\frac{h_iM_{i-1}}{6}\right)(x_i-x) \\ &+\left(\frac{y_i}{h_i}-\frac{h_iM_i}{6}\right)(x-x_{i-1}) \qquad (x_{i-1}\leqslant x\leqslant x_i). \end{aligned} \tag{1.5}$$

From (1.4), we have the expressions

$$\begin{aligned} s'(x_i-0)&=\frac{h_i}{6}M_{i-1}+\frac{h_i}{3}M_i+\frac{y_i-y_{i-1}}{h_i}, \\ s'(x_i+0)&=-\frac{h_{i+1}}{3}M_i-\frac{h_{i+1}}{6}M_{i+1}+\frac{y_{i+1}-y_i}{h_{i+1}}. \end{aligned} \tag{1.6}$$

The continuity of the first derivative at an internal knot, i.e., $s'(x_i - 0) = s'(x_i + 0)$, implies that

$$\mu_i M_{i-1} + 2M_i + \lambda_i M_{i+1} = d_i \qquad (i = 1, 2, \ldots, n-1), \tag{1.7}$$

where

$$\lambda_i = \frac{h_{i+1}}{h_i + h_{i+1}}, \qquad \mu_i = \frac{h_i}{h_i + h_{i+1}},$$

$$d_i = \frac{6}{h_i + h_{i+1}} \left(\frac{y_{i+1} - y_i}{h_{i+1}} - \frac{y_i - y_{i-1}}{h_i} \right) \qquad (i = 1, 2, \ldots, n-1). \tag{1.8}$$

Equations (1.7) are called the M-continuity equations of the interpolatory cubic spline function $s(x)$.

(2) Representation and m-continuity equations. By Hermite interpolation, $s(x)$ and its first and second derivatives can be written as

$$\begin{aligned} s(x) = {} & m_{i-1} \frac{(x_i - x)^2 (x - x_{i-1})}{h_i^2} - m_i \frac{(x - x_{i-2})^2 (x_i - x)}{h_i^2} \\ & + y_{i-1} \frac{(x_i - x)^2 [2(x - x_{i-1}) + h_i]}{h_i^3} \\ & + y_i \frac{(x - x_{i-1})^2 [2(x_i - x) + h_i]}{h_i^3}. \end{aligned} \tag{1.9}$$

$$\begin{aligned} s'(x) = {} & m_{i-1} \frac{(x_i - x)(2x_{i-1} + x_i - 3x)}{h_i^2} \\ & - m_i \frac{(x - x_{i-1})(2x_i + x_{i-1} - 3x)}{h_i^2} \\ & + 6 \frac{y_i - y_{i-1}}{h_i^3} (x_i - x)(x - x_{i-1}). \end{aligned} \tag{1.10}$$

$$\begin{aligned} s''(x) = {} & 2m_{i-1} \frac{3x - 2x_i - x_{i-1}}{h_i^2} + 2m_i \frac{3x - x_i - 2x_{i-1}}{h_i^2} \\ & + 6 \frac{y_i - y_{i-1}}{h_i^3} (x_i + x_{i-1} - 2x). \end{aligned} \tag{1.11}$$

For the one-sided limits of the second derivative at x_i, we have the equations

$$s''(x_i - 0) = \frac{2m_{i-1}}{h_i} + \frac{4m_i}{h_i} - 6 \frac{y_i - y_{i-1}}{h_i^2},$$

$$s''(x_i + 0) = -\frac{4m_i}{h_{i+1}} - \frac{2m_{i+1}}{h_{i+1}} + 6 \frac{y_{i+1} - y_i}{h_{i+1}^2}.$$

The continuity of the second derivatives at an internal knot, i.e., $s''(x_i-0)=s''(x_i+0)$, implies that

$$\lambda_i m_{i-1}+2m_i+\mu_i m_{i+1}=C_i \qquad (i=1,2,\ldots,n-1), \tag{1.12}$$

where λ_i and μ_i have been defined in (1.8) and

$$C_i=3\left(\lambda_i\frac{y_i-y_{i-1}}{h_i}+\mu_i\frac{y_{i+1}-y_i}{h_{i+1}}\right). \tag{1.13}$$

Equations (1.12) are called the m-continuity equations of the interpolatory cubic spline function $s(x)$.

2° End Conditions

The continuity equations, either (1.7) or (1.12), are $n-1$ linear and algebraic equations with $n+1$ unknowns. To find a unique solution, two additional equations are needed. In general, two conditions, the "end conditions," are specified at the end-points of the interval according to physical requirements. For instance, at the end-point $x=a$, the following end conditions may be specified:

I Specifying the slope $m_0=y_0'$. By the second equation of (1.6), we have

$$2M_0+M_1=\frac{6}{h_1}\left(\frac{y_1-y_0}{h_1}-y_0'\right). \tag{1.14}$$

II Specifying the second derivative $M_0=y_0''$. By (1.11) it is equivalent to

$$2m_0+m_1=3\frac{y_1-y_0}{h_1}-\frac{h_1}{2}y_0''. \tag{1.15}$$

In particular, $y_0''=0$ represents the simple support condition. In this case, the curvature of the spline curve at $x=a$ is zero. The interpolatory cubic spline is called the natural spline if it has zero curvature at both end points of $[a, b]$;

III Specifying the relationship

$$2M_0+\lambda_0 M_1=d_0, \tag{1.16}$$

where $0\leqslant\lambda_0\leqslant 1$ and d_0 is a suitable constant. Generally, if the first and the second derivatives at the end-point are not prescribed then (1.16) applies. For simplicity, we choose $\lambda_0=1$ and $d_0=d_1$. This is the analog of the draftsman's lofting process in which the wooden spline is extended outside the end-point and a duck is suitably put on it in order that the spline behaves fairly near the end-point. If we take $\lambda_0=-2$ and $d_0=0$, (1.16) becomes the "parabolic end condition."

For the m-continuity equations, we have the corresponding relationship

$$2m_0 + \mu_0 m_1 = C_0, \tag{1.17}$$

in which $0 \leq \mu_0 \leq 1$, and C_0 is a suitable constant. In general we can take $\mu_0 = 1$ and $C_0 = C_1$.

It is clear that the end conditions of type I and II can be incorporated respectively in (1.16) and (1.17) of type III.

Similarly, at the end point $x = b$, there are end conditions of three types that can be written as one equation

$$\mu_n M_{n-1} + 2M_n = d_n, \tag{1.18}$$

or

$$\lambda_n m_{n-1} + 2m_n = C_n. \tag{1.19}$$

Combining the two end conditions with the continuity equations, we obtain the complete continuity equations, which can be written in matrix form

$$\begin{bmatrix} 2 & \lambda_0 & & & & & & \\ \mu_1 & 2 & \lambda_1 & & & 0 & & \\ & \mu_2 & 2 & \lambda_2 & & & & \\ & & \ddots & \ddots & \ddots & & & \\ & & & \mu_{n-2} & 2 & \lambda_{n-2} & & \\ & 0 & & & \mu_{n-1} & 2 & \lambda_{n-1} \\ & & & & & \mu_n & 2 \end{bmatrix} \begin{bmatrix} M_0 \\ M_1 \\ M_2 \\ \vdots \\ M_{n-2} \\ M_{n-1} \\ M_n \end{bmatrix} = \begin{bmatrix} d_0 \\ d_1 \\ d_2 \\ \vdots \\ d_{n-2} \\ d_{n-1} \\ d_n \end{bmatrix} \tag{1.20}$$

or

$$\begin{bmatrix} 2 & \mu_0 & & & & & & \\ \lambda_1 & 2 & \mu_1 & & & 0 & & \\ & \lambda_2 & 2 & \mu_2 & & & & \\ & & \ddots & \ddots & \ddots & & & \\ & & & \lambda_{n-2} & 2 & \mu_{n-2} & & \\ & 0 & & & \lambda_{n-1} & 2 & \mu_{n-1} \\ & & & & & \lambda_n & 2 \end{bmatrix} \begin{bmatrix} m_0 \\ m_1 \\ m_2 \\ \vdots \\ m_{n-2} \\ m_{n-1} \\ m_n \end{bmatrix} = \begin{bmatrix} C_0 \\ C_1 \\ C_2 \\ \vdots \\ C_{n-2} \\ C_{n-1} \\ C_n \end{bmatrix}. \tag{1.21}$$

These coefficient matrices are tridiagonal.

So far nonperiodic end conditions have been discussed. When a closed curve is interpolated in terms of the polar coordinates, we must impose the following

IV Periodic end conditions

$$y_n = y_0, \qquad m_n = m_0, \qquad M_n = M_0. \tag{1.22}$$

In this case, the complete continuity equations have the matrix form

$$\begin{bmatrix} 2 & \lambda_1 & & & & & \mu_1 \\ \mu_2 & 2 & \lambda_2 & & 0 & & \\ & \mu_3 & 2 & \lambda_3 & & & \\ & & \ddots & \ddots & \ddots & & \\ & & & \mu_{n-2} & 2 & \lambda_{n-2} & \\ & 0 & & & \mu_{n-1} & 2 & \lambda_{n-1} \\ \lambda_n & & & & & \mu_n & 2 \end{bmatrix} \begin{bmatrix} M_1 \\ M_2 \\ M_3 \\ \vdots \\ M_{n-2} \\ M_{n-1} \\ M_n \end{bmatrix} = \begin{bmatrix} d_1 \\ d_2 \\ d_3 \\ \vdots \\ d_{n-2} \\ d_{n-1} \\ d_n \end{bmatrix} \tag{1.23}$$

or

$$\begin{bmatrix} 2 & \mu_1 & & & & & \lambda_1 \\ \lambda_2 & 2 & \mu_2 & & 0 & & \\ & \lambda_2 & 2 & \mu_3 & & & \\ & & \ddots & \ddots & \ddots & & \\ & & & \lambda_{n-2} & 2 & \mu_{n-2} & \\ & 0 & & & \lambda_{n-1} & 2 & \mu_{n-1} \\ \mu_n & & & & & \lambda_n & 2 \end{bmatrix} \begin{bmatrix} m_1 \\ m_2 \\ m_3 \\ \vdots \\ m_{n-2} \\ m_{n-1} \\ m_n \end{bmatrix} = \begin{bmatrix} C_1 \\ C_2 \\ C_3 \\ \vdots \\ C_{n-2} \\ C_{n-1} \\ C_n \end{bmatrix}, \tag{1.24}$$

in which

$$\lambda_n = \frac{h_1}{h_n + h_1}, \qquad \mu_n = \frac{h_n}{h_n + h_1}.$$

3° *Algorithm*

In order to evaluate the interpolatory cubic spline function $s(x)$, it is necessary to solve the complete continuity equations (1.20), (1.21), (1.23) and (1.24). In those tridiagonal matrices, we note that $|\lambda_i| + |\mu_i| = 1$ ($i = 1, 2, \ldots, n$) and $0 \leqslant \lambda_0, \mu_0, \lambda_n, \mu_n \leqslant 1$. Since the elements on the main diagonals of the matrices are equal to 2, all these matrices are diagonally dominant. Hence all these systems of equations have unique solutions.

Computing time and storage will be considerably reduced if we use the following algorithm to solve the above systems of equations. We take the M-continuity equation (1.20) for example to show the steps of the algorithm.

We introduce the quantities

$$\left.\begin{aligned} q_i &= \frac{-\lambda_i}{2 + \mu_i q_{i-1}}, \\ \mu_i &= \frac{d_i - \mu_i \mu_{i-1}}{2 + \mu_i q_{i-1}}, \end{aligned}\right\} \quad (i = 0, 1, \ldots, n)$$

and assume that $q_{-1}=u_{-1}=0$. By the recursive formula

$$M_n = u_n,$$
$$M_i = q_i M_{i+1} + u_i \qquad (i=n-1, n-2, \ldots, 1, 0),$$

M_n, $M_{n-1}, \ldots, M_0$, are successively evaluated.

The same algorithm applies to equation system (1.21). Systems (1.23) and (1.24) can be changed into the tridiagonal system by certain substitutions.

Incidentally, some authors are concerned with the "existence" of the interpolatory cubic spline functions. For the general end conditions, λ_0, μ_0, λ_n, μ_n may be greater than 2. Hence the coefficient matrix is no longer diagonally dominant, and the existence and uniqueness of the solution become indefinite. The condition under which the coefficient matrix is nonsingular is referred to as the "existence." A sufficient condition was given by Sun Jiachang (1978): if

$$\lambda_0 < 4\left(1+\frac{3h_2}{4h_1}\right), \qquad \mu_n < 4\left(1+\frac{3h_{n-1}}{4h_n}\right),$$

then the system (1.20) has a unique solution. A corresponding condition is available for the system (1.21). To our knowledge, in computational geometry, the cases in which λ_0 and μ_n assume large values probably do not occur. We shall see in Section 1.3 that the end conditions have influence only on a few pieces of the spline function near the end-points. The influence of the end conditions decays rapidly when the point moves away from the end-points.

We summarize the steps for evaluating interpolatory cubic spline functions as follows:

(1) Specify the end conditions according to practical requirements.
(2) Solve the equation system (1.20) or (1.21) by the algorithm we have mentioned to get the second derivative M_i or the first derivative m_i $(i=0, 1, \ldots, n)$.
(3) Substituting M_i or m_i back into the piecewise expressions of $s(x)$, (1.5) or (1.9), the value of the function $s(x)$ at any point $x \in [a, b]$ can be evaluated.

For computational convenience, we rewrite (1.5) and (1.9) in matrix form:

$$s(x) = [1 (x-x_{i-1}) (x-x_{i-1})^2 (x-x_{i-1})^3] \begin{bmatrix} \alpha_0 \\ \alpha_1 \\ \alpha_2 \\ \alpha_3 \end{bmatrix}_i \qquad (x_{i-1} \leq x \leq x_i)$$

$$(i=1, 2, \ldots, n),$$

where

$$\begin{bmatrix} \alpha_0 \\ \alpha_1 \\ \alpha_2 \\ \alpha_3 \end{bmatrix}_i = [A]_i \begin{bmatrix} y_{i-1} \\ y_i \\ m_{i-1} \\ m_i \end{bmatrix} = [B]_i \begin{bmatrix} y_{i-1} \\ y_i \\ M_{i-1} \\ M_i \end{bmatrix},$$

and

$$[A]_i = \begin{bmatrix} 1 & 0 & 0 & 0 \\ 0 & 0 & 1 & 0 \\ -\dfrac{3}{h_i^2} & \dfrac{3}{h_i^2} & -\dfrac{2}{h_i} & -\dfrac{1}{h_i} \\ \dfrac{2}{h_i^3} & -\dfrac{2}{h_i^3} & \dfrac{1}{h_i^2} & \dfrac{1}{h_i^2} \end{bmatrix}, \tag{1.25}$$

$$[B]_i = \begin{bmatrix} 1 & 0 & 0 & 0 \\ -\dfrac{1}{h_i} & \dfrac{1}{h_i} & -\dfrac{h_i}{3} & -\dfrac{h_i}{6} \\ 0 & 0 & \dfrac{1}{2} & 0 \\ 0 & 0 & -\dfrac{1}{6h_i} & \dfrac{1}{6h_i} \end{bmatrix}. \tag{1.26}$$

We shall see later that the bicubic spline functions and Coons patches have matrix expressions similar to that of $s(x)$.

In the next sections, we present several other expressions of general cubic spline functions and their three important mathematical properties.

For a fixed partition Δ: $a = x_0 < x_1 < \cdots < x_n = b$, the cubic spline function $s(x)$ is cubic on each subinterval $[x_{i-1}, x_i]$ $(1 = 1, 2, \ldots, n)$. Hence all such $s(x)$ form a linear space. By the condition (1) in Definition 1, $s(x)$ has $4n$ degrees of freedom. But by condition (2), there are $3(n-1)$ constraints, as $s(x)$ with both its first and second derivatives should be continuous at the internal knots x_i $(i = 1, 2, \ldots, n-1)$. Hence the resulting degree of freedom is $4_n - 3(n-1) = n+3$. We conclude that for the given partition Δ of $[a, b]$, cubic spline functions constitute a linear space of dimension $n+3$. The space has various bases, and the spline function has different representations with respect to different bases. The truncated power functions, cardinal spline and *B*-spline are three of the most important bases. Each of these bases and their uses will be discussed.

1.2 Truncated Power Functions

At the beginning of this chapter a mathematical model of the wooden spline with small deflection was observed. Segments of the deformed curve between two adjacent ducks satisfy the differential equation $d^4y/dx^4 = 0$. Now consider the whole wooden spline with concentrated load at each duck. Let x_i be the abscissa of ducks and b_i be the concentrated load $(i = 1, 2, \ldots, n-1)$. Hence the whole deformed curve satisfies the differential equation

$$\frac{d^4y}{dx^4} = \sum_{i=1}^{n-1} b_i \delta(x - x_i),$$

where $\delta(x)$ represents Dirac's delta function. By integrating four times, we obtain the solution

$$y = \sum_{i=0}^{3} a_i x^i + \sum_{i=1}^{n-1} \frac{b_i}{3!}(x - x_i)_+^3, \qquad x \in [a, b], \tag{1.27}$$

in which

$$x_+^3 = \begin{cases} x^3, & x \geq 0 \\ 0, & x < 0 \end{cases}$$

is called the truncated power function.

It is easy to see that $\{1, x, x^2, x^3, (x - x_1)_+^3, \ldots, (x - x_{n-1})_+^3\}$ constitutes a basis of the $(n+3)$-dimensional linear space of cubic spline functions.

Equation (1.27) is the expression of cubic spline functions in terms of truncated functions. It provides a unified analytical expression for the whole spline function, which may bring advantages for theoretical analysis. Around 1960, such expressions were used in mathematical lofting of ship bodies, but they were soon given up, since two serious problems had arisen:

(1) computation is unstable if x is far away from x_0;

(2) for interpolation purposes, the coefficients a_i and b_i in (1.27) should be determined by solving a system of linear algebraic equations. Since the matrix formed by the coefficients of the equations is highly ill-conditioned, the result of the computation will be far from the exact one.

1.3 Cubic Cardinal Splines

Motivated by the Lagrange formula for interpolation of algebraic polynomials, we can choose $n+3$ cubic spline functions $\phi_s(x)$ $(s = 0, 1, \ldots, n+2)$ which are linearly independent and are determined uniquely by the following interpolatory conditions:

$$\phi_i(x_j)=\delta_{ij} \qquad (i,j=0,1,\ldots,n),$$

$$\phi_i'(x_0)=\phi_i'(x_n)=0 \qquad (i=0,1,\ldots,n);$$

$$\phi_{n+1}(x_j)=0 \qquad (j=0,1,\ldots,n),$$

$$\phi'_{n+1}(x_0)=1,$$

$$\phi'_{n+1}(x_n)=0;$$

$$\phi_{n+2}(x_j)=0 \qquad (j=0,1,\ldots,n),$$

$$\phi'_{n+2}(x_0)=0,$$

$$\phi'_{n+2}(x_n)=1,$$

in which δ_{ij} is the Kronecker delta

$$\delta_{ij}=\begin{cases}1, & i=j,\\ 0, & i\neq j.\end{cases}$$

Thus, the solution of the interpolatory problem with end condition of type I could be expressed by

$$s(x)=\sum_{i=0}^{n} y_i\phi_i(x)+y_0'\phi_{n+1}(x)+y_n'\phi_{n+2}(x). \qquad (1.28)$$

Equation (1.28) is called the cardinal spline representation of cubic spline functions. For given interpolatory conditions, this is an explicit representation, while representations in Sections 1.1, 1.2 and the forthcoming Section 1.4 are implicit, as the coefficients of cubic spline functions have to be determined by solving systems of linear algebraic equations.

Cubic cardinal splines have been used by Fudan University and the Jiangnan Shipbuilding Factory in a program of mathematical lofting for ship bodies, and the results have been good. Cardinal splines also have many applications to numerical solutions of differential and integral equations.

To see what characteristics the cardinal spline functions have, we consider an infinite spline with equally spaced knots. In fact, the infinite spline does not exist, but it could be regarded as an approximation of a long spline with a great many knots that are almost uniformly spaced.

Let $\phi(x)$ be the spline defined on $(-\infty,+\infty)$, with all integers as its knots and satisfying interpolatory conditions

$$\phi(j)=\delta_{0j} \qquad (j=0,\pm1,\pm2,\ldots).$$

Assume that $\phi'(x)$ is bounded on the whole real axis. From the formulas in Section 1.1, we obtain

$$\phi(x)=\begin{cases}(3\lambda+2)x^3-3(\lambda+1)x^2+1, & 0\le x<1,\\ 3\lambda^j[(\lambda+1)(x-j)^3-(\lambda+2)(x-j)^2+(x-j)], & \\ j\le x<j+1 \quad (j=1,2,\dots), & \\ \phi(-x), & x<0,\end{cases}$$

where $\lambda=\sqrt{3}-2\approx-0.268$.

Note that $-1<\lambda<0$. Besides the fact that $\phi(x)$ equals 1 at $x=0$ and 0 at every nonzero integer, $\phi(x)$ has other properties:

(1) Two adjacent segments are opposite in sign.
(2) Each segment has only one extreme value, and the extreme value of the $(j+1)^{\text{th}}$ segment is equal to that of jth segment multiplied by λ.
(3) If m_j denotes the first derivative of $\phi(x)$ at the positive integer j, then $m_{j+1}=\lambda m_j$ for $j=1,2,\dots$.

By and large, the function $\phi(x)$ is an oscillatory function which decays as $x\to\infty$. The number λ is called the decay factor and is an important constant in the theory of spline functions. The function $\phi(x)$ is illustrated in Fig. 2-1.

The cardinal function $\phi_{n+1}(x)$ can be discussed in the positive axis $[0,+\infty)$ by the same methods, and properties of $\phi_{n+1}(x)$ similar to that of $\phi(x)$ will be obtained (cf. Fig. 2-2).

The function $\phi_{n+2}(x)$ is symmetric to $\phi_{n+1}(x)$.

Curves drawn by wooden splines with ducks attached to the data points of Fig. 2-1 and 2-2 coincide with that in the figures, respectively. The tests demonstrate that the cubic spline functions are satisfactory analogues of wooden splines in the case of small deflection.

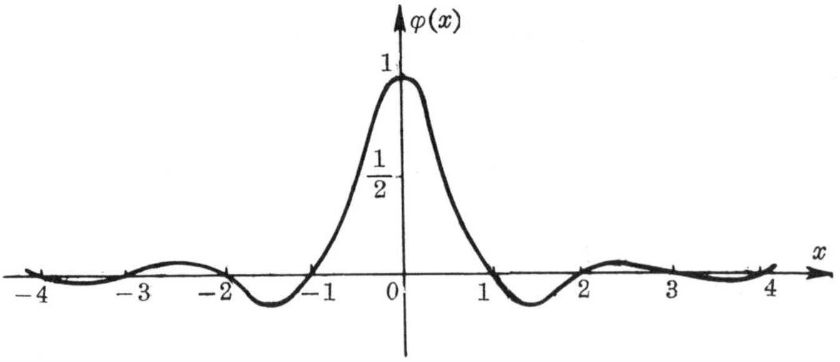

Figure 2-1

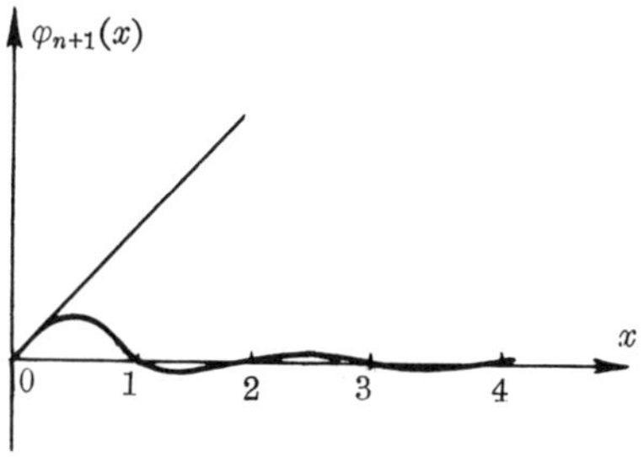

Figure 2-2

More detailed analysis shows that the cardinal spline functions of finite length with non-equally spaced knots are also decaying and oscillatory. If we change only the function value y_i at a knot i and keep other information fixed, the influence caused by the change to the $(i+j)^{\text{th}}$ segment of the cubic interpolatory spline function decays rapidly at speed λ^j. The same is true for the influence caused by a change of end conditions.

Rapid decay of error propagations and computational stability of cubic spline functions follow from the properties we just mentioned. Interpolatory algebraic polynomials of higher degree lack these merits. The analytic property of algebraic polynomials may cause considerable influence by a small alteration of function value at a certain knot, to the interpolant even in places far away from the knot. There is a price that must be paid for decayed error propagations: interpolatory cubic spline functions are of C^2-continuity only, rather than infinite smoothness.

1.4 *B*-Splines

B-splines of equispaced knots were used by I. J. Schoenberg in his first paper on spline functions in 1946. Since then, *B*-splines have been extended to general cases of non-equally spaced and multiple knots. At first, *B*-splines were introduced as a new method for smoothing statistical data, so it was natural to define them by Fourier transformations.

Unlike previous sections, we will not limit ourselves here to a discussion of cubic splines. For convenience, we define *B*-splines by central differences of the truncated power functions. The variable x varies on the whole real axis, and the distance between two adjacent knots equals 1.

Let x_+^k be the truncated power function of degree k. The central difference operator Δ is defined by

$$\Delta f(x) = f(x+\tfrac{1}{2}) - f(x-\tfrac{1}{2}),$$

$$\Delta^k f = \Delta(\Delta^{k-1} f).$$

Definition The B-spline function of degree k (order $k+1$) with equispaced knots is

$$M_k(x) = \frac{1}{k!}\Delta^{k+1}x_+^k. \tag{1.29}$$

It can be shown by induction that the analytic expression of the B-spline function of degree k is

$$M_k(x) = \frac{1}{k!}\sum_{j=0}^{k+1}(-1)^j C_{k+1}^j\left(x+\frac{k+1}{2}-j\right)_+^k, \tag{1.30}$$

and that the function $M_k(x)$ has the following properties:

(1) $M_k(x)$ and its first $k-1$ derivatives are continuous, but its kth derivative is discontinuous at

$$x = 0, \pm 1, \pm 2, \ldots \qquad \text{for odd } k;$$

$$x = \pm\tfrac{1}{2}, \pm\tfrac{3}{2}, \pm\tfrac{5}{2}, \ldots \qquad \text{for even } k;$$

(2) $M_k(x) = 0, \qquad x \bar{\in} \left(-\dfrac{k+1}{2}, \dfrac{k+1}{2}\right);$

(3) $M_k(x) > 0, \qquad x \in \left(-\dfrac{k+1}{2}, \dfrac{k+1}{2}\right);$

(4) $M_k(-x) = M_k(x);$

(5) $\displaystyle\int_{-\infty}^{+\infty} M_k(x)\,dx = 1;$

(6) $\sum_{i\in I} M_k(x-i) \equiv 1$, where I denotes the set of all integers.

The definition of the cubic spline functions discussed previously can be generalized to that of spline functions of degree k: for a given partition, it is a polynomial of degree k between two neighboring knots and is continuously differentiable $k-1$ times in its domain.

Let Φ_k be the linear space formed by all spline functions whose domain is the real axis $(-\infty, +\infty)$ with the knots $0, \pm 1, \pm 2, \ldots$ for odd k and $\pm\frac{1}{2}, \pm\frac{3}{2}, \pm\frac{5}{2}, \ldots$ for even k.

It can be shown that $\{M_k(x-i) \mid i \in I\}$ represents a basis for the linear space Φ_k, i.e., for any $s(x) \in \Phi_k$, there exists a unique sequence C_i $(i \in I)$

such that

$$s(x)=\sum_{i\in I} C_i M_k(x-i).$$

B-spline functions can also be defined in terms of the delta function. Note that

$$x_+^0=\int_{-\infty}^{x} \delta(t)\,dt$$

and

$$x_+^k=k\int_{-\infty}^{x} t_+^{k-1}\,dt.$$

Write

$$C\equiv\Delta\int_{-\infty}^{x}=\int_{x-1/2}^{x+1/2}.$$

Since the central difference and the integral operators are commutative, (1.29) can be rewritten in the compact form

$$M_k(x)=C^{k+1}\delta(x).$$

The operation $\int_{-\infty}^{x}$ in the operator C makes functions smoother, while the operator Δ is somewhat analogous to differentiation. Combining these two operations, $Cf(x)$ looks like $f(x)$ but should be smoother than $f(x)$. In approximation theory of functions, $Cf(x)$ is said to be the *Steklov function* of $f(x)$. C is also called the *smoothing operator* by some authors.

Properties (3) and (5) imply that the function $M_k(x)$ can be regarded as the distribution function of a probability density.

Properties (2) and (3) show that B-spline functions have finite local support. In its support, a B-spline consists of $k+1$ pieces of polynomials of degree k to reach C^{k-1} continuity.

The localness of B-spline curves (see Chapter IV), caused by the finite support property of B-spline functions, is of great importance in geometric design on an interactive computer graphics system.

The B-spline function is a very efficient tool of computation for the finite element method, as its property of finite support makes the width of the band formed by non-zero elements in the matrix of rigidity narrow. But when we use the cardinal splines described in Section 1.3 as basis functions, complicated computation will be caused by the matrix of rigidity, which is full of non-zero elements.

Explicit expressions for the B-spline functions $M_k(x)$ for $k=0, 1, 2, 3$, can be derived directly from the formula (1.30)

$$M_0(x)=\begin{cases}0 & (x>\frac{1}{2}),\\ \frac{1}{2} & (x=\frac{1}{2}),\\ 1 & (0\leqslant x<\frac{1}{2}),\\ M_0(-x) & (x<0).\end{cases}$$

$$M_1(x)=\begin{cases}0 & (x\geqslant 1),\\ 1-x & (0\leqslant x<1),\\ M_1(-x) & (x<0).\end{cases}$$

$$M_2(x)=\begin{cases}0 & (x\geqslant \frac{3}{2}),\\ \frac{1}{2}x^2-\frac{3}{2}x+\frac{9}{8} & (\frac{1}{2}\leqslant x<\frac{3}{2}),\\ -x^2+\frac{3}{4} & (0\leqslant x<\frac{1}{2}),\\ M_2(-x) & (x\leqslant 0).\end{cases}$$

$$M_3(x)=\begin{cases}0 & (x\geqslant 2),\\ -\frac{1}{6}x^3+x^2-2x+\frac{4}{3} & (1\leqslant x<2),\\ \frac{1}{2}x^3-x^2+\frac{2}{3} & (0\leqslant x<1),\\ M_3(-x) & (x<0).\end{cases}$$

They are illustrated in Fig. 2-3, from which we can see clearly the properties of B-spline functions mentioned above.

When the domain is a finite interval, say $[0, n]$, in which n is a positive integer, the B-spline functions still have the basis property. Take cubic B-splines as an example.

Let Φ_3 be the linear space consisting of all cubic spline functions defined on the interval $[0, n]$ with knots $x=0, 1, 2, \ldots, n$. We mentioned previously that $\dim \Phi_3 = n+3$. Thus the set of the following linearly independent B-spline functions

$$\{M_3(x-i);\ i=-1, 0, 1, 2, \ldots, n+1\}$$

represents a basis for Φ_3 (Fig. 2-4), i.e., for any $s(x)\in\Phi_3$, there exists a unique set of real numbers C_i $(i=-1, 0, 1, 2, \ldots, n+1)$ such that

$$s(x)=\sum_{i=-1}^{n+1} C_i M_3(x-i), \qquad x\in[0, n]. \tag{1.31}$$

Now apply the representation (1.31) to interpolation problems. Let function values at $n+1$ knots be given: $s(i)=y_i$ $(i=0, 1, \ldots, n)$. Note that

$$M_3(\pm 2)=0, \qquad M_3(\pm 1)=\tfrac{1}{6}, \qquad M_3(0)=\tfrac{2}{3}.$$

Putting $x=0, 1, \ldots, n$ into (1.31), the following $n+1$ equations,

$$C_{i-1}+4C_i+C_{i+1}=6y_i \qquad (i=0, 1, \ldots, n),$$

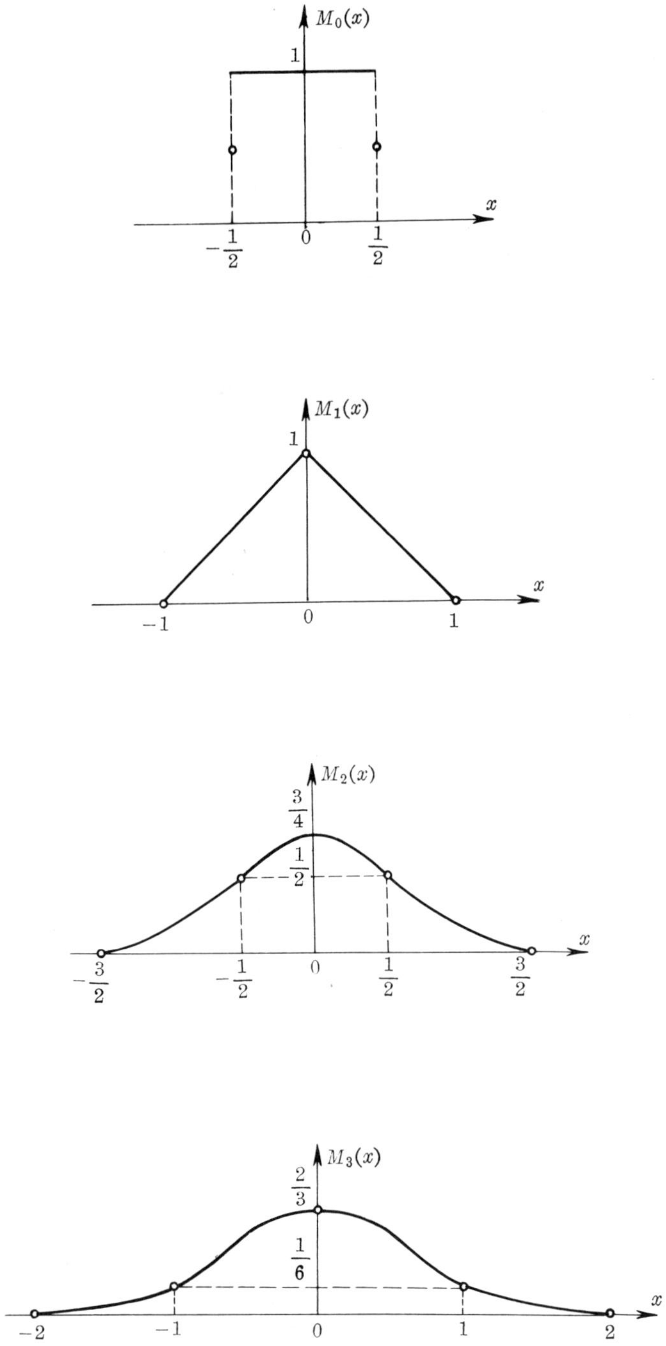
$M_0(x)$
1
x
$-\frac{1}{2}$
0
$\frac{1}{2}$
$M_1(x)$
1
x
-1
0
1
$M_2(x)$
$\frac{3}{4}$
$\frac{1}{2}$
x
$-\frac{3}{2}$
$-\frac{1}{2}$
0
$\frac{1}{2}$
$\frac{3}{2}$
$M_3(x)$
$\frac{2}{3}$
$\frac{1}{6}$
x
-2
-1
0
1
2

Figure 2-3

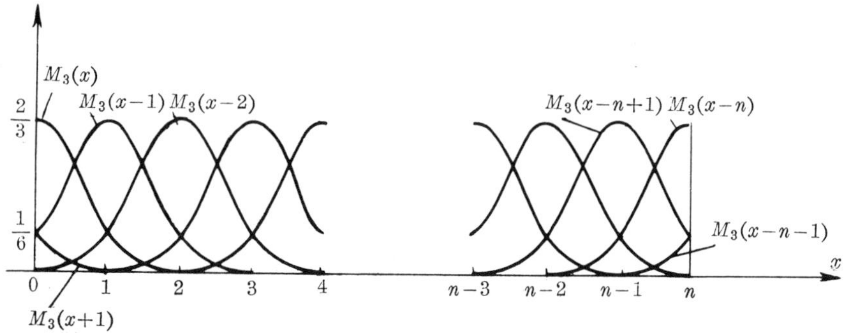

Figure 2-4

are obtained. Together with two additional equations formed by suitable end conditions, a complete system of $n+3$ linear algebraic equations enables us to find $n+3$ unknowns C_i, $i=-1, 0, 1, 2, \ldots, n+1$. This process is equivalent to solving the continuity equations (1.7) or (1.12). We still have to solve a system of equations with tridiagonal coefficient matrix, when B-spline functions are used as basis functions for spline interpolation.

The B-spline function, as a tool for the approximation of functions, enjoys the important variation diminishing property. This property means that the approximation scheme

(1) Approximates linear functions exactly.
(2) The number of intersections of the graph of the approximation with any straight line does not exceed the number of intersections of that straight line with the graph of the approximated function. This means that the approximation is always "smoother" than the function approximated.

By the property (2), we see that a convex approximated function yields a convex approximation. In brief, the variation diminishing approximation is convexity preserving. Since the local support and the variation diminishing property of B-spline functions are inherited by B-spline curves in computational geometry, a powerful role has been played by B-spline curves in geometric design.

1.5 Properties of Cubic Spline Functions

In this section, three of the most important properties of interpolatory cubic spline functions are presented. All these properties show that the interpolatory cubic spline functions have nice mathematical behavior which makes the cubic spline functions useful in many fields.

Theorem 1 (minimum norm property) *Let $f(x) \in C^2[a, b]$ and $s(x)$ be the natural cubic spline function interpolating to $f(x)$. Then we have*

$$\int_a^b [s''(x)]^2\,dx \leqslant \int_a^b [f''(x)]^2\,dx, \tag{1.32}$$

with equality holding iff $f(x) \equiv s(x)$.

Proof Consider the integral

$$\int_a^b [f''(x)-s''(x)]^2\,dx = \int_a^b [f''(x)]^2\,dx - \int_a^b [s''(x)]^2\,dx \\ -2\int_a^b [f''(x)-s''(x)]s''(x)\,dx. \tag{1.33}$$

Integrating by parts twice and using the interpolatory conditions, the last term in (1.33) becomes

$$\int_a^b [f''(x)-s''(x)]s''(x)\,dx = \sum_{i=1}^{n} \int_{x_{i-1}}^{x_i} [f''(x)-s''(x)]s''(x)\,dx$$

$$= \sum_{i=1}^{n} \left\{ [f'(x)-s'(x)]s''(x)\Big|_{x_{i-1}}^{x_i} - [f(x)-s(x)]s'''(x)\Big|_{x_{i-1}}^{x_i} + \int_{x_{i-1}}^{x_i} [f(x)-s(x)]s^{(4)}(x)\,dx \right\}$$

$$= [f'(x)-s'(x)]s''(x)\Big|_a^b = 0.$$

From (1.33), we see clearly that the equality of (1.32) holds iff $f''(x) \equiv s''(x)$, i.e., $f(x)-s(x)$ is a linear function. Note that $f(x)$ and $s(x)$ coincide at $n+1$ knots. Hence the linear function $f(x)-s(x)$ has $n+1 (\geqslant 2)$ zeros. Thus we have $f(x)=s(x)$ identically. This completes the proof.

The proof is still valid if the natural end conditions are replaced by the end conditions of type I. We see that the minimum norm property holds if $s(x)$ and $f(x)$ have the same slopes at the end-points.

The integration of the square of the second derivative in (1.32) equals approximately that of the square of the curvature of the curve with small deflection, i.e., the energy of the elastic beam of unit rigidity. Hence the minimum norm property is also called the minimum curvature property, which is equivalent to the minimum energy principle in mechanics. For the wooden spline with ducks attached to specified points, the equilibrium position assumes minimum energy. The position is represented by the natural interpolatory cubic spline. The fact revealed by Theorem 1 assures fairness and computational stability of the cubic spline function with small deflection.

Theorem 2 (best approximation property) *Let $f(x) \in C^2[a, b]$ and $s_f(x)$ be the cubic spline function interpolating to values and end slopes of f. Then for any cubic spline function $s(x)$ with respect the same partition of $s_f(x)$ we have*

$$\int_a^b [f''(x) - s_f''(x)]^2 \, dx \leq \int_a^b [f''(x) - s''(x)]^2 \, dx. \tag{1.34}$$

Proof. As before we consider the integral

$$\begin{aligned}\int_a^b [f''(x) - s''(x)]^2 \, dx &= \int_a^b [f''(x) - s_f''(x) + s_f''(x) - s''(x)]^2 \, dx \\ &= \int_a^b [f''(x) - s_f''(x)]^2 \, dx + \int_a^b [s_f''(x) - s''(x)]^2 \, dx \\ &\quad + 2\int_a^b [f''(x) - s_f''(x)][s_f''(x) - s''(x)] \, dx.\end{aligned}$$

Invoking the same technique as in the proof of Theorem 1, we can show that the last integration is zero. Then (1.34) follows immediately.

Theorem 3 (error estimate) *Let a function $f(x) \in C^4[a, b]$ and a partition Δ of $[a, b]$ be given. Let $s(x)$ be the cubic spline function interpolating to values of $f(x)$ and to its end derivatives of the first or second order. Then we have*

$$\|(f-s)^{(r)}\|_\infty \leq C_r \|f^{(4)}\|_\infty h^{4-r} \qquad (r = 0, 1, 2, 3),$$

where

$$C_0 = \tfrac{5}{384}, \qquad C_1 = \tfrac{1}{24}, \qquad C_2 = \tfrac{3}{8}, \qquad C_3 = \frac{\beta + \beta^{-1}}{2},$$

$$h = \max_i h_i, \qquad \beta = \frac{\max_i h_i}{\min_i h_i}.$$

Furthermore, the coefficients C_0 and C_1 are the best possible.

This theorem was established by C. A. Hall and W. W. Meyer in 1976. We do not have space for a detailed description of the proof. The theorem shows that the interpolatory cubic spline function $s(x)$, together with its first, second and third derivatives, converges uniformly to $f(x)$ and the corresponding derivatives as $h \to 0$. However, for convergence of the third derivatives, it is required that the ratio of maximum interval length to minimum interval length in the respective partitions is uniformly bounded.

2 Quadratic Spline Functions

Cubic spline functions and their variations are of special importance in computational geometry. The splines of higher degree are rarely used because there may be too many inflection points which may cause "unfairness" and their computations are rather complicated. However, spline functions of first degree—polygons formed by linking up each two adjacent data points with a line segment—are not in use either because they are not smooth enough.

Quadratic spline functions, consisting of piecewise parabolas and having continuous tangent at each junction, meet the needs when the requirement of smoothness is not strict. Also, they are advantageous for decreasing oscillations in the curves. It is very convenient to use them together with a pen plotter or a numerically controlled machine tool equipped with the function of parabolic interpolation.

The formulation and mathematical manipulation of interpolatory quadratic spline functions are similar to that of the interpolatory cubic spline functions. The only difference is the location of the junctions. For quadratic spline functions, the junctions are associated with the mid-points of each two adjacent knots. The same situation occurred in Section 1.4 where B-splines of even degree were discussed. The idea of interlacing junctions and interpolatory points is most likely motivated by B-splines of even degree.

Definition Let a partition of the interval $[a, b]$,

$$\Delta : a = x_0 < x_1 < \cdots < x_n = b,$$

and a set of real numbers y_i $(i = 1, 2, \ldots, n)$ be arbitrarily given. A function $s(x)$ is called an interpolatory quadratic spline function if the following conditions are satisfied:

(1) in each $[x_{i-1/2}, x_{i+1/2}]$, $s(x)$ is a quadratic, where $x_{i-1/2} = (x_{i-1} + x_i)/2$ $(i = 1, 2, \ldots, n)$, $x_{-1/2} \equiv x_0$ and $x_{n+1/2} \equiv x_n$ are said to be semi-knots,

(2) $s(x)$ has a continuous derivative of the first order in $[a, b]$, i.e., at each semi-knot $x_{i-1/2}$ $(i = 1, 2, \ldots, n)$, we have

$$s^{(k)}(x_{i-1/2} - 0) = s^{(k)}(x_{i-1/2} + 0), \qquad k = 0, 1; \tag{2.1}$$

(3) $s(x_i) = y_i$ $(i = 1, 2, \ldots, n)$.

We now establish the representation and the continuity equations in terms of $y_i = s(x_i)$, the first derivatives $m_i = s'(x_i)$ and the second derivatives $M_i = s(x_i)$ $(i = 1, 2, \ldots, n)$.

The ith quadratic function can be represented uniquely in the form

$$s(x) = y_i + m_i(x - x_i) + \tfrac{1}{2}M_i(x - x_i)^2 \qquad (i = 0, 1, \ldots, n),$$
$$x \in [x_{i-1/2}, x_{i+1/2}]. \tag{2.2}$$

Its derivative is

$$s'(x) = m_i + M_i(x - x_i). \tag{2.3}$$

The continuity conditions (2.1) can be written as

$$y_i - \tfrac{1}{2}m_i h_i + \tfrac{1}{8}M_i h_i^2 = y_{i-1} + \tfrac{1}{2}m_{i-1}h_i + \tfrac{1}{8}M_{i-1}h_i^2,$$
$$m_i - \tfrac{1}{2}M_i h_i = m_{i-1} + \tfrac{1}{2}M_{i-1}h_i \qquad (i = 1, 2, \ldots, n),$$

where $h_i = x_i - x_{i-1}$.

Solving for M_i from the above equations, we get

$$\left.\begin{aligned} M_{i-1} &= -\frac{4(y_i - y_{i-1})}{h_i^2} - \frac{3m_{i-1} + m_i}{h_i}, \\ M_i &= \frac{-4(y_i - y_{i-1})}{h_i^2} + \frac{3m_i + m_{i-1}}{h_i} \end{aligned}\right\} \quad (i = 1, 2, \ldots, n). \tag{2.4}$$

Comparing these two equations, we obtain the m-continuity equations

$$\lambda_i m_{i-1} + 3m_i + \mu_i m_{i+1} = C_i \qquad (i = 1, 2, \ldots, n-1), \tag{2.5}$$

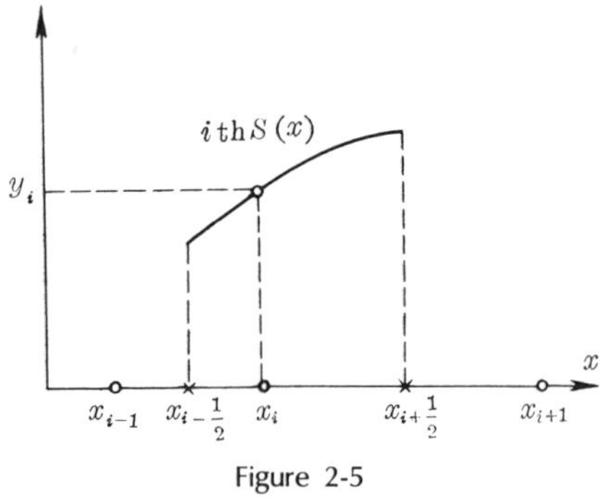

Figure 2-5

in which

$$\lambda_i = \frac{h_{i+1}}{h_i + h_{i+1}}, \qquad \mu_i = \frac{h_i}{h_i + h_{i+1}},$$

$$C_i = 4\left(\lambda_i \frac{y_i - y_{i-1}}{h_i} + \mu_i \frac{y_{i+1} - y_i}{h_{i+1}} \right).$$

The M-continuity equations can be obtained in a similar way:

$$\mu_i M_{i-1} + 3M_i + \lambda_i M_{i+1} = d_i \qquad (i = 1, 2, \ldots, n-1), \tag{2.6}$$

where

$$d_i = \frac{8}{h_i + h_{i+1}} \left(\frac{y_{i+1} - y_i}{h_{i+1}} - \frac{y_i - y_{i-1}}{h_i} \right).$$

Adding the end conditions of three types, a complete system of continuity equations will be formed. Since the coefficient matrix is strictly diagonally dominant, a solution of the system uniquely exists and can be found by the scheme mentioned in Section 1. A quadratic spline function has many properties similar to those of a cubic spline function, such as

(1) both have end conditions of three types;
(2) coefficient matrices of the continuity equations are all tridiagonal. In the quadratic case, elements on the main diagonal are three rather than two and the right-hand terms have been multiplied by a factor 4/3. In the next section, we will see that increasing the main diagonal elements brings a better convexity preserving property to the spline;
(3) for equally spaced knots, errors of interpolating data decay at the speed of λ^j, where

$$\lambda = -3 + 2\sqrt{2} \approx -0.172.$$

Why have the junctions for interpolating quadratic spline functions been chosen to be the points corresponding to the semi-knots? We give here some explanations. If the junctions are associated with the internal knots x_i $(i = 1, 2, \ldots, n-1)$, then a piece of the quadratic spline function is of the form

$$s(x) = a_i + b_i(x - x_i) + c_i(x - x_{i-1})(x - x_i),$$
$$x \in [x_{i-1}, x_i] \qquad (i = 1, 2, \ldots, n). \tag{2.7}$$

The interpolatory conditions

$$s(x_i) = y_i \qquad (i = 0, 1, \ldots, n)$$

and the one-sided end condition determine the spline function uniquely. In fact, the coefficients in (2.7) are

$$a_i = y_i, \qquad b_i = \frac{y_i - y_{i-1}}{h_i}. \tag{2.8}$$

Note that the first derivative should be continuous at each internal knot x_i, i.e., $s'(x_i - 0) = s'(x_i + 0)$ $(i = 1, 2, \ldots, n-1)$. Together with the end condition $s'(x_0) = y_0'$ it gives the recursive relations

$$c_{i+1} = -\frac{h_i}{h_{i+1}} c_i + \frac{1}{h_{i+1}}\left(\frac{y_{i+1} - y_i}{h_{i+1}} - \frac{y_i - y_{i-1}}{h_i}\right) \qquad (i = 1, 2, \ldots, n-1),$$
$$c_1 = \frac{\dfrac{y_1 - y_0}{h_1} - y_0'}{h_1}. \tag{2.9}$$

All coefficients a_i, b_i and c_i in (2.7) are determined uniquely by (2.8) and (2.9).

In the above scheme, only one end condition can be imposed. It is clear from (2.9) that the error in y_0', say $\Delta y_0'$, will be propagated to the last piece of the spline in equal oscillations, as will the error for the interpolated value y_i. Thus the advantage of decayed error propagation for spline functions has been lost. This is certainly not desirable.

We conclude this section with a numerical example. Knots $x_i = i$ and the data $y_i = 0$ $(i = 0, 1, \ldots, 5)$ are given in the interval $[0, 5]$. At first, we construct a quadratic spline function with end conditions $y_0' = 1$ and $y_5' = -1$ by the former scheme. The resulting function decays rapidly near the midpoint of the interval $[0, 5]$, as illustrated by the solid line in Fig. 2-6. If we impose the one-sided end condition and then construct the spline by the second scheme, solutions $a_i = b_i = 0$ and $C_i = (-1)^i$ $(i = 1, 2, \ldots, 5)$ are obtained from (2.8) and (2.9), respectively. An oscillatory parabolic spline with equal oscillations is shown by the dotted line in Fig. 2-6.

The above analysis also helps us to understand why the two end conditions for interpolatory cubic spline functions must be imposed on both sides rather than one side of the interval $[a, b]$. Suppose y_0' and y_0'' are given; this implies that m_0 and m_1 are known. By the m-continuity equations (1.12), $m_1, m_2, \ldots, m_n$ can be evaluated simply by the recursive formulas

$$m_{i+1} = \frac{1}{\mu_i}(c_i - \lambda_i m_{i-1} - 2m_i) \qquad (i = 1, 2, \ldots, n-1).$$

However, the scheme again causes equal oscillation in error propagation.

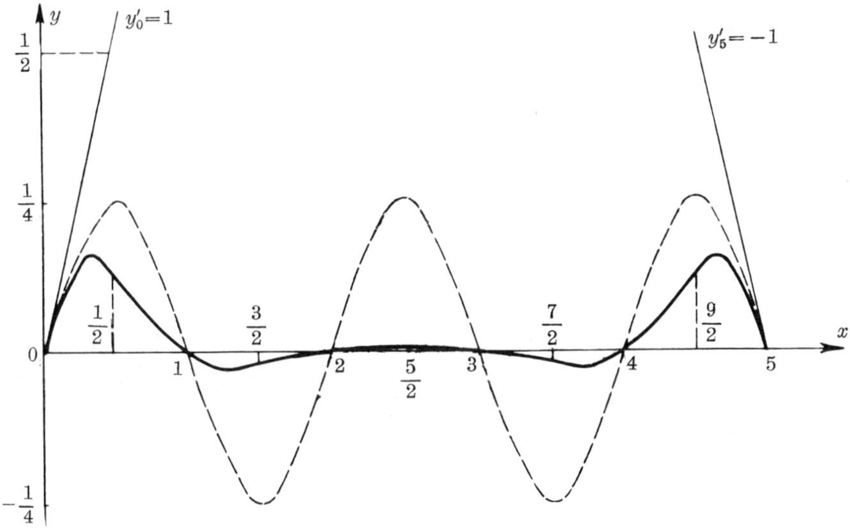

Figure 2-6

3 The Spline Function in Tension and the Convexity Preserving Property

In mathematical lofting and plane data fitting, interpolatory cubic spline functions are the most common and effective tools under the assumption of small deflection. But if the given data points are not fair enough, convex data points (i.e., points such that the polygon formed by joining adjacent data points with straight lines is convex) may produce unwanted inflection points on the corresponding interpolatory cubic spline, as illustrated in Fig. 2-7. The same situation occurs if we draw a curve passing through these data points with the help of a wooden spline.

It is desirable to have a convexity preserving interpolation technique that can avoid unwanted oscillations or inflections.

The spline function in tension, which has the convexity preserving property, was initiated by Schweikert in 1966 and was discussed later on

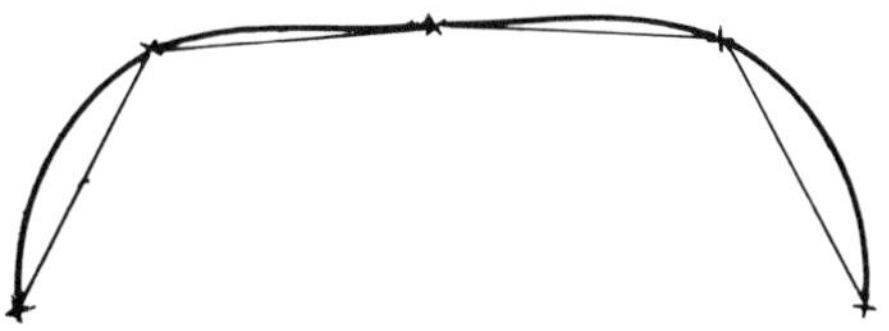

Figure 2-7

by many authors (Späth, [2] 1969, [3] 1971; Cline, 1974; Nielson, 1974; Pruess, 1976; Coons, [4] 1977). The theory is still in progress. The convexity preserving problem is related not only to geometric design but also to shape preserving interpolation in the approximation theory of functions (Passow and Roulier, 1977).

3.1 Mechanical Model and Continuity Equations

Suppose that a tunnel is dug along the axis of a common wooden spline and that a rubber band is then inserted into the tunnel and drawn tightly so that the wooden spline is in tension along the axis. The tightness is indicated by the tension parameter. We refer to the modified wooden spline as the spline in tension, which has the following equilibrium equation (see Fig. 2-8):

$$EI\frac{d^2k}{ds^2}\cdot ds = dN,$$

$$dN = \rho^* \, d\theta,$$

in which ρ^* represents the tension of the rubber band and EI is the rigidity of the wooden spline. We call $\rho = \sqrt{\rho^*/EI}$ the tension parameter. Note that the above equilibrium equation can be rewritten in terms of the curvature $k = d\theta/ds$ as

$$\frac{d^2k}{ds^2} - \rho^2 k = 0, \tag{3.1}$$

and its solution is a hyperbolic function of the arc length s:

$$k = C_0 \operatorname{ch} \rho s + C_1 \operatorname{sh} \rho s, \tag{3.2}$$

where C_0 and C_1 are two constants of integration.

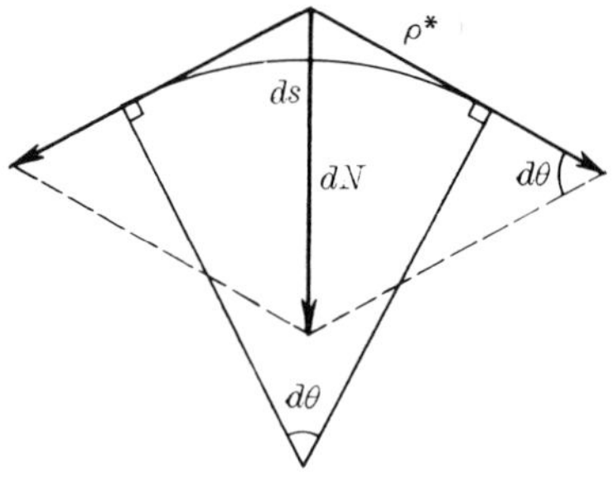

Figure 2-8

Suppose that a Cartesian coordinate system is chosen. Under the assumption of small deflection, we have the curvature $k \approx y''$ and the arc length $s \approx x$. Then the equilibrium equation (3.1) becomes approximately

$$\frac{d^4 y}{dx^4} - \rho^2 \frac{d^2 y}{dx^2} = 0, \tag{3.3}$$

whose solution is the sum of hyperbolic and linear functions. Generally the tension parameter ρ_i is different from one subinterval to another and thus (3.3) is a differential equation satisfied by the function restricted to two adjacent knots. The function $y(x)$ belongs to $C^2[a, b]$. From now on we use the notation $T(x)$ for the interpolatory spline function in tension on the interval $[a, b]$. Write

$$h_i = x_i - x_{i-1}, \qquad T''_i = T''(x_i), \qquad S_i = \operatorname{sh} \rho_i h_i, \qquad C_i = \operatorname{ch} \rho_i h_i.$$

The equation

$$\frac{d^4 T}{dx^4} - \rho_i^2 \frac{d^2 T}{dx^2} = 0, \qquad x \in [x_{i-1}, x_i] \; (i = 1, 2, \ldots, n)$$

has the interpolatory solution

$$\begin{aligned} T(x) = {} & \frac{1}{\rho_i^2 S_i} [T''_{i-1} \operatorname{sh} \rho_i (x_i - x) + T''_i \operatorname{sh} \rho_i (x - x_{i-1})] \\ & + \left(y_{i-1} - \frac{T''_{i-1}}{\rho_i^2} \right) \frac{x_i - x}{h_i} + \left(y_i - \frac{T''_i}{\rho_i^2} \right) \frac{x - x_{i-1}}{h_i}, \\ & x \in [x_{i-1}, x_i] \qquad (i = 1, 2, \ldots, n). \end{aligned} \tag{3.4}$$

Since $T(x) \in C^2[a, b]$, we obtain the continuity equations

$$e_i T''_{i-1} + (d_i + d_{i+1}) T''_i + e_{i+1} T''_{i+1} = F_i \qquad (i = 1, 2, \ldots, n-1). \tag{3.5}$$

in which

$$e_i = \frac{1}{\rho_i^2} \left(\frac{1}{h_i} - \frac{\rho_i}{S_i} \right), \qquad d_i = \frac{1}{\rho_i^2} \left(\frac{\rho_i C_i}{S_i} - \frac{1}{h_i} \right), \qquad F_i = \frac{y_{i+1} - y_i}{h_{i+1}} - \frac{y_i - y_{i-1}}{h_i}.$$

Using elementary calculus, we can easily show that the coefficients e_i and d_i have the following properties:

$$\begin{aligned} & e_i, d_i > 0, \qquad \lim_{\rho_i \to 0} e_i = \frac{h_i}{6}, \qquad \lim_{\rho_i \to 0} d_i = \frac{h_i}{3}, \\ & 0 < \frac{e_i}{d_i} \le \tfrac{1}{2}, \qquad \lim_{\rho_i \to +\infty} \frac{e_i}{d_i} = 0 \qquad (i = 1, 2, \ldots, n). \end{aligned} \tag{3.6}$$

There are mainly two types of end conditions:

(1) end slopes are given: $T'(a)=y'(a)$, $T'(b)=y'(b)$;
(2) end deflections are given: $T''(a)=y''(a)$, $T''(b)=y''(b)$.

End conditions of type I may be written in more detail as

$$\begin{aligned} d_1T''_0+e_1T''_1&=\frac{y_1-y_0}{h_1}-y'(a),\\ e_nT''_{n-1}+d_nT''_n&=y'(b)-\frac{y_n-y_{n-1}}{h_n}. \end{aligned} \tag{3.7}$$

Equations in (3.5) together with (3.7) constitute the complete system of continuity equations, whose coefficient matrix is also tridiagonal. It is clear from (3.6) that the matrix is diagonally dominant, so that the system of continuity equations has a unique solution. If $\rho_i=0$ then $e_i=h_i/6$ and $d_i=h_i/3$, thus equations in (3.5) reduce to the M-continuity equations of ordinary interpolatory cubic spline functions.

3.2 Conditions for Convexity Preserving

Rewrite the continuity equations (3.5) and the end conditions (3.7) of type I as

$$\beta_iT''_{i-1}+T''_i+\alpha_iT''_{i+1}=\bar{F}_i \qquad (i=0,1,\dots,n), \tag{3.8}$$

in which

$$\alpha_i=\frac{e_{i+1}}{d_i+d_{i+1}},\qquad \beta_i=\frac{e_i}{d_i+d_{i+1}},\qquad \bar{F}_i=\frac{F_i}{d_i+d_{i+1}}\qquad (i=1,2,\dots,n-1),$$

$$\alpha_0=\frac{e_1}{d_1},\qquad \beta_n=\frac{e_n}{d_n},\qquad F_0=\frac{y_1-y_0}{h_1}-y'(a),$$

$$F_n=y'(b)-\frac{y_n-y_{n-1}}{h_n},\qquad \bar{F}_0=\frac{F_0}{d_1},\qquad \bar{F}_n=\frac{F_n}{d_n}.$$

Hereafter an element with subscript -1 or $n+1$ is assumed equal to zero. Equations in (3.8) can be rewritten in matrix form as

$$(I+A)T=\bar{F}, \tag{3.9}$$

where I designates $(n+1)\times(n+1)$ identity matrix. T and $\bar{F}$ are both

$(n+1)$-dimensional column vectors formed by elements T_i'' and $\bar{F}_i$ $(i=0, 1, \ldots, n)$, respectively. The matrix

$$A=\begin{bmatrix} 0 & \alpha_0 & & & & \\ \beta_1 & 0 & \ddots & & & 0 \\ & \ddots & \ddots & & & \\ & & \beta_i & 0 & \alpha_i & \\ & & & \ddots & \ddots & \ddots \\ & 0 & & \ddots & 0 & \alpha_{n-1} \\ & & & & \beta_n & 0 \end{bmatrix} \geqslant 0;$$

nonnegativity of the matrix A follows from the fact α_i, $\beta_i > 0$. From (3.9) we get

$$T=(I-A^2)^{-1}[(I-A)\bar{F}], \tag{3.10}$$

in which

$$(I-A^2)^{-1}=\sum_{i=0}^{\infty} A^{2i} > 0.$$

Convergence of the matrix series is ensured by the fact $0<\alpha_i$, $\beta_i \leqslant \frac{1}{2}$.

If given data points are convex, then we can choose suitable tension parameters ρ_i $(i=1, 2, \ldots, n)$ such that the corresponding spline function in tension is convex.

Take the second derivative of $T(x)$ from (3.4)

$$T''(x)=\frac{1}{S_i}[T''_{i-1} \operatorname{sh} \rho_i(x_i - x) + T''_i \operatorname{sh} \rho_i(x - x_{i-1})], \qquad x_{i-1} \leqslant x \leqslant x_i.$$

Note that $S_i > 0$ and that $\operatorname{sh} \rho_i(x_i - x) \geqslant 0$, $\operatorname{sh} \rho_i(x - x_{i-1}) \geqslant 0$ for $x \in [x_{i-1}, x_i]$. Hence conditions for convexity preserving could be formulated as follows: for a given $(n+1)$-dimensional column vector F with positive components F_i $(i=0, 1, \ldots, n)$, tension parameters ρ_i $(i=1, 2, \ldots, n)$ can be suitably chosen such that $T>0$. Thus from (3.10) we get a sufficient condition for convexity preserving:

$$(I-A)\bar{F}>0,$$

that is

$$F_i > \alpha_{i-1}F_{i-1} + \beta_{i+1}F_{i+1} \qquad (i=0, 1, \ldots, n). \tag{3.11}$$

Therefore, the problem of finding tension parameters ρ_i for convexity preserving purposes is equivalent to solving the set (3.11) of nonlinear inequalities under the restrictions $\rho_i \geq 0$ $(i=1, 2, \ldots, n)$. Since $F_i > 0$ $(i = 0, 1, \ldots, n)$ and

$$\lim_{\rho_i \to \infty} \alpha_{i-1} = \lim_{\rho_i \to \infty} \beta_i = 0,$$

solutions do exist. A practical method for finding convexity preserving tension parameters is to use iteration and approximation techniques. For instance, set $\rho_i = 0$ $(i=1, 2, \ldots, n)$ as the initial approximation, and then check whether or not the set (3.11) of inequalities holds. If the ith inequality does not hold, then give a suitable increment to ρ_i and ρ_{i+1} until all inequalities in (3.11) hold.

For $\rho_i = 0$ $(i=1, 2, \ldots, n)$, $T(x)$ reduces to the ordinary interpolatory cubic spline function. In this case

$$e_i = \frac{h_i}{6}, \qquad d_i = \frac{h_i}{3}, \qquad \alpha_{i-1} = \tfrac{1}{2}\lambda_{i-1}, \qquad \beta_{i+1} = \tfrac{1}{2}\mu_{i+1},$$

and (3.11) becomes

$$2F_i > \lambda_{i-1}F_{i-1} + \mu_{i+1}F_{i+1} \qquad (i=0, 1, \ldots, n), \tag{3.12}$$

in which $\lambda_0 = \mu_n = 1$.

Set

$$F_i^* = \frac{F_i}{h_i + h_{i+1}},$$

which equals the second divided difference of the interpolated data y_i. Hence (3.12) can be written as

$$F_i^* > \tfrac{1}{2}(\mu_i F_{i-1}^* + \lambda_i F_{i+1}^*) \qquad (i=0, 1, \ldots, n). \tag{3.13}$$

This is a sufficient condition for convexity preserving of the interpolatory cubic spline function, which can be used as a criterion for fairing data points in mathematical lofting and in geometric design. To ensure that there are no inflection points on the curve, after suitably changing the direction of the axes of the coordinate system, the following two steps should be taken:

(1) rough fairing: adjust the data points so that $F_i^* > 0$, $i = 0, 1, 2, \ldots, n$;

(2) fine fairing: adjust the data points again to satisfy the inequalities in (3.12).

It is easy to see that the second step does not destroy the results gained by the first. It has been proved in practice that this method for fairing curves is simple and efficient.

The sufficient condition (3.13) for convexity preserving of interpolatory cubic spline functions is due to Wang Rishuang (1979). The results have been extended to splines in tension and to cases of large deflection by Liu Dingyuan ([2], 1979).

For interpolatory quadratic spline functions, note that elements on the main diagonal of the coefficient matrix of the continuity equations are all 3. It follows from this observation that a sufficient condition for convexity preserving is

$$F_i^* > \tfrac{1}{3}(\mu_i F_{i-1}^* + \lambda_i F_{i+1}^*) \qquad (i = 0, 1, \ldots, n). \tag{3.14}$$

For equally spaced knots, $\lambda_i = \mu_i = \frac{1}{2}$. In this case, we can see from (3.13) that the interpolatory cubic spline function has the convexity preserving property if the ratio of the two consecutive F_i^* does not exceed 2. For the interpolatory quadratic spline function the constant 2 could be replaced by 3. It means that the quadratic spline has a convexity preserving property better than that of the cubic. Its smoothness and continuity, however, are not as good as that of the cubic.

For some cases it is easier to estimate the first derivative m_i at the knot x_i $(i = 0, 1, \ldots, n)$. We wish to study the convexity of the spline function in terms of m_i. Take a piece of the spline function associated with the subinterval $[x_0, x_1]$. The function value, the first and the second derivatives at x_i, are denoted by y_i, m_i and M_i, respectively, for $i = 0, 1$. Set

$$h = x_1 - x_0,$$

$$Dy = \frac{y_1 - y_0}{x_1 - x_0}.$$

It follows from (1.15) and (1.14) that

$$M_0 = -\frac{2}{h}(2m_0 + m_1 - 3Dy),$$

$$M_1 = \frac{2}{h}(m_0 + 2m_1 - 3Dy).$$

There is no inflection point on this segment iff $M_0 \cdot M_1 > 0$, i.e.,

$$[2(m_0 - Dy) - (Dy - m_1)][(m_0 - Dy) - 2(Dy - m_1)] < 0,$$

or equivalently

$$\frac{1}{2} < \frac{m_0 - Dy}{Dy - m_1} < 2. \tag{3.15}$$

This is a necessary and sufficient condition for the convexity preserving of the interpolatory cubic spline functions.

For the interpolatory quadratic spline functions, it follows from (2.4) that the second derivatives and the divided difference satisfy the relationship

$$M_0 = \frac{1}{h}[4Dy - 3m_0 - m_1],$$

$$M_1 = \frac{-1}{h}[4Dy - m_0 - 3m_1].$$

Since inflection points can occur only at semi-knots, there is no inflection point on the spline curve iff $M_0 \cdot M_1 > 0$, or equivalently

$$\frac{1}{3} < \frac{m_0 - Dy}{Dy - m_1} < 3. \tag{3.16}$$

This is a necessary and sufficient condition for the convexity preserving of the interpolatory quadratic spline function.

Comparing (3.16) with (3.15), we see also that the interpolatory quadratic spline function has a convexity preserving property better than that of the cubic.

CHAPTER III

Parametric Cubic Spline Curves

1 Background and Developments

In Chapter II, we discussed cubic spline functions and pointed out that their mechanical background is the wooden spline with small deflection. Theoretical analysis and applications have shown that, in the case of small deflection, the curve represented by the interpolatory cubic spline function is satisfactory in the sense that the curve is very close to the one which is drawn by using a wooden spline.

Nevertheless, a large deflection curve, i.e., a curve $y = y(x)$ with $|y'| \gg 1$, may occur in practical problems. In this case, there exists a remarkable deviation between y'' and the curvature k of the curve, and thus the interpolatory cubic spline function is no longer a good approximation to the curve formed by the wooden spline. Let us consider the following numerical example.

Suppose we are given the data points

x	8.125	8.4	9	9.485	9.6	9.959	10.166	10.2
y	0.0774	0.099	0.28	0.6	0.708	1.2	1.8	2.177

and the end conditions of type I:

$$m_0 = 0.01087, \qquad m_7 = 100.$$

From the M-continuity equations (1.7) and (1.14) in the last chapter, the second derivatives y_i'' $(i=0, 1, 2, \ldots, 7)$ can be solved. The first derivative y_i' at each data point can be evaluated by (1.6). The curvature k_i of the interpolatory cubic spline curve at each data point is then computed for $i=0, 1, 2, \ldots, 7$. We have the following list:

y''	0.300	0.895	−0.517	5.637	−42.069	116.494	−519.809	8000
k	0.300	0.855	−0.459	0.923	−27.747	0.055	−0.021	0.008

The numerical result shows that the curvature varies in sign and has big jumps in magnitude. The resulting curve is not desirable as there are six points of inflection on it. Keeping the data points and the end tangent lines fixed and rotating the coordinate system $\{\boldsymbol{O}, x, y\}$ by 45° counter-clockwise about the origin $\boldsymbol{O}$, a new system $\{\boldsymbol{O}, \bar{x}, \bar{y}\}$ is obtained. It turns out $|\bar{y}'|<1$ in the new system. The second derivative and the curvature at each data point are shown by the following table.

$\bar{y}''$	1.344	0.863	0.562	0.443	0.489	0.522	0.819	1.299
$\bar{k}$	0.491	0.444	0.471	0.440	0.489	0.455	0.455	0.459

We can see clearly from the table that the curvature has an even change and the resulting curve is fair.

Two drawbacks of spline functions used in computational geometry have been shown by the above example:

(1) In the case of large deflection, the interpolatory cubic spline may lose fairness.

(2) The interpolatory curve represented by the cubic spline function is dependent on the choice of coordinate systems in which the data points and the end conditions are evaluated. In other words, the interpolatory curve is not geometrically invariant.

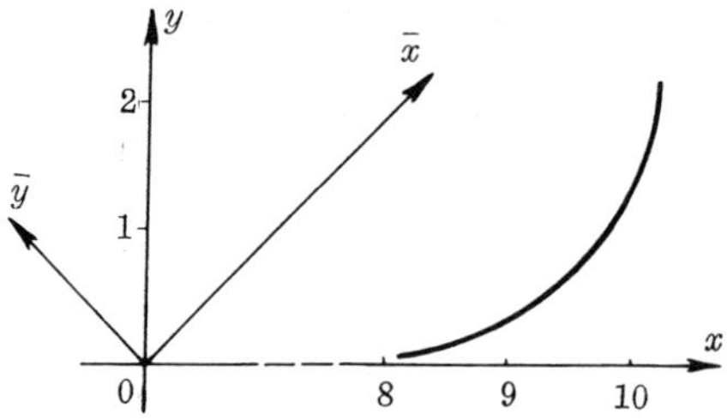

Figure 3-1

The first drawback may be remedied in some cases. In fact, our example has shown us a kind of remedy: suitably rotate the coordinate system in order to turn the "large deflection" into a small one. However, the method is applicable only to some curves. It does not work for a curve containing a semicircle; no matter how you rotate the coordinate system, you can not reach a system in which the curve would be of small deflection. Needless to say, the same observation holds for closed curves.

The second drawback is the essential one. In computational geometry, geometric figures are the objects to be studied. Once a coordinate system is established, geometric figures can be described in terms of functions. The approximation theory of functions, a sophisticated field in which spline functions play an important role, is expected to be useful. The deeper the investigation of geometric design goes, the more knowledge about geometric characters of figures is required. By the geometric characters we mean, for example, inflection-points and singularities on curves, convexity of surfaces and so on. As spline functions are not geometrically invariant, it is inconvenient to use them for the study of geometric properties of figures.

To solve these problems, the technique of parametric splines was proposed: Each component of a curve is represented by a spline function, and a combination of these three components forms a parametric spline curve.

Some properties of the curve can be discovered by studying the functional properties of each component independently, but deeper investigation of geometric characters of the curve cannot be done in such a way. It is harder to treat the curve as a whole. For example, it is difficult to discuss the curvature of the curve, as some nonlinear problems are involved.

In this book, parametric curves will be studied by the techniques of classical algebraic geometry. In order to control such curve segments, their affine invariants and the distributions of real singularities and inflection-points will be discussed.

Affine invariants and geometric properties of plane parametric cubic curves will be discussed in this chapter. Meanwhile, several kinds of spline curves formed by segments of parametric cubic curves will be constructed. Parametric splines of such forms are especially suitable for interpolations.

2 Parametric Cubic Curves and the Related Affine Invariants

Let

$$\begin{aligned} x &= a_0 + a_1 t + \tfrac{1}{2} a_2 t^2 + \tfrac{1}{6} a_3 t^3, \\ y &= b_0 + b_1 t + \tfrac{1}{2} b_2 t^2 + \tfrac{1}{6} b_3 t^3 \end{aligned} \tag{2.1}$$

be the parametric equations of a plane parametric cubic curve. In order to find the affine classifications characterized by the numbers of real singularities and inflection points, the affine invariants of (2.1) and their related properties will be considered (Sub Buchin [2], 1976) in great detail here and in the following sections. This is because the parametric curves are much more complicated than those represented by polynomials. For example, the parametric cubic curve

$$x = 5t - 11.5t^2 + 7.5t^3, \qquad (0 \geqslant t \geqslant 1)$$
$$y = 2t - t^2 - 0.67t^3$$

does not have an inflection point but has a singularity, while its x-coordinate has an inflection point (see Fig. 3-2). We cannot in general deduce the geometric characters of the parametric curve only from the properties of its individual components.

We point out at first that the parameter t in (2.1) cannot be taken as the arc length s of the parametric curve. In fact, write

$$\frac{dx}{dt} = x', \qquad \frac{d^2x}{dt^2} = x'',$$

etc. If $t = x$, from the identity

$$x'^2 + y'^2 \equiv 1$$

it follows that

$$x'x'' + y'y'' \equiv 0,$$

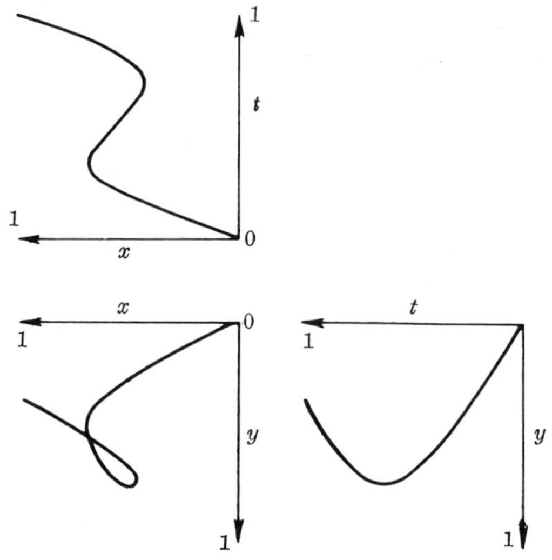

Figure 3-2

i.e.,

$$\tfrac{1}{2}(a_3^2+b_3^2)t^3+\tfrac{3}{2}(a_2a_3+b_2b_3)t^2+(a_2^2+b_2^2+a_1a_3+b_1b_3)t+(a_1a_2+b_1b_2)\equiv 0.$$

We obtain at once

$$a_3=0, \qquad b_3=0, \qquad a_2=0, \qquad b_2=0.$$

Hence the curve (2.1) degenerates into a straight line.

The parametric cubic curve (2.1) is called the cubic rational integral curve in the theory of algebraic curves. It has two inflection points (including imaginary ones) and a singularity which has to be either a cusp or a loop. To determine if there is a real singularity or real inflection point on the curve (2.1), the affine transformation

$$\begin{aligned} \bar{x} &= \alpha x+\beta y+\xi, \\ \bar{y} &= \gamma x+\delta y+\eta, \end{aligned} \tag{2.2}$$

is applied. Assume that

$$J\equiv \alpha\delta-\beta\gamma\neq 0.$$

Under the transformation, equations (2.2) of the curve become

$$\begin{aligned} \bar{x} &= \bar{a}_0+\bar{a}_t t+\tfrac{1}{2}\bar{a}_2t^2+\tfrac{1}{6}\bar{a}_3t^3, \\ \bar{y} &= \bar{b}_0+\bar{b}_1t+\tfrac{1}{2}\bar{b}_2t^2+\tfrac{1}{6}\bar{b}_3t^3. \end{aligned} \tag{2.3}$$

Singularity and inflection points on the curve (2.1) are transformed into singularity and inflection points on the curve (2.3), respectively. We are concerned with the relative affine invariants of the affine transformation (2.2), as they are closely related to the real singularity and real inflection points of the curve. General parametric curves and their affine invariants will be treated in detail in Section 1 of Chapter VIII.

Projective transformations are not considered in this book, since under these transformations singularities and inflection points may be carried to infinity, and an ellipse may become the two branches of a hyperbola. These properties are not desirable for our purposes.

Easy computations show that the new coefficients $\bar{a}_i$ and $\bar{b}_i$ $(i=0,1,2,3)$ are given in terms of the old coefficients by the equations

$$\begin{aligned} \bar{a}_1 &= \alpha a_1+\beta b_1, \qquad & \bar{b}_1 &= \gamma a_1+\delta b_1; \\ \bar{a}_2 &= \alpha a_2+\beta b_2, \qquad & \bar{b}_2 &= \gamma a_2+\delta b_2; \\ \bar{a}_3 &= \alpha a_3+\beta b_3, \qquad & \bar{b}_3 &= \gamma a_3+\delta b_3. \end{aligned}$$

Write

$$\begin{aligned} p &= a_2b_3 - a_3b_2, \\ q &= a_3b_1 - a_1b_3, \\ r &= a_1b_2 - a_2b_1. \end{aligned} \tag{2.4}$$

These are the three components of the vector product $\boldsymbol{a}\times\boldsymbol{b}$ of vectors $\boldsymbol{a}=(a_1, a_2, a_3)$ and $\boldsymbol{b}=(b_1, b_2, b_3)$. We have

$$\bar{p} = Jp, \qquad \bar{q} = Jq, \qquad \bar{r} = Jr. \tag{2.5}$$

This means that p, q and r are all the affine invariants of weight 1 with respect to the affine transformation (2.2).

We assume that a_3 and b_3 are not both zero; otherwise the curve (2.1) is not cubic. Without loss of generality, let $b_3 \neq 0$. It follows easily from (2.1) that

$$b_3x - a_3y + a_3b_0 - a_0b_3 = \tfrac{1}{2}pt^2 - qt.$$

If $p=0$, then $q\neq 0$. Thus

$$\bar{x} = \frac{1}{q}(-b_3x + a_3y + a_0b_3 - a_3b_0),$$

$$\bar{y} = \frac{6}{b_3}y,$$

and we have

$$\bar{y} = a + b\bar{x} + c\bar{x}^2 + \bar{x}^3.$$

This implies that the new curve (2.3) is a curve represented by a cubic polynomial that has an inflection point but does not have a singularity. Careful analysis will show that in the case $p=0$, the parametric curbic curve (2.1) is itself an ordinary cubic curve.

Inflection points of the parametric cubic curve (2.1) are determined by the equation

$$x'y'' - x''y' = 0,$$

i.e.,

$$pt^2 - 2qt + 2r = 0. \tag{2.6}$$

When $p\neq 0$, the curve (2.1) has two real inflection points iff

$$q^2 - 2pr > 0. \tag{2.7}$$

We now turn our discussion to the singularity of the general parametric cubic curve (2.1). It is known from (2.5) that any quadratic form of p, q and r, such as q^2-2pr, is a relative affine invariant of weight 2 with respect to the affine transformation (2.2). Hence its sign is of significance in affine geometry.

To simplify the curve (2.1), the affine transformation

$$\begin{aligned} x^* &= \frac{2}{p}(-b_3x+a_3y+a_0b_3-a_3b_0)-\frac{q^2}{p^2}, \\ y^* &= \frac{6}{b_3}y, \end{aligned} \tag{2.8}$$

is performed, with determinant

$$J=-\frac{12}{p}\neq 0.$$

The equations of the image of curve (2.1) are

$$\begin{aligned} x^* &= -t^{*2}, \\ y^* &= t^{*3}+at^{*2}+bt^*+c, \end{aligned} \tag{2.9}$$

where

$$t^*=t+\frac{q}{p}.$$

Eliminating the parameter t^* from (2.9), we get

$$f(x^*, y^*)\equiv(y^*+ax^*-c)^2+x^*(x^*-b)^2=0. \tag{2.10}$$

The singularity of the curve is determined by the system of equations

$$f=0, \qquad \frac{\partial f}{\partial x^*}=0, \qquad \frac{\partial f}{\partial y^*}=0.$$

Putting

$$H=\begin{vmatrix} \dfrac{\partial^2 f}{\partial x^{*2}} & \dfrac{\partial^2 f}{\partial x^*\,\partial y^*} \\ \dfrac{\partial^2 f}{\partial x^*\,\partial y^*} & \dfrac{\partial^2 f}{\partial y^{*2}} \end{vmatrix},$$

the curve (2.1) has no real singularity; it has a cusp or has a loop according to $H>0$, $H=0$, or $H<0$, respectively.

For $b=0$, the curve (2.10) has a cusp

$$x^*=0, \qquad y^*=c,$$

associated with parameter

$$t=\frac{q}{p}. \tag{2.11}$$

For $b<0$, the curve has a cusp

$$x^*=b, \qquad y^*=c-ab,$$

associated with two values of parameter

$$t_\varepsilon=\frac{q}{p}+\varepsilon\sqrt{-b} \qquad (\varepsilon=\pm 1). \tag{2.12}$$

If $b>0$, the curve does not have a real singularity but has two real inflection-points. In fact, it follows from (2.9) that

$$p^*=-12, \qquad q^*=0, \qquad r^*=2b,$$

hence

$$q^{*2}-2p^*r^*=48b.$$

By (2.5) and $J=-12/p$, we obtain

$$J^2(q^2-2pr)=48b$$

and then

$$b=3\left\{\left(\frac{q}{p}\right)^2-2\frac{r}{p}\right\}. \tag{2.13}$$

Thus we have found one of the most important relative affine invariants of curve (2.1):

$$I=\left(\frac{q}{p}\right)^2-2\frac{r}{p}. \tag{2.14}$$

The presence of a real singularity and real inflection points on the curve (2.1) is characterized by the sign of I:

$\boldsymbol{I>0}$, two real inflection points, no real singularity;
$\boldsymbol{I=0}$, a cusp, no real inflection points; (2.15)
$\boldsymbol{I<0}$, a loop, no real inflection points.

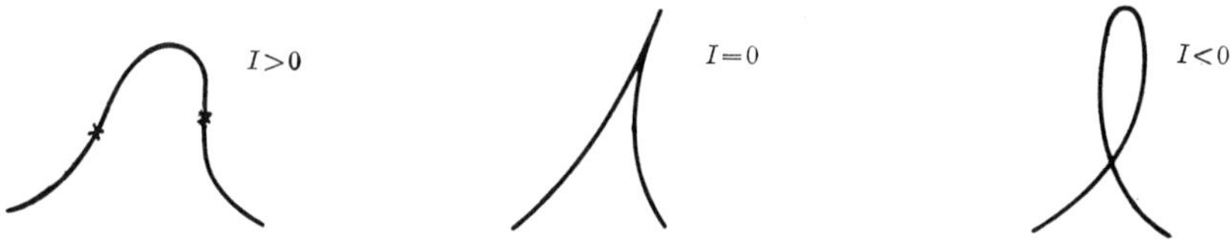

Figure 3-3

For illustrations, see Fig. 3-3.

The relative affine invariant I has weight (-2) with respect to linear transformation of the parameter. In fact, if

$$t = C\bar{t} + f \qquad (C \neq 0),$$

then p, q and r become $C^5 p$, $C^4(q - fp)$ and $C^3(r - fq + \frac{1}{2}f^2 p)$, respectively. Hence $q^2 - 2pr$ becomes $C^8(q^2 - 2pr)$, and I is replaced by $C^{-2}I$. This shows that the sign of I remains fixed under linear substitutions of the parameter.

3 Necessary and Sufficient Conditions for Inflection Points

In this section, we turn our attention to the segment of the plane parametric cubic curve

$$\begin{aligned} x &= a_0 + a_1 t + \tfrac{1}{2}a_2 t^2 + \tfrac{1}{6}a_3 t^3, \\ y &= b_0 + b_1 t + \tfrac{1}{2}b_2 t^2 + \tfrac{1}{6}b_3 t^3, \end{aligned} \qquad (0 \leq t \leq T) \qquad (3.1)$$

and consider when inflection points occur on the segment. This problem has not yet been completely solved. For instance, if $p \neq 0$ and $I > 0$, then we know by (2.15) that there are two inflection points on the curve (2.1), but they may not belong to the curve segment (3.1).

For $p = 0$, as we mentioned previously, the curve segment is an ordinary cubic curve. It is quite simple to determine whether or not there are inflection points on such a segment: If the curvature has opposite signs at two end points of the segment, then an inflection point occurs inevitably on this segment; otherwise no inflection point appears. It remains to consider the case $p \neq 0$.

Parametric values corresponding to the real inflection points on the curve segment (3.1) should be the roots of the equation (2.6). The equation (2.6) has two real roots in the interval $[0, T]$ if

I $q^2 - 2pr > 0$,
II $pr > 0$,
III $qr > 0$,
IV $T^2 - 2\frac{q}{p}T + 2\frac{r}{p} > 0$,
V $T > \frac{q}{p}$.

In applications, we set

$$T = \sqrt{[x(T) - x(0)]^2 + [y(T) - y(0)]^2},$$

in other words, T is taken to be the chord length of the curve segment. In this case, one more condition,

VI $(a_1 + \frac{1}{2}a_2 T + \frac{1}{6}a_3 T^2)^2 + (b_1 + \frac{1}{2}b_2 T + \frac{1}{6}b_3 T^2)^2 = 1$,

should be added.

A criterion to determine the number of inflection points follows immediately: To ensure that no more than one real inflection point occurs in (3.1), it is necessary and sufficient that p, q and r, the three components of the vector product $\boldsymbol{a} \times \boldsymbol{b} = (a_1, a_2, a_3) \times (b_1, b_2, b_3)$, do not have the same sign, or $q^2 - 2pr < 0$, or the positive root T of VI does not satisfy IV and V simultaneously.

Now we consider the sign of the product of the curvature at two end points of the segment

$$\begin{aligned} \operatorname{sign}(\kappa(0)\kappa(T)) &= \operatorname{sign}(\rho(0)\rho(T)) \\ &= \operatorname{sign}[r(pT^2 - 2qT + 2r)], \end{aligned}$$

in which

$$\rho(t) = pt^2 - 2qt + 2r.$$

It follows from II and IV that

$$\kappa(0)\kappa(T) > 0.$$

On the contrary, the last inequality and II imply IV.

We conclude that there are two real inflection points on the segment (3.1) iff

1. the curvature assumes the same sign at two end points of the segment,
2. p, q and r have the same sign,
3. $q^2 - 2pr > 0$,
4. $T > q/p$.

In the last inequality, T represents the positive root of the equation VI.

Xin Yuanlong has found an example in which the conditions I–VI are all satisfied. In his example, we are given

$$a_1=0, \quad a_2=1, \quad a_3=-\tfrac{3}{2};$$
$$b_1=-1, \quad b_2=0, \quad b_3=\tfrac{3}{4};$$
$$T=3\tfrac{1}{5}.$$

Simple calculation yields

$$p=\tfrac{3}{4}, \quad q=\tfrac{3}{2}, \quad r=1.$$

The equation (2.6) has two roots $2\pm\frac{2}{3}\sqrt{3}$. To identify the distribution of the inflection-points of the curve segment, equation (3.1) has to be reduced to the form of (2.9), for which

$$t^*=t-2, \quad a=6, \quad b=4, \quad c=-8.$$

Thus

$$D=a^2-3b=24.$$

This curve is illustrated in Fig. 3-4, which does not coincide with the original curve, but is its image under an affine transformation. These two curves share the same distribution of inflection points.

Values of the parameter

$$t_1, t_2=(-a\pm\sqrt{D})/3$$

and

$$\tau_1, \tau_2=\pm\sqrt{\frac{b}{3}}$$

are associated with two extreme points and two inflection points respectively.

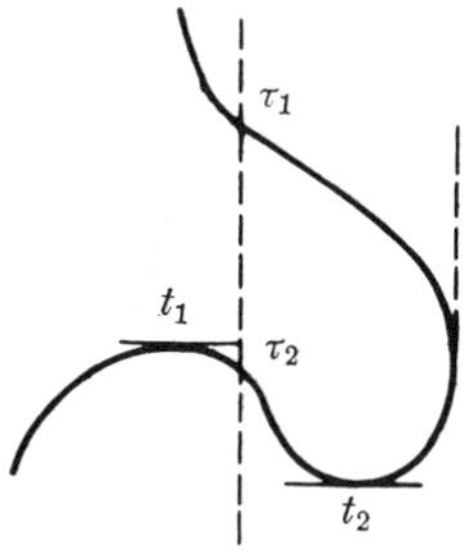

Figure 3-4

This example indicates that two real inflection points do exist on certain segments of parametric cubic curves, no matter how difficult it seems for conditions I–VI to be satisfied simultaneously.

In applications of computational geometry to practical problems, we often take $T=1$. In this case, a necessary and sufficient condition for two real inflection-points is expressed by

I′ $q^2-2pr>0$,
II′ $pr>0$,
III′ $qr>0$,
IV′ $2r/p-2q/p+1>0$,
V′ $q/p<1$.

Inequality IV′ can be replaced by the fact that the curvature assumes opposite signs at the two end points of the segment.

Finally, inequalities involving T can be derived from the equality VI. These inequalities can be used as necessary but not sufficient conditions for the occurrence of two real inflection points. Put

$$A_1=a_1+\tfrac{1}{2}a_2T+\tfrac{1}{6}a_3T^2,$$

$$B_1=b_1+\tfrac{1}{2}b_2T+\tfrac{1}{6}b_3T^2.$$

Then VI becomes $A_1^2+B_1^2=1$. Using the Cauchy–Schwarz inequality

$$(A_1^2+B_1^2)(A_2^2+B_2^2)\geqslant(A_1A_2+B_1B_2)^2,$$

the inequalities

$$(1)\quad a_3^2+b_3^2\geqslant(\tfrac{1}{2}pT-q)^2,$$

$$(2)\quad a_2^2+b_2^2\geqslant(\tfrac{1}{6}pT^2-r)^2,$$

$$(3)\quad a_1^2+b_1^2\geqslant T^2(\tfrac{1}{6}qT-\tfrac{1}{2}r)^2,$$

are obtained by different choices of A_2 and B_2. If at least one of the above three inequalities does not hold, then we conclude that two real inflection points do not occur on the curve segment simultaneously.

4 A Theorem Concerning Segments of Parametric Cubic Curves

A drawback of segments of parametric cubic curves is indicated by the fact that unwanted inflection points or singularities may occur on these segments. As designers used to worry about difficulties in controlling singularities and inflection points, applications of parametric cubic curves, which are of exceptional geometric merit, have been greatly limited. Techniques for eliminating unwanted singularities and inflection points will be given in this section. Suppose that tangent directions are fixed at the two end points of a segment, and only the magnitudes of the tangents are allowed to be varied in scalar multiples λ and μ ($\lambda > 0$, $\mu > 0$), respectively. In the first quadrant of the coordinate system (λ, μ) in the plane, there exists a rectangular region $\mathscr{D}$ which is called the normal region, such that for each pair $(\lambda, \mu) \in \mathscr{D}$ the corresponding segment of the parametric cubic curve does not have either an inflection point or a singularity (Su Buchin, 1977).

For convenience, a rectangular coordinate system $\{\boldsymbol{O}, x, y\}$ in the plane is established such that

$$\begin{aligned} x(0) &= 0, & y(0) &= 0; \\ x(1) &= l, & y(1) &= 0; \end{aligned} \tag{4.1}$$

and that

$$\begin{aligned} x'(0) &= \lambda a_0, & y'(0) &= \lambda b_0; \\ x'(1) &= \mu a_1, & y'(1) &= \mu b_1, \end{aligned} \tag{4.2}$$

in which l designates the distance between the two end points $\boldsymbol{O}$ and $\boldsymbol{L}$, and (a_0, b_0) and (a_1, b_1) represent the tangent directions at the end-points. From Fig. 3-5, we see that

$$a_0, \qquad a_1 > 0, \qquad b_0 > 0 > b_1, \qquad \lambda, \mu > 0.$$

The parametric cubic curve interpolating to (4.1) and (4.2), using Hermite interpolation, is expressed by equations

$$\begin{aligned} x(t) &= \bar{a}_1 t + \tfrac{1}{2}\bar{a}_2 t^2 + \tfrac{1}{6}\bar{a}_3 t^3, \\ y(t) &= \bar{b}_1 t + \tfrac{1}{2}\bar{b}_2 t^2 + \tfrac{1}{6}\bar{b}_3 t^3 \end{aligned} \qquad (0 \leq t \leq 1), \tag{4.3}$$

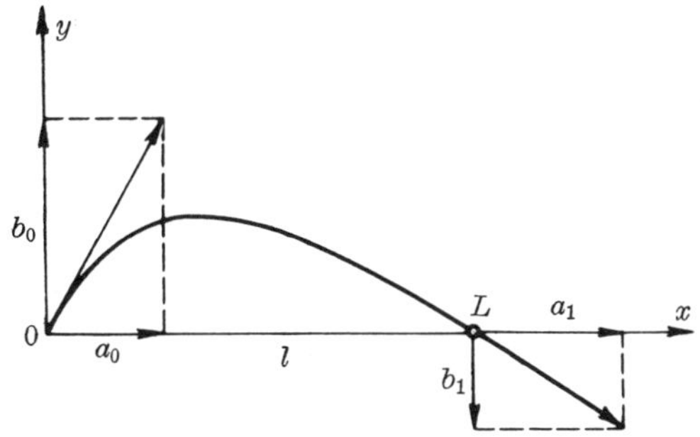

Figure 3-5

in which

$$\bar{a}_1 = \lambda a_0, \qquad \bar{a}_2 = 2(3l - 2\lambda a_0 - \mu a_1), \qquad \bar{a}_3 = 6(-2l + \lambda a_0 + \mu a_1);$$
$$\bar{b}_1 = \lambda b_0, \qquad \bar{b}_2 = -2(2\lambda b_0 + \mu b_1), \qquad \bar{b}_3 = 6(\lambda b_0 + \mu b_1). \tag{4.4}$$

Then we have

$$\begin{aligned} p &= 12\{(-\lambda b_0 + \mu b_1)l + \lambda\mu\Delta\}, \\ q &= 6\lambda(\mu\Delta - 2b_0 l), \\ r &= 2\lambda(\mu\Delta - 3b_0 l), \end{aligned} \tag{4.5}$$

where $\Delta = a_1 b_0 - a_0 b_1 > 0$.

Substituting these quantities into the invariant $q^2 - 2pr$, we obtain

$$q^2 - 2pr = -12\lambda\mu\Delta^2\left\{\left(\lambda + \frac{4b_1 l}{\Delta}\right)\left(\mu - \frac{4b_0 l}{\Delta}\right) + \frac{4b_0 b_1 l^2}{\Delta^2}\right\}. \tag{4.6}$$

Since λ, $\mu > 0$, it follows immediately by (2.15) that there is a loop, a cusp, or two inflection points on the whole parametric cubic curve iff

$$\left(\lambda + \frac{4b_1 l}{\Delta}\right)\left(\mu - \frac{4b_0 l}{\Delta}\right) + \frac{4b_0 b_1 l^2}{\Delta^2} \gtreqless 0$$

holds respectively.

Hence the first quadrant of the (λ, μ) plane is divided by a hyperbola C with the equation

$$\left(\lambda + \frac{4b_1 l}{\Delta}\right)\left(\mu - \frac{4b_0 l}{\Delta}\right) + \frac{4b_0 b_1 l^2}{\Delta^2} = 0 \tag{4.7}$$

into regions D_1, D_2 and I. We have $(\lambda, \mu) \in D_1 \cup D_2$, $(\lambda, \mu) \in I$ or $(\lambda, \mu) \in C$ if and only if there is a loop, two inflection points, or a cusp on the entire parametric cubic curve (Fig. 3-6).

For segments of parametric cubic curves, we will prove the following theorem concerning distributions of inflection points and singularities.

Theorem *If a point (λ, μ) is taken from the rectangular region*

$$\mathscr{D}: \qquad 0 < \lambda < -\frac{3b_1 l}{\Delta}, \qquad 0 < \mu < \frac{3b_0 l}{\Delta}$$

to construct the segment of the parametric cubic curve (4.3), *then the segment does not contain unwanted inflection points or singularities.*

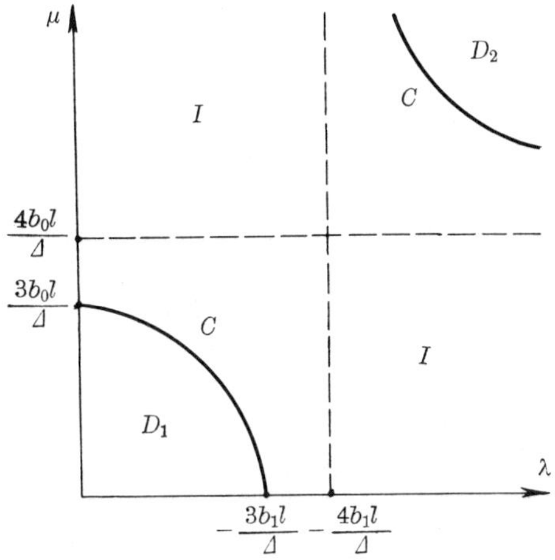

Figure 3-6

Proof. First of all we point out that for any $(\lambda, \mu) \in \mathscr{D}$, the corresponding segment (4.3) does not contain unwanted inflection points. To show this, we divide $\mathscr{D}$ into four rectangles R, R_1, R_2 and $\bar{R}$ which have a common vertex

$$\boldsymbol{P}\left(\frac{-2b_1l}{\Delta}, \frac{2b_0l}{\Delta}\right).$$

This point lies on the hyperbola C which is related to the possible cusps (see Fig. 3-7).

(1) For points in

$$\boldsymbol{R}\left(\frac{-2b_1l}{\Delta} \leqslant \lambda < \frac{-3b_1l}{\Delta}, \frac{2b_0l}{\Delta} \leqslant \mu < \frac{3b_0l}{\Delta}\right),$$

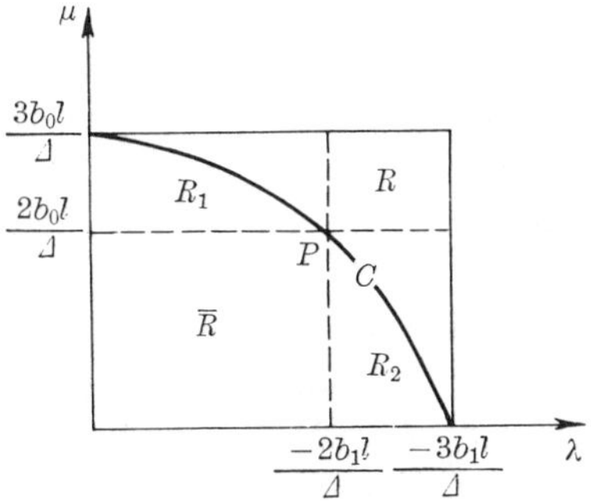

Figure 3-7

we have $r<0$ and $q\geqslant 0$ by (4.5). Since

$$p-2q+2r=4\mu(\lambda\Delta+3b_1l)<0$$

holds generally, the curvature has the same sign at the end points. By the criteria in Section 3, we know that there are no unwanted inflection points on the segment: It is obvious for $q>0$, and for $q=0$, i.e., $\mu\Delta-2b_0l=0$, it follows from

$$p=q+6\mu(\lambda\Delta+2b_1l) \tag{4.8}$$

that $p>0$. Thus unwanted inflection points do not occur unless $\lambda\Delta+2b_1l=0$, which means that (λ, μ) is just the point $\boldsymbol{P}$ on C.

(2) If

$$(\lambda, \mu)\in R_1\left(0<\lambda\leqslant-\frac{2b_1l}{\Delta}, \frac{2b_0l}{\Delta}\leqslant\mu<\frac{3b_0l}{\Delta}\right),$$

then $r<0$, $q\geqslant 0$. From (4.8) we know that $p-q\leqslant 0$. Thus $q/p\geqslant 1$ for $p>0$ and $q/p\leqslant 0$ for $p<0$. We conclude that there are no unwanted inflection points on the curve segment.

(3) If

$$(\lambda, \mu)\in R_2\left(\frac{-2b_1l}{\Delta}\leqslant\lambda<-\frac{3b_1l}{\Delta}, 0<\mu\leqslant\frac{2b_0l}{\Delta}\right),$$

then $q<0$ and $p-q\geqslant 0$ by (4.8). Hence $q/p<0$ for $p>0$ and $q/p\geqslant 1$ for $p<0$. We have the same conclusion.

(4) If

$$(\lambda, \mu)\in \bar{R}\left(0<\lambda<\frac{-2b_1l}{\Delta}, 0<\mu<\frac{2b_0l}{\Delta}\right),$$

then from (4.6) we have $q^2-2pr<0$. This means that no unwanted inflection points occur.

Next we examine if there is a cusp on the parametric cubic curve segment associated with the pair (λ, μ) which lies on the curve segment C.

For the point $\boldsymbol{P}$ on which $\lambda=-2b_1l/\Delta$, $\mu=2b_0l/\Delta$, from (4.4) we have $\bar{a}_3=\bar{b}_3=0$. Hence the curve (4.3) degenerates to a quadratic on which there is no cusp.

The curve segment C is divided by the point $\boldsymbol{P}$ into two segments characterized by $\mu\Delta-2b_0l>0$ and $\mu\Delta-2b_0l<0$, respectively (Fig. 3-7). For the first part of C, we have $0<\lambda<-2b_1l/\Delta$, $q>0$ and $p=q^2/(2r)<0$. Hence $q/p<0$, so that by (2.11) we know that the corresponding curve segment does not contain any cusp if (λ, μ) belongs to this part of C.

For the second part of C, we have $-2b_1 l/\Delta < \lambda < -3b_1 l/\Delta$ and $q<0$. It follows from (4.8) that $p-q>0$ and $p=q^2/(2r)<0$. The corresponding curve segment still does not contain any cusp as $q/p>1$.

To complete the proof of the theorem, we discuss whether or not loops occur on the segment. In this case, the only possibility is that the point (λ, μ) falls into the region bounded by the two coordinate axes and the curve segment C (see Fig. 3-7).

As previously stated, $b<0$ is equivalent to

$$2pr > q^2.$$

But if $r<0$, then

$$p<0. \tag{4.9}$$

Loops occur on the segment (4.3) corresponding to the point (λ, μ) iff the two roots t_1 and t_{-1} defined by (2.12) belong to the interval (0, 1). This says that

$$0<\frac{q}{p}+\varepsilon\sqrt{-b}<1 \qquad (\varepsilon=\pm 1). \tag{4.10}$$

From (4.10) we obtain

$$0<\frac{q}{p}<1. \tag{4.11}$$

Comparing this with (4.9) we get

$$p-q<0, \qquad q<0,$$

and thus

$$\mu<\frac{2b_0 l}{\Delta}, \qquad \lambda<-\frac{2b_1 l}{\Delta}. \tag{4.12}$$

Inequality (4.10) with a negative ε, i.e., $0<(q/p)-\sqrt{-b}<1$, gives

$$-b<\left(\frac{q}{p}\right)^2,$$

which can be rewritten as

$$2\frac{r}{p}<\frac{4}{3}\left(\frac{q}{p}\right)^2$$

by (2.13). Similarly, (4.10) with a positive ε, i.e., $0<(q/p)+\sqrt{-b}<1$, gives only

$$-b<\left(1-\frac{q}{p}\right)^2,$$

which can be rewritten as

$$2\frac{r}{p}<\frac{1}{3}\left(1-\frac{q}{p}\right)^2+\left(\frac{q}{p}\right)^2$$

by (2.13) again.

We have obtained in this way two sets of inequalities, namely (4.11) and

$$\left(\frac{q}{p}\right)^2<\frac{2r}{p}<\min\left[\frac{4}{3}\left(\frac{q}{p}\right)^2,\frac{1}{3}\left(1-\frac{q}{p}\right)^2+\left(\frac{q}{p}\right)^2\right].$$

If we set $\xi=q/p$, then they can be reformulated by

$$0<\xi<1, \qquad \xi^2<\frac{2r}{p}<\min\left(\tfrac{4}{3}\xi^2,\tfrac{1}{3}(1-\xi)^2+\xi^2\right). \tag{4.13}$$

To prove the non-existence of λ and μ, we assume to the contrary that

$$\lambda=-2m\frac{b_1 l}{\Delta}, \qquad \mu=2n\frac{b_0 l}{\Delta},$$

so that (4.12) becomes

$$0<m,\ n<1. \tag{4.14}$$

From (4.5) we have

$$\xi=\frac{m(1-n)}{m+n-2mn}, \tag{4.15}$$

$$\frac{2r}{p}=\frac{m(3-2n)}{3(m+n-2mn)}. \tag{4.16}$$

On the other hand, we discuss (4.13) in three cases according to

$$(1-\xi)^2<\xi^2, \qquad (1-\xi)^2=\xi^2, \qquad \text{and} \quad (1-\xi)^2>\xi^2.$$

Case I. $(1-\xi)^2<\xi^2$. Now (4.13) can be replaced by the inequalities

$$\tfrac{1}{2}<\xi<1, \qquad \xi^2<\frac{2r}{p}<\tfrac{1}{3}(1-\xi)^2+\xi^2. \tag{4.17}$$

Substituting (4.15) into the first inequalities in (4.17), we have

$$m+n-2mn<2m(1-n)<2(m+n-2mn),$$

and by (4.14) we know that

$$m+n-2mn=m(1-n)+n(1-m)>0.$$

It is easy to derive $m>n$. Combining this inequality with (4.14), we can write

$$0<n<m<1.$$

Set

$$L=3m^2(1-n)^2,$$
$$M=m(3-2n)(m+n-2mn),$$
$$R=n^2(1-m)^2+3m^2(1-n)^2.$$

Substituting (4.15) and (4.16) into the second part of (4.17), with some simplification, we get

$$L<M<R. \tag{4.18}$$

It is easy to see

$$M-L=nm(1-n)+(3-2n)n(1-m),$$

so by (4.14) we have $L<M$.

To see if the last part of (4.18) holds, we consider the difference

$$R-M=2n[m-\tfrac{1}{4}(3+\sqrt{9-8n})][m-\tfrac{1}{4}(3-\sqrt{9-8n})].$$

By (4.14), $3>\sqrt{9-8n}>1$. To ensure $R>M$, we must have

$$(1)\quad 4m-3>\sqrt{9-8n},$$

or

$$(2)\quad 4m-3<-\sqrt{9-8n}.$$

From (1) we have $4m-3>1$, i.e., $m>1$, and $4m-3<-3$, i.e., $m<0$ from (2). Both cases contradict (4.14).

We have proved in this case that such m and n do not exist.

Case II. $(1-\xi)^2=\xi^2$. The equation implies that $\xi=\frac{1}{2}$. Hence (4.15) gives

$$\frac{m(1-n)}{m+n-2mn}=\frac{1}{2},$$

i.e., $m=n$. Inequalities (4.13) become

$$\frac{1}{4}<\frac{m(3-2n)}{3(m+n-2mn)}<\frac{1}{3},$$

that is,

$$\frac{3}{2}<\frac{3-2m}{1-m}<2,$$

as we have seen $n=m$. From the last part of the above inequalities we get $3<2$, a contradiction.

Case III. $(1-\xi)^2>\xi^2$.

Now (4.13) is replaced by

$$0<\xi<\tfrac{1}{2},\qquad \xi^2<\frac{2r}{p}<\tfrac{4}{3}\xi^2.$$

As in Case I, we get

$$0<m<n<1 \tag{4.19}$$

and

$$3m(1-n)^2 < (3-2n)(m+n-2mn) < 4m(1-n)^2.$$

The first part of the above inequalities always holds, as we have

$$(3-2n)(m+n-2mn) - 3m(1-n)^2 = n\{1-mn+2(1-m)(1-n)\} > 0.$$

But the second part does not hold, as

$$4m(1-n)^2 - (3-2n)(m+n-2mn) = m-n-2n(1-n) < 0.$$

Hence m and n do not exist in this case. This completes the proof.

5 Extending (λ, μ) to the Whole Plane

Now we extend the results obtained in the previous section to the whole plane (Liu Dingyuan [4], 1981).

The parametric cubic curve (2.1) can be written in vector form

$$\boldsymbol{P}(t) = \tfrac{1}{6}\boldsymbol{P}_3 t^3 + \tfrac{1}{2}\boldsymbol{P}_2 t^2 + \boldsymbol{P}_1 t + \boldsymbol{P}_0. \tag{5.1}$$

The quantities p, q and r in (2.4) are represented by

$$\begin{aligned} p &= [\boldsymbol{P}_2\boldsymbol{P}_3], \\ q &= [\boldsymbol{P}_3\boldsymbol{P}_1], \\ r &= [\boldsymbol{P}_1\boldsymbol{P}_2]. \end{aligned} \tag{5.2}$$

where the brackets [ ] denote the determinant formed by the components of the two vectors appearing in the brackets.

Set

$$G = q^2 - 2pr. \tag{5.3}$$

Suppose that two end-points $\boldsymbol{M}_0$, $\boldsymbol{M}_1$ and the tangent vectors $\boldsymbol{A}_0$, $\boldsymbol{A}_1$ at $\boldsymbol{M}_0$, $\boldsymbol{M}_1$, respectively, are given. By Hermite interpolation, the parametric cubic curve segment has the representation

$$\boldsymbol{P}(t) = \overrightarrow{\boldsymbol{OM}_0} + t^2(3-2t)\boldsymbol{L} + t(t-1)^2\boldsymbol{A}_0 + t^2(t-1)\boldsymbol{A}_1, \qquad 0 \leqslant t \leqslant 1, \tag{5.4}$$

where $\boldsymbol{L} = \overrightarrow{\boldsymbol{M}_0\boldsymbol{M}_1}$. Hence

$$\begin{aligned} &\boldsymbol{P}'(0) = \boldsymbol{A}_0, \qquad \boldsymbol{P}''(0) = 6\boldsymbol{L} - 4\boldsymbol{A}_0 - 2\boldsymbol{A}_1; \\ &\boldsymbol{P}'(1) = \boldsymbol{A}_1, \qquad \boldsymbol{P}''(1) = -6\boldsymbol{L} + 2\boldsymbol{A}_0 + 4\boldsymbol{A}_1. \end{aligned} \tag{5.5}$$

On the other hand, it follows from (5.1) that

$$\boldsymbol{P}'(0) = \boldsymbol{P}_1, \qquad \boldsymbol{P}''(0) = \boldsymbol{P}_2, \qquad \boldsymbol{P}''(1) = \boldsymbol{P}_2 + \boldsymbol{P}_3. \tag{5.6}$$

Thus we obtain

$$p = -24\Delta[(\lambda - 1)(\mu - 1) - 1],$$
$$q = 12\Delta\lambda(2 - \mu), \tag{5.7}$$
$$r = 4\Delta\lambda(3 - \mu),$$

$$G = -48\Delta^2\lambda\mu[(\lambda - 4)(\mu - 4) - 4], \tag{5.8}$$

in which $\Delta = \frac{1}{2}[\overrightarrow{\boldsymbol{M}_0\boldsymbol{M}}\ \overrightarrow{\boldsymbol{M}\boldsymbol{M}_1}]$ denotes the signed area of the triangle $\boldsymbol{M}_0\boldsymbol{M}\boldsymbol{M}_1$ and $\boldsymbol{M}$ is the intersection of the tangent lines at $\boldsymbol{M}_0$ and $\boldsymbol{M}_1$. In our discussion, $\Delta \neq 0$ and

$$\boldsymbol{A}_0 = \lambda\overrightarrow{\boldsymbol{M}_0\boldsymbol{M}},$$
$$\boldsymbol{A}_1 = \mu\overrightarrow{\boldsymbol{M}\boldsymbol{M}_1}. \tag{5.9}$$

We shall refer to λ and μ as the relative lengths of the tangent vectors at the end points (Fig. 3-8). They are affine invariants for the parametric cubic segment, as the ratio of lengths of the two vectors having the same direction is invariant under affine transformations.

We now consider the relationship between (λ, μ) and the distribution of real singularities and inflection points. First of all, an affine coordinate system $\{\boldsymbol{O}, \lambda, \mu\}$ is established in the plane, as shown by Fig. 3-9. In the figure, the plane is divided into several regions by the λ-axis, the μ-axis, the straight lines $\lambda = 3$ and $\mu = 3$, the hyperbola $(\lambda - 4)(\mu - 4) - 4 = 0$, l_2—the segment of the parabola $\mu^2 - 3\mu + \lambda = 0$ limited by the second quadrant—and l_4—the segment of the parabola $\lambda^2 - 3\lambda + \mu = 0$ limited by the fourth quadrant. For example, N_1 represents the region in Fig. 3-9 characterized by $0 < \lambda < 3$ and $0 < \mu < 3$. The symbol C_1 denotes the branch of the hyperbola

$$(\lambda - 4)(\mu - 4) - 4 = 0,$$

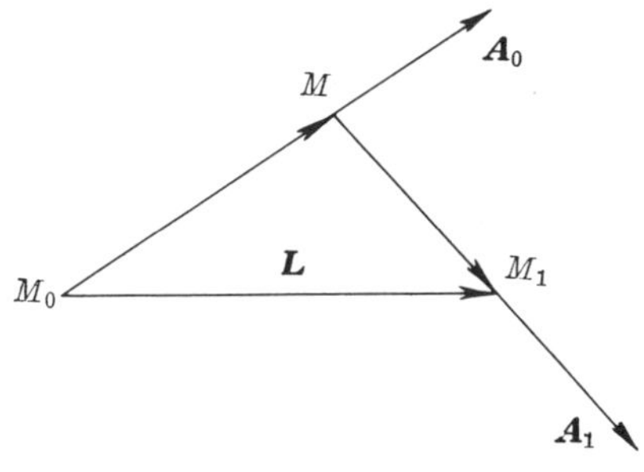

Figure 3-8

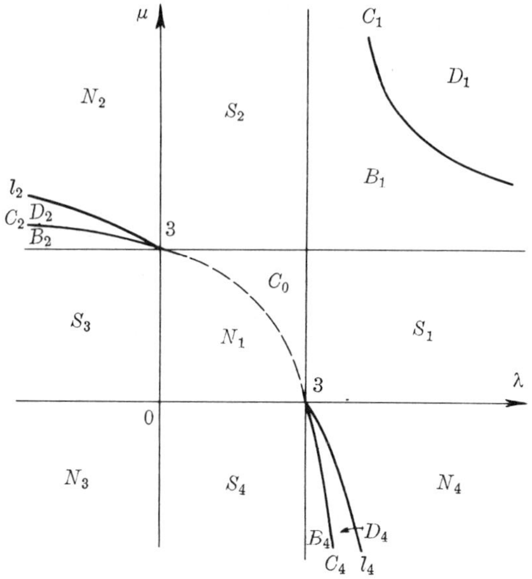

Figure 3-9

which has straight lines $\lambda = 4$ and $\mu = 4$ as its asymptotic lines, and C_0, C_2 and C_4 denote the segments of the other branch limited by the first, second and fourth quadrants, respectively.

From now on, by singularities we mean the real ones. The same applies to inflection points.

Recall the distribution of singularities and inflection points of the whole parametric cubic curve obtained in Section 1. If $p \neq 0$, the point $\boldsymbol{P}(t_0)$ on the curve (5.1) is

(1) a loop if

$$t_\varepsilon = \frac{q + \varepsilon\sqrt{-3G}}{p} \qquad (\varepsilon = \pm 1),$$
$$G < 0; \tag{5.10}$$

(2) a cusp if

$$t_\varepsilon = \frac{q}{p},$$
$$G = 0; \tag{5.11}$$

and

(3) there are two inflection points on the curve iff

$$t_\varepsilon = \frac{q+\varepsilon\sqrt{G}}{p},$$
$$G>0. \tag{5.12}$$

Note that the parameter t_ε in (5.10), (5.11) and (5.12) is independent of the quantity Δ, which appeared in the right-hand side of (5.7) and (5.8). Without loss of generality, we assume that $\Delta<0$.

Two cases, $p \neq 0$ and $p=0$, will be discussed separately.

I. $p \neq 0$.

(1) The curve segment has a loop in $t \in (0,1)$ iff

$$0<\frac{q+\varepsilon\sqrt{-3G}}{p}<1,$$
$$G<0. \tag{5.13}$$

(a) If $p>0$, then (5.13) is equivalent to

$$q+\sqrt{-3G}<p,$$
$$q-\sqrt{-3G}>0,$$
$$G<0.$$

After rationalization

$$p^2+4q^2-2pq-6pr>0,$$
$$2q^2-3pr>0,$$
$$p>q>0,$$
$$G<0.$$

Substituting (5.7) into the above inequalities, we obtain

$$\lambda(\mu^2-3\mu+\lambda)>0,$$
$$\mu(\lambda^2-3\lambda+\mu)>0,$$
$$\mu(\lambda-2)>0,$$
$$\lambda(\mu-2)>0,$$
$$G<0.$$

We must point out that the parabolas $\mu^2-3\mu+\lambda=0$ and $\lambda^2-3\lambda+\mu=0$ intersect at two real points, (0, 0) and (2, 2), and that $p=0$ represents two branches of the hyperbola $(\lambda-1)(\mu-1)=1$, with (0, 0) and (2, 2) as their vertices (see Fig. 3-10). We immediately conclude that there is a loop on the curve segment if $(\lambda, \mu)\in D_1$, while no loop occurs if $(\lambda, \mu)\in N_3$.

(b) For $p<0$, we obtain analogously

$$\begin{aligned}\lambda(\mu^2-3\mu+\lambda)&>0,\\ \mu(\lambda^2-3\lambda+\mu)&>0,\\ \mu(\lambda-2)&<0,\\ \lambda(\mu-2)&<0,\\ G&<0.\end{aligned}$$

Hence there is a loop on the curve segment if $(\lambda, \mu)\in D_2$ or D_4, while no loop occurs if $(\lambda, \mu)\in N_1$, N_2 or N_4.

(2) The curve segment has a cusp when $t\in(0, 1)$ iff

$$\begin{aligned}&0<\frac{q}{p}<1,\\ &G=0.\end{aligned}\tag{5.14}$$

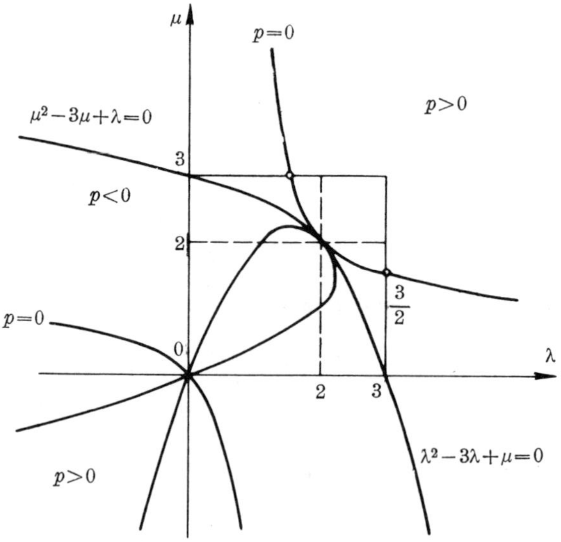

Figure 3-10

(a) If $p>0$, (5.14) can be rewritten as

$$\mu(\lambda-2)>0,$$
$$\lambda(\mu-2)>0,$$
$$G=0,$$

by using (5.7). Hence the curve segment has a cusp if $(\lambda, \mu)\in C_1$.

(b) If $p<0$, we similarly get

$$\mu(\lambda-2)<0,$$
$$\lambda(\mu-2)<0,$$
$$G=0.$$

It is clear that there is a cusp on the curve segment if $(\lambda, \mu)\in C_2$ or C_4 while no cusp accurs if $(\lambda, \mu)\in C_0$.

(3) From (5.5) and (5.6), we can easily evaluate the curvature at the end points:

$$k_0=\frac{[\boldsymbol{P}'(0)\boldsymbol{P}''(0)]}{|\boldsymbol{P}'(0)|^3}=\operatorname{sign}(\lambda)\frac{3-\mu}{\lambda^2}\cdot\frac{4\Delta}{|\overrightarrow{\boldsymbol{M}_0\boldsymbol{M}}|^3},$$

$$k_1=\frac{[\boldsymbol{P}'(1)\boldsymbol{P}''(1)]}{|\boldsymbol{P}'(1)|^3}=\operatorname{sign}(\mu)\frac{3-\lambda}{\mu^2}\cdot\frac{4\Delta}{|\overrightarrow{\boldsymbol{M}\boldsymbol{M}_1}|^3}.$$

The inequality $k_0k_1<0$ is equivalent to

$$\lambda\mu(3-\lambda)(3-\mu)<0.$$

Hence the curve segment has an inflection point iff (λ, μ) belongs to one of the four regions S_1, S_2, S_3 or S_4.

The curve segment has two inflection points iff

$$0<\frac{q+\varepsilon\sqrt{G}}{p}<1, \qquad G>0. \tag{5.15}$$

(a) In the case of $p>0$, (5.15) is equivalent to

$$p-q>\sqrt{G},$$
$$q>\sqrt{G},$$
$$G>0.$$

After rationalization, we have by using (5.7)

$$\begin{aligned} \mu(\lambda-3)&>0,\\ \lambda(\mu-3)&>0,\\ \mu(\lambda-2)&>0,\\ \lambda(\mu-2)&>0,\\ G&>0, \end{aligned} \tag{5.16}$$

so that the segment has two inflection points if $(\lambda, \mu) \in B_1$.

(b) For $p<0$, we similarly get

$$\begin{aligned} \mu(\lambda-3)&<0,\\ \lambda(\mu-3)&<0,\\ \mu(\lambda-2)&<0,\\ \lambda(\mu-2)&<0,\\ G&>0. \end{aligned} \tag{5.17}$$

Hence the segment has two inflection points if (λ, μ) belongs to B_2 or B_4.

Furthermore we point out that the region N_1 does not contain the point corresponding to the inflection-point. In fact for $p>0$, it is seen from (5.16) that the intersection of $\lambda>3$, $\mu>3$ and N_1 is empty. For $p<0$, the intersection of $\lambda<2$, $\mu<2$ and the subregion of N_1 limited by $G>0$ is also empty by (5.17).

II. $p=0$. In this case the curve does not contain a singularity but contains an inflection point associated with the parameter value

$$t=\frac{r}{q}. \tag{5.18}$$

Hence the curve segment determined by the parameter $t \in (0,1)$ has one inflection point iff

$$0<\frac{3-\mu}{3(2-\mu)}<1,$$

i.e., $\mu<\frac{3}{2}$ or $\mu>3$. Since $p=0$ represents the hyperbola indicated in Fig. 3-10, we conclude that, for $p=0$, if $(\lambda, \mu) \in N_1$ then the curve segment contains no singularity or inflection point, and if $(\lambda, \mu) \in S_1 \cup S_2 \cup S_3 \cup S_4$, then the segment contains an inflection point.

In summary, a theorem concerning the distribution of singularities and inflection points of the segment (5.4) is obtained:

Theorem. *If*

$$(\lambda, \mu) \in \begin{cases} \bigcup_{i=1}^{4} N_i \\ \bigcup_{i=1}^{4} S_i \\ D_1 \cup D_2 \cup D_4 \\ C_1 \cup C_2 \cup C_4 \\ B_1 \cup B_2 \cup B_4 \end{cases}$$

$$\textit{then (5.4) contains} \begin{cases} \textit{no singularity and inflection point;} \\ \textit{one inflection point;} \\ \textit{a loop;} \\ \textit{a cusp;} \\ \textit{two inflection points.} \end{cases}$$

When the end points and tangent vectors at these points are given, the parametric cubic curve segment is uniquely determined. Keeping tangential directions fixed, the shape control for the segment can be realized by changing the length of the tangent vectors at the end-points by adjusting (λ, μ). The theorem provides a scheme for the adjustment which plays an important role in shape control. Figure 3-11 shows several curve segments associated with different pairs (λ, μ).

We shall say a few words here about the exceptional case $\Delta = 0$ in which either the tangent vectors at the two end points are parallel or one of the tangent vectors is parallel to the chord $\boldsymbol{L}$ (if the two tangent vectors are both parallel to the chord, then the segment (5.4) degenerates to a line segment). By using the same argument, the distribution of singularity and inflection points can be determined as follows.

(1) Assume $\boldsymbol{A}_0 \| \boldsymbol{A}_1$.

If $\boldsymbol{A}_0$ and $\boldsymbol{A}_1$ are in the same direction, then (5.4) has an inflection point; if $\boldsymbol{A}_0$ and $\boldsymbol{A}_1$ are in the opposite direction, then no singularity or inflection point occurs.

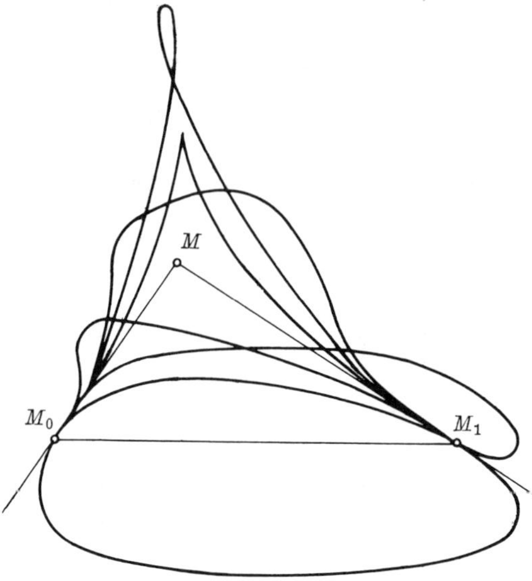

Figure 3-11

(2) Assume $\boldsymbol{A}_1 \| \boldsymbol{L}$ but $\boldsymbol{A}_0 \nparallel \boldsymbol{L}$.
Let $\boldsymbol{A}_1 = \mu \boldsymbol{L}$. Then we have
no singularity or inflection point if $\mu \leqslant 0$;
one inflection point if $0 < \mu \leqslant 3$;
two inflection points if $3 < \mu < 4$;
one cusp if $\mu = 4$;
one loop if $\mu > 4$.
For different shapes of curve segments, see Fig. 3-12.

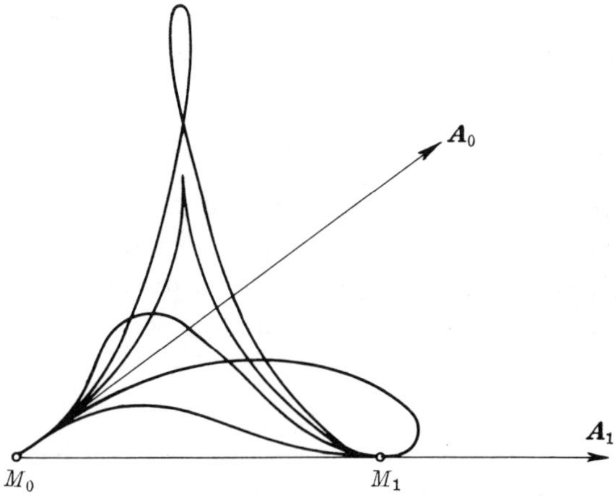

Figure 3-12

6 Parametric Cubic Spline Curves of Cumulative Chord Length

The general theory of parametric cubic curves was examined in previous sections. Based on this theory, several kinds of cubic parametric spline curves, which are useful in different cases, will be constructed.

Let $n+1$ data points $\boldsymbol{P}_i(x_i, y_i)$ $(i=0, 1, \ldots, n)$ be given in a plane Cartesian coordinate system. The chord length between two consecutive data points is given by

$$l_i = \sqrt{(x_i - x_{i-1})^2 + (y_i - y_{i-1})^2} \qquad (i = 1, 2, \ldots, n).$$

A cubic parametric spline curve is defined in the following manner. Let $t_i = \sum_{j=1}^{i} l_j$ $(i=1, 2, \ldots, n)$. Each t_i represents the cumulative chord length. A partition $\Delta: 0 = t_0 < t_1 < \cdots < t_n$ of the axis of parameter t is then induced. With respect to the partition Δ, using x_i and y_i $(i = 0, 1, 2, \ldots, n)$ as interpolated data, two interpolatory cubic spline functions $x(t)$ and $y(t)$ are obtained. Combining $x(t)$ and $y(t)$ we get the parametric curve $\boldsymbol{P}(t) = (x(t), y(t))$, which is called the parametric cubic spline curve of cumulative chord length. The spline curve has continuous tangent vector and curvature, as each component is of C^2-continuity at every knot.

Such a spline curve is suitable for interpolating to curves with large deflection. Since $|\Delta x_i/\Delta t_i|$ and $|\Delta y_i/\Delta t_i|$ are less than 1, each component is of small deflection in the (x, t) plane or the (y, t) plane, no matter how the curve in the (x, y) plane is. We have shown in Section 2 that arc length cannot be chosen as the parameter of an algebraic parametric curve. However, if the adjacent data points are so close that the chord length is approximately equal to the arc length of the curve, the parameter t has the geometric meaning of approximate arc length of the curve. It is possible that the parametric spline curve is nicely behaved.

Practice has shown that parametric cubic spline curves of the cumulative chord length are satisfactory in fitting curves with large deflection. For example, if we use the parametric cubic spline curve for interpolating the data points illustrated in Section 1, curvature at each data point will be found

k	0.500	0.469	0.496	0.449	0.497	0.479	0.481	0.473

which is quite close to that evaluated by the interpolatory cubic function with respect to the coordinate system obtained by rotating the original one by 45°. The relative error does not exceed 5%. It will be seen from the following table that interpolatory results are even closer.

Cubic spline function interpolating to the rotated data points		Parametric cubic spline curve of cumulative chord length	
x	y	x	y
8.2547	0.0830	8.255	0.083
8.3844	0.0968	8.384	0.097
8.5141	0.1186	8.514	0.119
8.6437	0.1486	8.644	0.149
8.7734	0.1878	8.773	0.188
8.9031	0.2367	8.903	0.237
9.0328	0.2960	9.033	0.296
9.1625	0.3664	9.163	0.367
9.2922	0.4495	9.292	0.450
9.4219	0.5468	9.422	0.547
9.5516	0.6605	9.552	0.661
9.6813	0.7951	9.681	0.795
9.8109	0.9589	9.811	0.959
9.9406	1.1657	9.941	1.166
10.0703	1.4486	10.070	1.450

Parametric cubic spline curves of cumulative chord length have been widely used because of their simple computation and good interpolations effects. We may fit curves as well in three dimensions, forming splines for x, y and z in terms of chord length.

However, there has been a lack of theoretical study and analysis of these parametric spline curves. In applications, at least the following questions should be answered:

(1) Are they geometrically invariant?
(2) What is their mechanical background and how is the fairness?
(3) How do we check singularities and unwanted inflection points?

In Section 3, the theory of affine invariants for the parametric curves was used for the study of unwanted inflection points. We continue that study here.

First of all, we rewrite the equation of the parametric cubic spline curve of cumulative chord length in vector form. Assume that the ith curve segment, i.e., the segment between the data point $\boldsymbol{P}_{i-1}$ and $\boldsymbol{P}_i$, has the equation

$$\boldsymbol{P}(t) = \boldsymbol{R}_3 t^3 + \boldsymbol{R}_2 t^2 + \boldsymbol{R}_1 t + \boldsymbol{R}_0, \qquad t_{i-1} \leqslant t \leqslant t_i, \tag{6.1}$$

in which $t_i = \sum_{j=1}^{i} l_j$ $(i = 1, 2, \ldots, n)$ represent the knots in the parametric axis and $l_i = \overline{\boldsymbol{P}_{i-1}\boldsymbol{P}_i}$ denotes the chord length.

Continuity of the first and second derivative vectors at the data point $\boldsymbol{P}_i$ gives

$$\begin{aligned} \boldsymbol{P}'(t_i - 0) &= \boldsymbol{P}'(t_i + 0) \equiv \boldsymbol{m}_i, \\ \boldsymbol{P}''(t_i - 0) &= \boldsymbol{P}''(t_i + 0) \equiv \boldsymbol{M}_i. \end{aligned} \tag{6.2}$$

Analogous to cubic spline functions, by using relations between the first derivative vector $\boldsymbol{m}_i$ and the second derivative vector $\boldsymbol{M}_i$ at the data point $\boldsymbol{P}_i$

$$\begin{aligned} l_i\boldsymbol{M}_i &= -2(3\boldsymbol{e}_i - \boldsymbol{m}_{i-1} - 2\boldsymbol{m}_i), \\ l_{i+1}\boldsymbol{M}_i &= 2(3\boldsymbol{e}_{i+1} - 2\boldsymbol{m}_i - \boldsymbol{m}_{i+1}), \end{aligned} \tag{6.3}$$

we obtain the $\boldsymbol{m}$-continuity equations

$$\lambda \boldsymbol{m}_{i-1} + 2\boldsymbol{m}_i + \mu_i \boldsymbol{m}_{i+1} = 3(\lambda_i \boldsymbol{e}_i + \mu_i \boldsymbol{e}_{i+1}) \qquad (i = 1, 2, \ldots, n-1), \tag{6.4}$$

where

$$\lambda_i = \frac{l_{i+1}}{l_i + l_{i+1}}, \qquad \mu_i = \frac{l_i}{l_i + l_{i+1}},$$

and $\boldsymbol{e}_i = (1/l_i)\overrightarrow{\boldsymbol{P}_{i-1}\boldsymbol{P}_i}$ denotes the unit vector on the chord $\boldsymbol{P}_{i-1}\boldsymbol{P}_i$.

Correspondingly, we have the M-continuity equations

$$\mu_i \boldsymbol{M}_{i-1} + 2\boldsymbol{M}_i + \lambda_i \boldsymbol{M}_{i+1} = 6\,\frac{\boldsymbol{e}_{i+1} - \boldsymbol{e}_i}{l_i + l_{i+1}} \qquad (i = 1, 2, \ldots, n-1). \tag{6.5}$$

Adding two appropriate end conditions to the continuity equations (6.4) or (6.5), a complete system of linear equations will be obtained. In practical problems, it is suggested that tangent vectors at the end points should be chosen as unit vectors, i.e., $|\boldsymbol{m}_0| = |\boldsymbol{m}_n| = 1$. We shall see from the following discussion that such a choice will be good for fairness of the curve.

The ith segment, i.e., the segment between data points $\boldsymbol{P}_{i-1}$ and $\boldsymbol{P}_i$, has the equation in matrices form

$$\boldsymbol{P}(t) = [1, (t - t_{i-1}), (t - t_{i-1})^2, (t - t_{i-1})^3] \begin{bmatrix} \boldsymbol{a}_0 \\ \boldsymbol{a}_1 \\ \boldsymbol{a}_2 \\ \boldsymbol{a}_3 \end{bmatrix}_i$$

$$(t_{i-1} \leqslant t \leqslant t_i;\ i = 1, 2, \ldots, n),$$

where

$$\begin{bmatrix} a_0 \\ a_1 \\ a_2 \\ a_3 \end{bmatrix}_i = [A]_i \begin{bmatrix} P_{i-1} \\ P_i \\ m_{i-1} \\ m_i \end{bmatrix} = [B]_i \begin{bmatrix} P_{i-1} \\ P_i \\ M_{i-1} \\ M_i \end{bmatrix},$$

and matrices $[A]_i$ and $[B]_i$ have been expressed by (1.25) and (1.26) in Chapter II, respectively, but h_i must be replaced by l_i. $\boldsymbol{P}_i$ denotes the position vector of the data point $\boldsymbol{P}_i(x_i, y_i)$ $(i = 0, 1, \ldots, n)$.

Solving the complete system of continuity equations for $\boldsymbol{m}_i$ or $\boldsymbol{M}_i$ and using the above interpolatory formula, a spline curve will be uniquely determined. The quantitities involved in continuity equations and interpolatory formulas are those which are related only to the position vectors of the data points and chord lengths l_i, and are independent of the choice of coordinate system. This verifies that parametric cubic spline curves of cumulative chord length are geometrically invariant (more precisely, metrically invariant). This is the answer to the first question. In this book, we regard the splines which are geometrically invariant as "spline curves," but those which depend upon choice of coordinate systems as "spline functions."

The above discussions also apply to the three-dimensional case. From now on we limit our discussion to the planar case.

To answer the second question, we linearize the continuity equations. Projecting the m-continuity equations (6.4) onto $\boldsymbol{e}_{i+1}$ in its normal direction, we obtain

$$\begin{aligned} &\lambda_i m_{i-1} \cos(\theta_{i-1} - \phi_i) + 2m_i \cos\theta_i + \mu_i m_{i+1} \cos(\theta_{i+1} + \phi_{i+1}) \\ &\quad = 3(\lambda_i \cos\phi_i + \mu_i), \\ &\lambda_i m_{i-1} \sin(\theta_{i-1} - \phi_i) + 2m_i \sin\theta_i + \mu_i m_{i+1} \sin(\theta_{i+1} + \phi_{i+1}) \\ &\quad = -3\lambda_i \sin\phi_i \qquad (i = 1, 2, \ldots, n-1), \end{aligned} \tag{6.6}$$

in which $m_i = |\boldsymbol{m}_i|$, and the signed angles made by rotating $\boldsymbol{e}_{i+1}$ to $\boldsymbol{m}_i$, $\boldsymbol{e}_i$ to $\boldsymbol{e}_{i+1}$, are denoted by θ_i and ϕ_i respectively. An angle is positive if it is measured counterclockwise (Fig. 3-13).

We linearize equations (6.6) by expanding the trigonometric functions involved in power series. Taking the main part of each term, we have

$$\begin{aligned} &\lambda_i m_{i-1} + 2m_i + \mu_i m_{i+1} = 3 + O(\phi^2), \\ &\lambda_i m_{i-1}\theta_{i-1} + 2m_i\theta_i + \mu_i m_{i+1}\theta_{i+1} \\ &\quad = -\lambda_i(3 - m_{i-1})\phi_i - \mu_i m_{i+1} + O(\phi^3) \qquad (i = 1, 2, \ldots, n-1), \end{aligned} \tag{6.7}$$

where $\phi = \max_i |\phi_i|$.

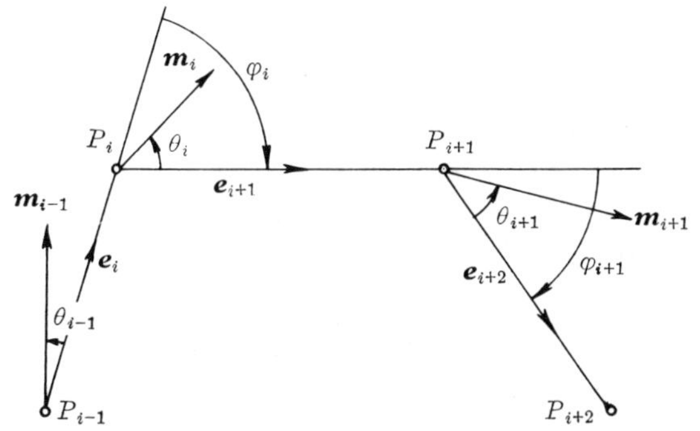

Figure 3-13

With end conditions $m_0 = m_n = 1$ in mind, we solve the first equation in (6.7) and get

$$m_i = 1 + O(\phi^2). \tag{6.8}$$

For small ϕ (i.e., $\phi \leqslant 30°$), the spline is said to be of locally small deflection. Neglecting $O(\phi^2)$, the tangent vector $\boldsymbol{m}_i$ at the data point $\boldsymbol{P}_i$ is a unit vector, as shown by (6.8). The second equation in (6.7) becomes

$$\lambda_i\theta_{i-1} + 2\theta_i + \mu_i\theta_{i+1} = -2\lambda_i\phi_i - \mu_i\phi_{i+1} + O(\phi^3) \qquad (i = 1, 2, \ldots, n-1), \tag{6.9}$$

which are called θ-continuity equations. They represent the relationship satisfied by the angle θ_i between the tangent and chord lines.

Taking the vector product of both sides of (6.3) with the vector $\boldsymbol{m}_i$ and using (6.8), we obtain

$$\begin{aligned} l_i k_i &= 2(2\phi_i + \theta_{i-1} + 2\theta_i) + O(\phi^3), \\ l_{i+1} k_i &= -2(\phi_{i+1} + 2\theta_i + \theta_{i+1}) + O(\phi^3). \end{aligned} \tag{6.10}$$

Attention should be paid to the directions of the signed angles θ_i and ϕ_i. In (6.10) k_i denotes the curvature of the spline curve at data point $\boldsymbol{P}_i$. Replacing the subscript i by $i-1$ in the second expression, we solve from it and the first expression for

$$\begin{aligned} \theta_{i-1} &= -\frac{l_i}{6}(2k_{i-1} + k_i) + O(\phi^3), \\ \theta_i &= \frac{l_i}{6}(k_{i-1} + 2k_i) - \phi_i + O(\phi^3). \end{aligned} \tag{6.11}$$

Replacing i in the first equation in (6.11) by $i+1$, we observe that both expressions in (6.11) have the same left-hand side. Therefore

$$\mu_i k_{i-1} + 2k_i + \lambda_i k_{i+1} = 3K_i + O(\phi^2) \qquad (i = 1, 2, \ldots, n-1), \qquad (6.12)$$

where K_i is equal to the curvature of the circle passing through three consecutive data points $\boldsymbol{P}_{i-1}$, $\boldsymbol{P}_i$ and $\boldsymbol{P}_{i+1}$. In fact $K_i = 2\phi_i/(l_i + l_{i+1}) + O(\phi_i^2)$. The equations in (6.12) are called the k-continuity equations. In a discussion for the strict mathematical model of wooden splines, we shall show that their k-continuity equations coincide with (6.12) and their difference is only in the term $O(\phi^2)$. This shows that the curvature of the wooden spline at each data point is approximated by that of the spline curve with order $O(\phi^2)$, whence the approximation of the curve itself is $O(\phi^4)$. This fact ensures theoretically the fairness of parametric cubic spline curves of cumulative chord length. Wooden splines provide again their mechanical background.

Now we turn to the third question. For each segment of the spline curve we normalize the parameter by the transformation $T = (t - t_{i-1})/li$ $(i = 1, 2, \ldots, n)$, so that $T \in [0, 1]$. The tangent vectors of the ith segment with respect to the new parameter T at the end points are denoted by $\boldsymbol{A}_{i0}$ and $\boldsymbol{A}_{i1}$, so that

$$\boldsymbol{A}_{i0} = \left.\frac{d\boldsymbol{P}}{dT}\right|_{T=0} = \left.\frac{d\boldsymbol{P}}{dt}\right|_{t=t_{i-1}} \frac{dt}{dT} = l_i \boldsymbol{m}_{i-1}.$$

Similarly $\boldsymbol{A}_{i1} = l_i \boldsymbol{m}_i$. The signed angles between $\boldsymbol{e}_i$ and $\boldsymbol{A}_{i0}$, and $\boldsymbol{e}_i$ and $\boldsymbol{A}_{i1}$, are denoted by θ_{i-1} and θ_i^*, respectively (Fig. 3-14). Assume $m_0 = m_n = 1$ as before.

The following theorem answers the third question.

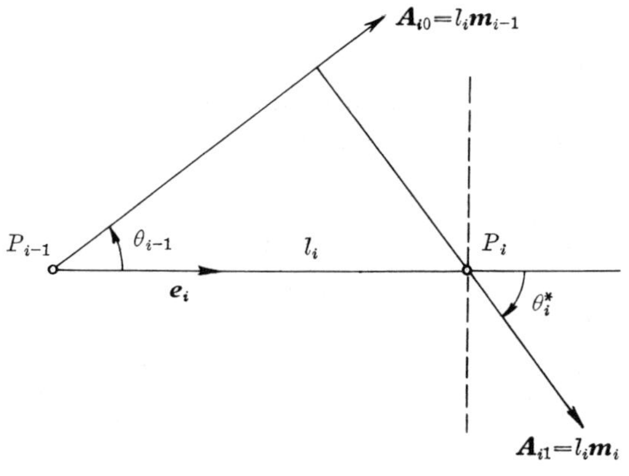

Figure 3-14

Theorem *If*

$$|\theta_{i-1}|+|\theta_i^*|\leqslant\frac{\pi}{2}\qquad(i=1,2,\ldots,n),\tag{6.13}$$

then each segment of the parametric cubic spline curve of cumulative chord length does not contain either singularities or two inflection points.

Proof Due to (6.13), the angle between two tangent vectors $\boldsymbol{m}_{i-1}$ and $\boldsymbol{m}_i$ is not greater than $\pi/2$. It follows from (6.4) that

$$|2\boldsymbol{m}_i|\leqslant|(\lambda_i\boldsymbol{m}_{i-1}+\mu_i\boldsymbol{m}_{i+1})+2\boldsymbol{m}_i|=3|\lambda_i\boldsymbol{e}_i+\mu_i\boldsymbol{e}_{i+1}|\leqslant 3\qquad(i=1,2,\ldots,n-1).$$

Therefore

$$m_i\leqslant\tfrac{3}{2}\qquad(i=0,1,\ldots,n).$$

We see that

$$|\boldsymbol{A}_{i0}|,|\boldsymbol{A}_{i1}|\leqslant\tfrac{3}{2}l_i\qquad(i=1,2,\ldots,n).\tag{6.14}$$

Denote the relative lengths of the tangent vectors at the end points of the ith segment by λ_i and μ_i (note that they are not the coefficients λ_i and μ_i in the continuity equations for spline functions). Without loss of generality, we assume that $\theta_{i-1}>0$. By using the theorem in Section 5, we consider the following five cases.

(1) $-(\pi/2)\leqslant\theta_i^*<0$. We have $\lambda_i,\mu_i>0$ in this case. Hence $\min(\lambda_i,\mu_i)<3$ by (6.14). Therefore $(\lambda_i,\mu_i)\in I$ (see Fig. 3-15). We conclude that the ith segment of the curve does not have a singularity and does not have two or more inflection points.

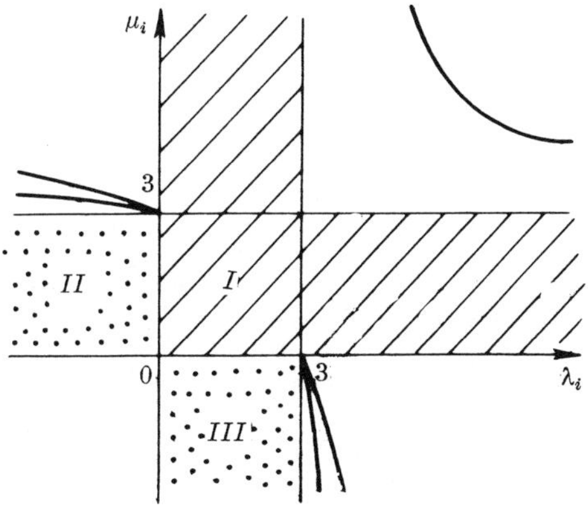

Figure 3-15

(2) $0<\theta_i^*<\theta_{i-1}$. We have

$$\lambda_i<0,$$

$$0<\mu_i<3,$$

and thus $(\lambda_i, \mu_i)\in II$. The ith segment does not have a singularity but has one inflection point.

(3) $\theta_{i-1}<\theta_i^*\leq\pi/2$. We have

$$0<\lambda_i<3,$$

$$\mu_i<0,$$

and then $(\lambda_i, \mu_i)\in III$.

(4) $\theta_i^*=\theta_{i-1}$.

(5) $\theta_i^*=0$. The same conclusion as in case (2) is still valid for cases (3)-(5).

From (6.13) we see that $\theta_i^*\in[-\pi/2, \pi/2]$, which shows that the above five cases are complete. The theorem has been proved.

The additional restriction (6.13) is a sufficient condition for common use to avoid a singularity or two inflection points occurring on the spline curve. In mathematical lofting and geometric design, the curves involved are mostly of locally small deflection and (6.13) is always satisfied. Generally speaking, a spline curve may have a singularity or two inflection-points without this restriction.

We consider an example. As illustrated by Fig. 3-16, assume $\boldsymbol{P}_0$, $\boldsymbol{P}_1$ and $\boldsymbol{P}_2$ are three data points in the plane, with $l_1=l_2=1$ and $\angle \boldsymbol{P}_0P_1\boldsymbol{P}_2=120°$. Tangent vectors $\boldsymbol{m}_0$ and $\boldsymbol{m}_2$ are taken such that $\boldsymbol{m}_2=-\boldsymbol{m}_0$. The angle between $\boldsymbol{m}_2$ and $\overrightarrow{\boldsymbol{P}_0\boldsymbol{P}_2}$ is denoted by α. From the continuity equations we find $\boldsymbol{m}_1=\frac{3}{4}(\boldsymbol{e}_1+\boldsymbol{e}_2)$, and thus $m_1=3\sqrt{3}/4\approx1.299$.

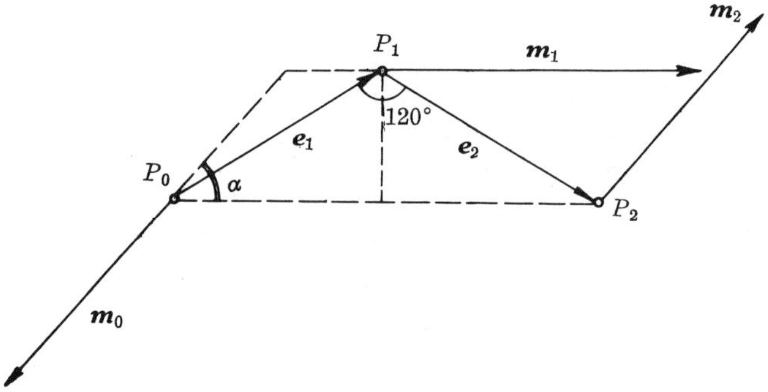

Figure 3-16

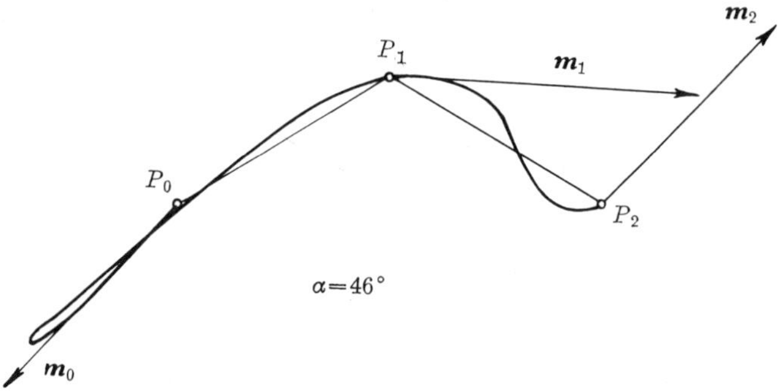

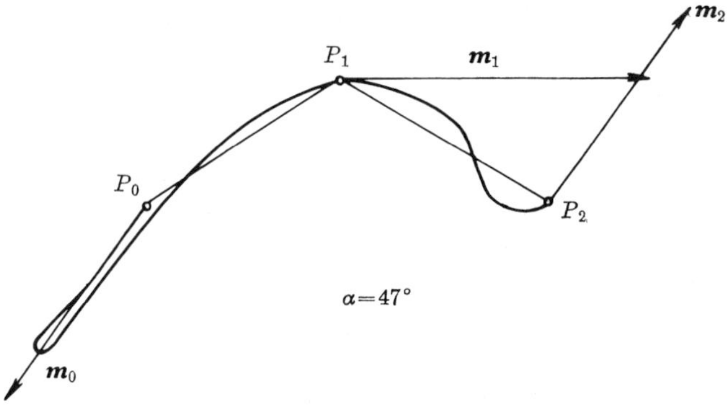

Figure 3-17

The relative lengths of the tangent vectors at the end points $\boldsymbol{P}_0$ and $\boldsymbol{P}_1$ of the first segment are, respectively,

$$\lambda_1 = -\frac{1}{\dfrac{1}{2\sin\alpha}} = -2\sin\alpha,$$

$$\mu_1 = \frac{\dfrac{3\sqrt{3}}{4}}{\dfrac{\sqrt{3}}{2} - \dfrac{\operatorname{ctg}\alpha}{2}} = \frac{3\sqrt{3}}{2(\sqrt{3} - \operatorname{ctg}\alpha)}.$$

(1) For $\alpha = 46°$, we have

$$\lambda_1 \approx -1.438,$$

$$\mu_1 \approx \frac{3 \times 1.732}{2(1.732 - 0.966)} \approx 3.40.$$

By the theorem in Section 5 we see that there is a loop on the first segment.
(2) For $\alpha = 47°$, we have

$$\lambda_1 \approx -1.462,$$

$$\mu_1 \approx \frac{3 \times 1.732}{2(1.732 - 0.933)} \approx 3.24.$$

By the theorem we just mentioned the first segment has two inflection points.

The above two cases are illustrated by Fig. 3-17.

7 Composite Curves of Parametric Cubic Segments

7.1 Continuity Conditions

In this section we consider the construction of composite curves from the various types of plane parametric cubic curve segments. From a practical point of view, it is necessary to attain GC^2-continuity at each join. By GC^2-continuity for the parametric curves we mean the continuity of the position, the tangent line and the curvature of adjacent segments at the join. The parametric cubic spline curve of cumulative chord length is certainly of GC^2-continuity, as the first and second derivative vectors with respect to the parameter, i.e., the cumulative chord length, are continuous, as we have shown in the previous section.

Suppose two parametric segments $\boldsymbol{P}_1(t)$ and $\boldsymbol{P}_2(t)$ are given, in which $t \in [0, 1]$. We want to join these segment at $\boldsymbol{P}_0(1) = \boldsymbol{P}_1(0)$ with GC^2-continuity. Necessary and sufficient conditions are given in the following theorem.

Theorem *For two plane segments $\boldsymbol{P}_1(t)$ and $\boldsymbol{P}_2(t)$ to attain GC^2-continuity at the join, it is necessary and sufficient that there exist real numbers $\alpha > 0$ and β such that*

$$\begin{aligned} &\boldsymbol{P}_1(1) = \boldsymbol{P}_2(0), \\ &\boldsymbol{P}_1'(1) = \alpha \boldsymbol{P}_2'(0), \\ &\boldsymbol{P}_1''(1) = \alpha^2 \boldsymbol{P}_2''(0) + \beta \boldsymbol{P}_2'(0). \end{aligned} \tag{7.1}$$

Proof Assume that $\boldsymbol{P}_1(t)$ and $\boldsymbol{P}_2(t)$ have continuous tangent vectors at the joint. Then the first and second equalities in (7.1) are satisfied, where $\alpha > 0$.

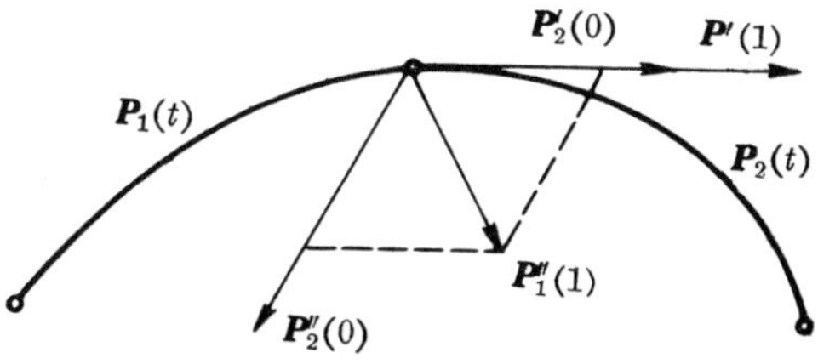

Figure 3-18

(1) Suppose $P_2'(0) \parallel P_2''(0)$. As illustrated by Fig. 3-18, there exist real numbers β and γ such that

$$P_1''(1) = \beta P_2'(0) + \gamma P_2''(0).$$

Evaluating the curvature of $P_1(t)$ at the join, we get

$$k_1 = \frac{[P_1'(1) \quad P_1''(1)]}{|P_1'(1)|^3} = \frac{[\alpha P_2'(0) \quad (\beta P_2'(0) + \gamma P_2''(0))]}{\alpha^3 |P_2'(0)|^3}$$

$$= \frac{\gamma [P_2'(0) \quad P_2''(0)]}{\alpha^2 |P_2'(0)|^3} = \frac{\gamma}{\alpha^2} k_2.$$

Continuity of curvature is equivalent to $k_1 = k_2$, and this implies $\gamma = \alpha^2$. Thus the third equality in (7.1) is justified.

(2) Suppose $P_2'(0) \parallel P_2''(0)$.

In this case $k_2 = 0$. Hence $k_1 = k_2 = 0$. It follows that $P_1'(1) \parallel P_1''(1)$. We obtain again the third equality of (7.1).

Conversely, by the formula for curvature of parametric curves we see that the conditions in (7.1) are sufficient for GC^2-continuity. This completes the proof.

Denote the ith segment of the parametric cubic spline curve by $P_i(t)$. We see clearly that two segments $P_i(t)$ and $P_{i+1}(t)$ have at their join the conditions (7.1) with coefficients $\beta_i = 0$ and $\alpha_i = l_i / l_{i+1}$.

As shown by (7.1), the most general spline curves of C^2-continuity are not uniquely determined, since at each internal data point there are two degrees of freedom, i.e., α and β, to be chosen. By adjusting these two numbers, we may construct various types of spline curves to meet certain requirements.

As early as 1963, parametric cubic spline curves were developed by Ferguson, called Ferguson curves by Bézier. These curves formed the foundation for the FMILL system developed by Boeing Aircraft Company in the United States. Ferguson curves correspond to one of the simplest choices: $\alpha = 1$ and $\beta = 0$, suitable only for uniformly spaced data points. In this case we have to choose the magnitude unit of the coordinate system such that $l_i \approx 1$, $i = 1, 2, \ldots, n$. When the data points are not uniformly spaced, the Ferguson curve will be not good in the sense that for longer l_i the corresponding segment is rather flat and very close to the chord, and for shorter l_i the segment may contain two inflection points or a singularity. In 1967 Hosaka suggested taking $\alpha_i = l_i / l_{i+1}$. In this case the Ferguson curve reduces to the parametric spline curve of cumulative chord length.

7.2 Parametric Cubic Spline Curves with Shape Preserving Properties

In computational geometry, there are interpolatory problems such as the following: For given ordered data points P_i $(i = 0, 1, \ldots, n)$ in the plane, find a "shape preserving" interpolatory curve. By "shape preserving," we mean that if a part of the polygon $\boldsymbol{P}_0\boldsymbol{P}_1 \cdots \boldsymbol{P}_n$ is convex then so is the corresponding segment on the interpolatory curve, and if the polygon changes its direction at a certain data point, then the corresponding segment should have an inflection point but no singularity.

Bézier curves and B-spline curves, which will be studied in the next chapter, are very efficient tools for shape preserving approximation, but they are not schemes of interpolation.

The problem becomes easier if we relax the requirements of continuity. Obviously, the simplest solution of the shape preserving interpolation with C^0-continuity is the polygon formed by joining each two neighbouring data points by line segments. The shape preserving interpolation with GC^1-continuity can be constructed in such a way: The tangent direction is prescribed at each data point by certain methods, followed by Hermite interpolation for each two consecutive data points. Biarc spline curves are practical schemes for shape preserving interpolation with GC^1-continuity. They will be discussed later.

The parametric cubic spline curves of cumulative chord length are of GC^2-continuity but are not shape preserving. Although the splines in tension are shape preserving with GC^2-continuity, there is only a tension parameter for each segment, and no more degree of freedom exists. Moreover, when the tension parameters become large enough, the spline in tension approximates the polygon formed by chords. This shows that the spline in tension has a lack of flexibility in some applications.

In some problems, more degrees of freedom are needed. For instance, it is desirable to assign a tangent direction and curvature to each data point arbitrarily. Each segment of the spline becomes the Hermite interpolation in the approximation theory of functions: The function values and the first and second derivatives at two end points are given. The resulting function must be a polynomial of degree five. The corresponding curve is hard to control as it may have three inflection points.

In this section, we construct a shape preserving and interpolatory spline with GC^2-continuity by using parametric cubic segments. As we mentioned in Section 7.1, the tangent direction and curvature at each data point P_i are regarded as two degrees of freedom, in order to provide more flexibility (Liu Dingyuan [2], 1979).

The relationships between curvatures k_0, k_1 and the relative magnitudes λ, μ of the tangent vectors $\boldsymbol{m}_0$, $\boldsymbol{m}_1$, respectively, at the end points of a plane parametric cubic segment are

$$k_0 = \frac{4\Delta}{a^3}\frac{3-\mu}{\lambda^2}\operatorname{sign}(\lambda),$$

$$k_1 = \frac{4\Delta}{b^3}\frac{3-\lambda}{\mu^2}\operatorname{sign}(\mu),$$

in which a and b represent the two sides of the triangle $\boldsymbol{P}_0\boldsymbol{P}\boldsymbol{P}_1$ illustrated by Fig. 3-19, and

$$\Delta = \tfrac{1}{2}[\boldsymbol{P}_0\boldsymbol{P}\boldsymbol{P}\boldsymbol{P}_1],$$

the signed area of the triangle. For $\Delta \neq 0$, the relationships can be rewritten as

$$\begin{aligned} \mu &= 3 - \operatorname{sign}(\lambda) A\lambda^2, \\ \lambda &= 3 - \operatorname{sign}(\mu) B\mu^2, \end{aligned} \tag{7.2}$$

where

$$\begin{aligned} A &= \frac{a^3}{4\Delta} k_0, \\ B &= \frac{b^3}{4\Delta} k_1. \end{aligned} \tag{7.3}$$

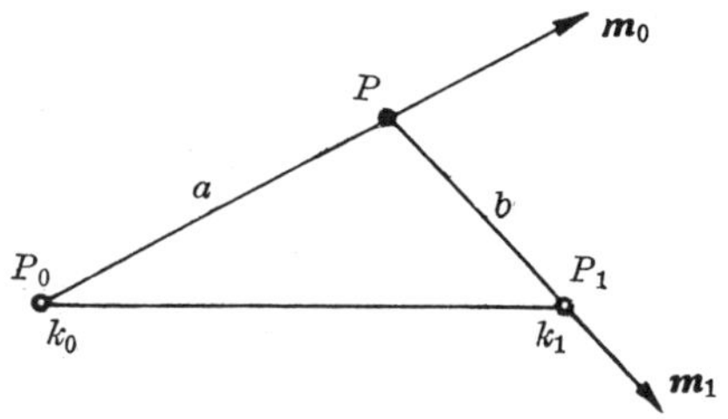

Figure 3-19

For given curvatures k_0, k_1 and the triangle $\boldsymbol{P}_0\boldsymbol{P}\boldsymbol{P}_1$ formed by the tangent lines, equations (7.2) determine the coordinates of the intersections of two parabolas in the (λ, μ) plane.

Constructing the spline curve consists of the following steps:

(1) determine the directions of $\boldsymbol{m}_0$ and $\boldsymbol{m}_1$;
(2) specify the curvatures k_0 and k_1 at $\boldsymbol{P}_0$ and $\boldsymbol{P}_1$, respectively;
(3) evaluate the relative magnitudes λ and μ.

Thus the tangent vectors $\boldsymbol{m}_0$ and $\boldsymbol{m}_1$ at the data points are completely determined, and then each segment is determined by Hermite interpolation.

Data points $\boldsymbol{P}_i$ $(i = 0, 1, \ldots, n)$ are given in the plane, shown by Fig. 3-20, in which notations are the same as in Section 6.

(1) *Determination of the direction of the tangent vector $\boldsymbol{m}_i$ at $\boldsymbol{P}_i$.* The direction of $\boldsymbol{m}_i$ is determined by the coefficient C_i for which $0 < C_i < 1$ and

$$\theta_i = -C_i\phi_i \qquad (i = 1, 2, \ldots, n-1), \tag{7.4}$$

while θ_0 and θ_n are specified to fix the tangent vectors $\boldsymbol{m}_0$ and $\boldsymbol{m}_n$ at the end points of the curve.

(2) *Determination of curvature k_i at P_i.* First of all, the following criteria help us to check whether the inflection points occur on each segment.

(*i*) If $\phi_{i-1}\phi_i > 0$, then the ith segment does not contain inflection points;

(*ii*) if $\phi_{i-1}\phi_i < 0$, then the ith segment contains one inflection point.

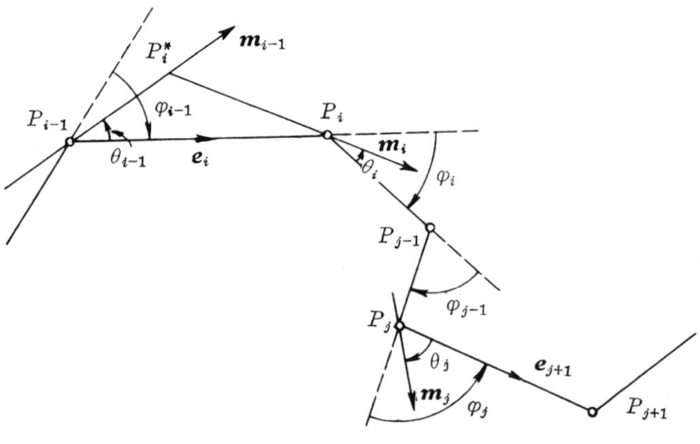

Figure 3-20

To ensure that i^{th} segment does not contain a singularity or an unwanted inflection-point, a sufficient condition will be given below.

For the sake of simplicity, the subscript i will be temporarily omitted and the two end points of the ith segment will be denoted simply by $\boldsymbol{P}_0$ and $\boldsymbol{P}_1$. Other notations remain the same as in Fig. 3-20, (7.2) and (7.3).

We consider the following two cases.

(i) The segment does not contain an inflection point.

In this case k_0, k_1 and Δ have the same sign. From (7.3) we have A, $B>0$. A pair of parabolas expressed by (7.2) is shown by Fig. 3-21. For fairness of the spline curve, we are interested in the solutions of (7.2) only in the region λ, $\mu>0$.

Assume that $\Delta>0$. The first curve in (7.2) intersects the λ-axis at $(\sqrt{3/A}, 0)$, while the second curve in (7.2) intersects the μ-axis at $(0, \sqrt{3/B})$. If

$$\sqrt{\frac{3}{A}}, \sqrt{\frac{3}{B}}<3,$$

or equivalently

$$k_0>\frac{4\Delta}{3a^3},$$

$$k_1>\frac{4\Delta}{3b^3},$$

then the solution to (7.2) in the first quadrant of the (λ, μ) plane is represented uniquely by the intersection of the two real parabolas illustrated by Fig. 3-21.

If

$$\sqrt{\frac{3}{A}}, \sqrt{\frac{3}{B}}>3,$$

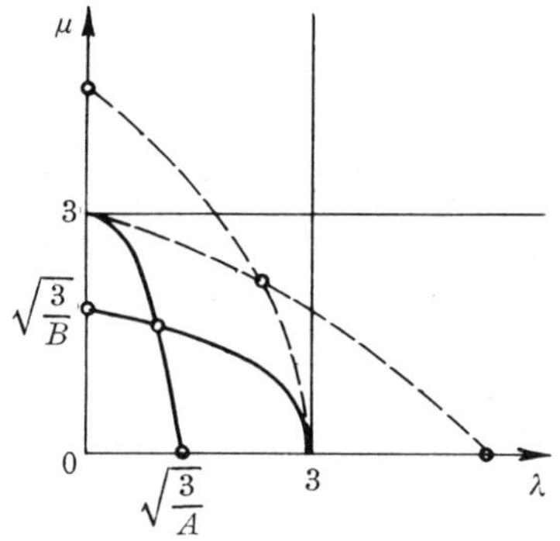

Figure 3-21

or equivalently

$$k_0 < \frac{4\Delta}{3a^3},$$

$$k_1 < \frac{4\Delta}{3b^3},$$

then the solution to (7.2) is represented uniquely by the intersection of the dotted parabolas in the same figure.

In these two cases, solutions (λ, μ) satisfy the conditions $0 < \lambda, \mu < 3$. This means that the points (λ, μ) belong to the region I in Fig. 3-15. Thus the corresponding curve segment does not contain a singularity or inflection-point.

Considering there is still the case of $\Delta < 0$, the above restrictions to k_0 and k_1 should be modified as

$$|k_0| > \frac{4|\Delta|}{3a^3}, \qquad |k_0| < \frac{4|\Delta|}{3a^3},$$
$$\text{and}$$
$$|k_1| > \frac{4|\Delta|}{3b^3} \qquad |k_1| < \frac{4|\Delta|}{3b^3}.$$

These are ranges of k_0 and k_1 for the segment without inflection points.

(ii) The segment contains an inflection point.

In this case, k_0 and k_1 have opposite signs. It follows from (7.3) that A and B have opposite signs too. Hence the curves represented by (7.2) have only the two possibilities shown in Fig. 3-22.

It is seen that two parabolas of anti-symmetry have a unique intersection falling into the region, associated with a single inflection point on the curve segment.

In view of fairness, only solutions to (7.2) which fall into the second and fourth quadrants of the (λ, μ) plane shall be considered. In other words,

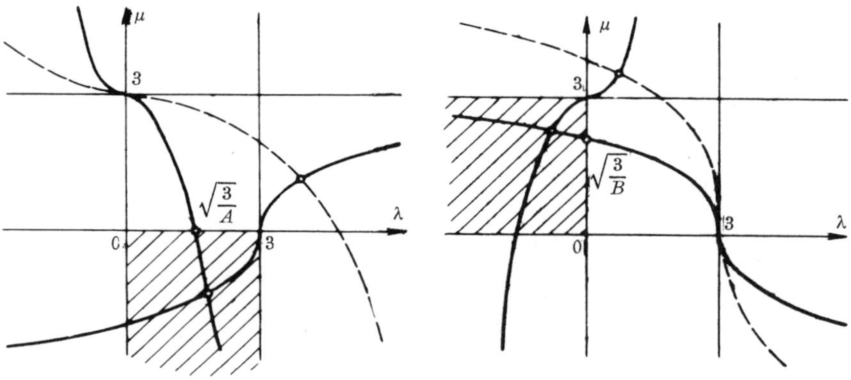

Figure 3-22

only the intersections in the shaded regions of Fig. 3-22 shall be taken into account. This means that $\sqrt{3/A}<3$ or $\sqrt{3/B}<3$, or equivalently

$$|k_0|>\frac{4|\Delta|}{3a^3} \qquad \text{or} \qquad |k_1|>\frac{4|\Delta|}{3b^3}.$$

These inequalities determine the ranges of k_0 and k_1 for the segment with a single inflection point.

Now let us return to our previous discussions. The $(i+1)^{\text{th}}$ data point is denoted again by $\boldsymbol{P}_i$. The triangle formed by tangent lines of the ith segment, denoted by $\boldsymbol{P}_{i-1}\boldsymbol{P}_i^*\boldsymbol{P}_i$, is illustrated in Fig. 3-20. The two sides and the signed area of the triangle are designated by

$$a_i=|\boldsymbol{P}_{i-1}\boldsymbol{P}_i^*|, \qquad b_i=|\boldsymbol{P}_i^*\boldsymbol{P}_i|, \qquad \Delta_i=\tfrac{1}{2}[\boldsymbol{P}_{i-1}\boldsymbol{P}_i^*\boldsymbol{P}_i^*\boldsymbol{P}_i],$$

respectively. We employ the following notations:

$$\begin{aligned} k_{i-1}^{+}&=\frac{4|\Delta_i|}{3a_i^3}, \\ k_i^{-}&=\frac{4|\Delta_i|}{3b_i^3}, \qquad (i=1,2,\ldots,n). \\ k_0^{-}&=k_n^{+}=0 \end{aligned}$$

In summary, we can choose the curvature k_i at $\boldsymbol{P}_i$ in such a way that k_i and ϕ_i have the same sign, and

$$|k_i|>\max(k_i^{+},k_i^{-}) \qquad (i=0,1,\ldots,n), \tag{7.5}$$

in which ϕ_0 and ϕ_n are given by the end conditions.

(3) Finally, after determining k_i at each $\boldsymbol{P}_i$, we solve (7.2) for λ and μ to obtain the relative magnitudes λ_i and μ_i of the tangent vectors at the end-points of the ith segment. Hence the ith $(i=1,2,\ldots,n)$ segment of the curve is completely determined.

7.3 Constructing Spline Curves in Tension with Large Deflection in Terms of Parametric Cubic Segments

To solve convexity preserving interpolation problems, the spline functions in tension were introduced in Section 3 of Chapter II. There the results came out under the assumption of the curve being of small deflection. In the case of large deflection, computations will be unstable in finding the spline functions in tension, since differences of large numbers will be involved in the evaluations of F_i using the continuity equations (3.8) of Chapter II. Furthermore, the tension parameters may become very large if they are estimated by the conditions (3.11) of Chapter II for convexity preserving. Spline functions in tension are expressed in terms of exponential functions which are computationally more complicated than algebraic polynomials.

In (7.1), the GC^2-continuity conditions for plane parametric cubic segments, there are two degrees of freedom to be determined.

(1) If $\alpha = 1$, $\beta = 0$, then we obtain the parametric cubic spline curves of Ferguson type.
(2) If $\alpha_i = l_i/l_{i+1}$, $\beta_i = 0$ $(i = 1, 2, \ldots, n-1)$, then the parametric cubic spline curves of cumulative chord lengths are obtained.
(3) If the coefficients C_i in (7.4) and the curvatures k_i $(i = 1, 2, \ldots, n-1)$ in (7.5) are taken to be the two degrees of freedom, then we have the interpolatory parametric cubic spline curves with shape preserving property.

There remains the fourth construction: taking $a_i = l_i/l_{i+1}$ and β_i as tension parameters $(i = 1, 2, \ldots, n-1)$, we have the spline curves in tension with GC^2-continuity, which are suitable for the cases of large deflection.

1° Continuity Equations

Let $n+1$ data points $\boldsymbol{P}_i$ $(i = 0, 1, \ldots, n)$ be given in the plane. The ith parametric cubic segment, i.e., the segment between $\boldsymbol{P}_{i-1}$ and $\boldsymbol{P}_i$, has the expression in terms of vectors

$$\begin{aligned} \boldsymbol{P}_i(t) = \boldsymbol{P}_{i-1} + t^2(3-2t)\boldsymbol{L}_i + t(t-1)^2\boldsymbol{P}_i'(0) \\ + t^2(t-1)\boldsymbol{P}_i'(1), \qquad 0 \leqslant t \leqslant 1 \qquad (i = 1, 2, \ldots, n), \end{aligned} \tag{7.6}$$

in which $\boldsymbol{L}_i = \boldsymbol{P}_i - \boldsymbol{P}_{i-1}$, and $l_i = |\boldsymbol{L}_i|$ is the chord length. The unit vector in the direction of the chord is expressed by $\boldsymbol{e}_i = (1/l_i)\boldsymbol{L}_i$.

The ith and $(i+1)^{\text{th}}$ segments reach GC^2-continuity at $\boldsymbol{P}_i$ iff there exist coefficients η_i and $\xi_i > 0$ such that

$$\left.\begin{aligned} \boldsymbol{P}_i'(1) &= \xi_i \boldsymbol{P}_{i+1}'(0), \\ \boldsymbol{P}_i''(1) &= \xi_i^2 \boldsymbol{P}_{i+1}''(0) - \eta_i \boldsymbol{P}_i'(1), \end{aligned}\right. \qquad (i = 1, 2, \ldots, n-1). \tag{7.7}$$

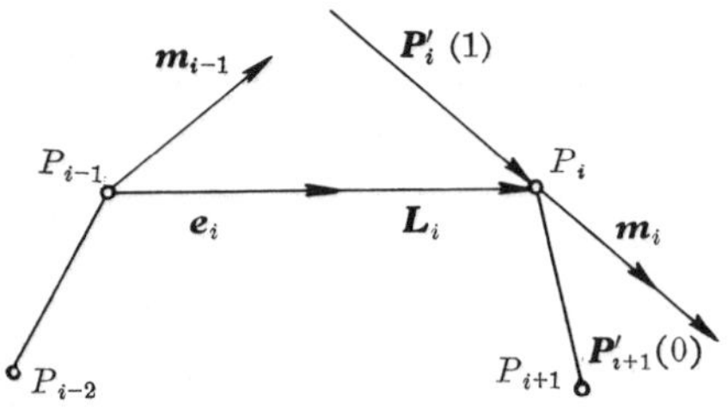

Figure 3-23

The first and second derivative vectors of the segment (7.6) satisfy the relations

$$
\begin{aligned}
&P_i''(1) = -2[3L_i - P_i'(0) - 2P_i'(1)],\\
&P_{i+1}''(0) = 2[3L_{i+1} - 2P_{i+1}'(0) - P_{i+1}'(1)],
\end{aligned}
\qquad (i = 1, 2, \ldots, n-1). \qquad (7.8)
$$

which are similar to that of cubic spline functions. Inserting them into (7.7), we obtain the equations

$$
P_i'(0) + \left[2\xi_i(\xi_i + 1) + \frac{\xi_i \eta_i}{2}\right] P_{i+1}'(0) + \xi_i^2 P_{i+1}'(1)
$$

$$
= 3(L_i + \xi_i^2 L_{i+1}) \qquad (i = 1, 2, \ldots, n-1). \qquad (7.9)
$$

Set $\xi_i = l_i / l_{i+1}$. By the first equation in (7.7), we denote

$$
m_i = \frac{1}{l_i} P_i'(1) = \frac{1}{l_{i+1}} P_{i+1}'(0) \qquad (i = 1, 2, \ldots, n-1).
$$

Thus the above equations can be written as

$$
\lambda_i m_{i-1} + \rho_i m_i + \mu_i m_{i+1} = 3E_i \qquad (i = 1, 2, \ldots, n-1), \qquad (7.10)
$$

in which

$$
\lambda_i = \frac{l_{i+1}}{l_i + l_{i+1}}, \qquad \mu_i = \frac{l_i}{l_i + l_{i+1}}, \qquad \rho_i = 2 + \tfrac{1}{2}\lambda_i \eta_i, \qquad E_i = \lambda_i e_i + \mu_i e_{i+1}.
$$

We assume that $\eta_i \geqslant 0$, thus $\rho_i \geqslant 0$, which are referred to as tension parameters. If $\eta_i = 0$ and $\rho_i = 2$ for all i, (7.10) reduces to the continuity equations of parametric cubic spline curves of cumulative chord lengths. It is easily seen that to include the spline curves of cumulative chord lengths as a special case, we have set the free parameters $\xi_i = l_i / l_{i+1}$.

Several nonperiodic end conditions for the continuity equations (7.10) can be written as the unified form

$$
\begin{aligned}
\rho_0 m_0 + \mu_0 m_1 &= 3E_0,\\
\lambda_n m_{n-1} + \rho_n m_n &= 3E_n,
\end{aligned}
\qquad (7.10)'
$$

in which the tension parameters ρ_0, $\rho_n \geqslant 2$, and $0 < \lambda_n$, $\mu_0 < 1$, $0 < |E_0|$, $|E_n| < 1$. A complete system of equations with tridiagonal coefficient matrix is formed by (7.10) and (7.10)′. The coefficient matrix is diagonally dominant, so that the system has a unique solution. Expressing the system of vector equations in terms of their two components, the resulting systems can be solved by the algorithm mentioned in Section 1.1 of Chapter II. In this case (7.6) should be used as the interpolation formulas, in which $P_i'(0) = l_i m_{i-1}$

and $P_i'(1) = l_i m_i$. Thus the spline curve so obtained is certainly of GC^2-continuity.

2° Conditions for Convexity Preserving

Denote by a_{ij} $(i, j = 0, 1, \ldots, n)$ the elements in the inverse matrix of the coefficient matrix of the complete system mentioned above. Then the solution of the system has the form

$$\boldsymbol{m}_i = 3 \sum_{j=0}^{n} a_{ij} \boldsymbol{E}_j \qquad (i = 0, 1, \ldots, n).$$

Using a result of Kershaw (1970) concerning the inverse of a tridiagonal matrix,

$$\frac{1}{\rho_i} < a_{ii} < \frac{1}{\rho_i} A_i,$$

$$0 < (-1)^{i-j} a_{ij} < \left(\prod_{r=r_1}^{r_2} \rho_r \right)^{-1} A_j \qquad (i \neq j), (i, j = 0, 1, \ldots, n),$$

where

$$A_i = \frac{\omega_i}{\omega_i - 1},$$

$$\omega_i = \min(\rho_{i-1}\rho_i, \rho_i\rho_{i+1}),$$

$$r_1 = \min(i, j),$$

$$r_2 = \max(i, j),$$

we can prove the following lemma.

Lemma *If $\rho_{i-1} = \rho_i = \rho_{i+1} \geqslant 5$, then we have*

$$\begin{cases} \sin \alpha_i < \dfrac{3.3}{\rho_i}, \\[2ex] |\boldsymbol{m}_i| < \dfrac{4.4}{\rho_i} \end{cases} \qquad (i = 0, 1, \ldots, n), \tag{7.11}$$

where α_i denotes the angle formed by $\boldsymbol{m}_i$ and $\boldsymbol{E}_i$, and $\rho_{-1} = \rho_{n+1} = 0$.

However, we skip the proof.

The lemma indicates that if $\rho_{i-1} = \rho_i = \rho_{i+1}$ becomes sufficiently large, then $|\boldsymbol{m}_i| \to 0$ and the direction of $\boldsymbol{m}_i$ tends to that of $\boldsymbol{E}_i$. Hence if we take $\rho_{i-2} = \rho_{i-1} = \rho_i = \rho_{i-1}$ large enough, then $|\boldsymbol{m}_{i-1}|, |\boldsymbol{m}_i| \to 0$ and the directions of $\boldsymbol{m}_{i-1}$ and $\boldsymbol{m}_i$ tend to that of $\boldsymbol{E}_{i-1}$ and $\boldsymbol{E}_i$, respectively. We know that $\boldsymbol{E}_j$ is a weighted mean of $\boldsymbol{e}_j$ and $\boldsymbol{e}_{j+1}$ $(j = 1, 2, \ldots, n-1)$. Hence the convexity of given data points, i.e., the fact that all ϕ_j have the same sign, implies

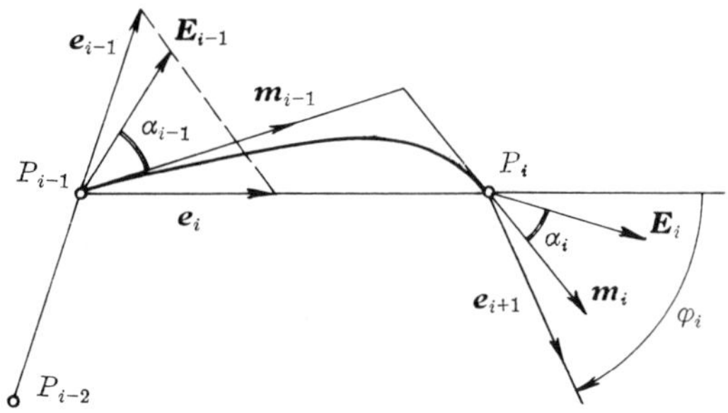

Figure 3-24

that the relative magnitudes of the tangent vectors at the end points of the ith segment are all positive and tend to zero. This ensures there is neither a singularity nor an inflection point on the ith segment (see Fig. 3-24).

What do we mean by the "tension parameter being large enough"? Precisely speaking, if

$$\rho_{i-2} = \rho_{i-1} = \rho_i = \rho_{i+1}$$

$$\geqslant \max\left(\frac{6.2}{\lambda_{i-1}|\sin\phi_{i-1}|}, \frac{3.3}{\mu_{i-1}|\sin\phi_{i-1}|}, \frac{3.3}{\lambda_i|\sin\phi_i|}, \frac{6.2}{\mu_i|\sin\phi_i|}\right), \tag{7.12}$$

then the ith segment does not contain either a singularity or an inflection point. Here we give up the proof. For further detail readers are referred to (Liu Dingyuan [2], 1979).

However, (7.12) is a conservative estimate. It shows that it is possible to construct spline curves in tension with the convexity preserving property for cases of large deflection in terms of parametric cubic segments. In practice, for the purpose of convexity preserving, an iterative scheme for choosing ρ_i can be designed just as we have done in the last chapter for spline functions in tension. We shall not carry the discussion any further.

3° *Properties of Spline Curves in Tension with Large Tension Parameters*

Define a new vector

$$\begin{aligned} \boldsymbol{C}_i &\equiv \boldsymbol{P}_i(t) - \boldsymbol{P}_{i-1} - t^2(3-2t)\boldsymbol{L}_i \\ &= t(t-1)^2\boldsymbol{P}_i'(0) + t^2(t-1)\boldsymbol{P}_i'(1) \\ &= t(t-1)^2 l_i \boldsymbol{m}_{i-1} + t^2(t-1) l_i \boldsymbol{m}_i, \qquad 0 \leqslant t \leqslant 1, \end{aligned}$$

based upon (7.6). Note that for $t \in [0, 1]$, we have

$$\max|t(t-1)^2| = \max|t^2(t-1)| = \tfrac{4}{27},$$

and thus

$$|\boldsymbol{C}_i(t)| \leq \tfrac{4}{27} l_i(|\boldsymbol{m}_{i-1}| + |\boldsymbol{m}_i|) < \frac{4}{3} \frac{l_i}{\rho_i}$$

by the second equation in (7.11).

This has the following interpretation: Given $\rho_{i-2} = \rho_{i-1} = \rho_i = \rho_{i+1} (\geq 5)$, the ith segment is contained by a strip of width $4l_i/3\rho_i$, with the chord $\boldsymbol{P}_{i-1}\boldsymbol{P}_i$ as one of its sides (see Fig. 3-25). It is clear that the ith segment $\boldsymbol{P}_i(t)$ will approach the chord $\boldsymbol{P}_{i-1}\boldsymbol{P}_i$ as $\rho_{i-2} = \rho_{i-1} = \rho_i = \rho_{i+1} \to \infty$. In this case the tangent directions at the two end-points tend to $\boldsymbol{E}_{i-1}$ and $\boldsymbol{E}_i$, respectively.

Compute the curvature at $\boldsymbol{P}_{i-1}$:

$$\begin{aligned} k_{i-1} &= \frac{[\boldsymbol{P}_i'(0)\ \boldsymbol{P}_i''(0)]}{|\boldsymbol{P}_i'(0)|^3} \\ &= \frac{6[\boldsymbol{P}_i'(0)\ \boldsymbol{L}_i] - 2[\boldsymbol{P}_i'(0)\ \boldsymbol{P}_i'(1)]}{|\boldsymbol{P}_i'(0)|^3} \\ &= \frac{6[\boldsymbol{m}_{i-1}\ \boldsymbol{e}_i] - 2[\boldsymbol{m}_{i-1}\ \boldsymbol{m}_i]}{l_i|\boldsymbol{m}_{i-1}|^3}. \end{aligned}$$

Obviously $k_{i-1} \to \infty$ as $\rho_{i-2} = \rho_{i-1} = \rho_i \to \infty$.

In summary we have the following conclusions:

(1) the whole spline curve approaches the polygon formed by the chords;
(2) $\boldsymbol{m}_i \to \boldsymbol{E}_i$ $(i = 0, 1, \ldots, n)$,
(3) $k_i \to \infty$ $(i = 0, 1, \ldots, n)$,

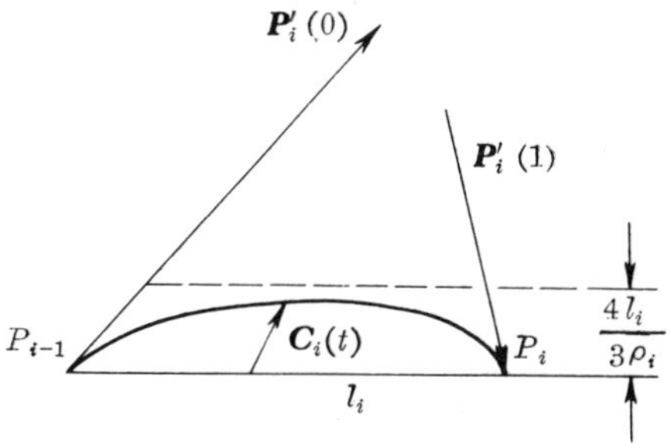

Figure 3-25

as $\rho_i \to \infty$ $(i=0, 1, \ldots, n)$. In this case the spline globally approximates the polygon formed by the chords. The spline curve changes its direction at each data point rapidly and smoothly but maintains its GC^2-continuity. This is the geometric figure for the parametric spline curve in tension with large tension parameters.

7.4 Spline Curves with Normalized Tangent Vectors

In 1974, Manning constructed an interpolatory spline curve of GC^2-continuity by using parametric cubic segments in the plane. In the present section, we introduce briefly the construction of such splines, then show the following fact: If the given data points satisfy the requirement of locally small deflection, then such splines coincide with the spline of cumulative chord length when the higher-order terms are neglected.

Assume that the cubic segment $\boldsymbol{P}(t)$, $t \in [0, 1]$, has the end-points $\boldsymbol{P}_0$ and $\boldsymbol{P}_1$, and that $\boldsymbol{P}'(0)$ and $\boldsymbol{P}'(1)$ are its tangent vectors at these points respectively. In Fig. 3-26, $\boldsymbol{P}'(0)$ and $\boldsymbol{P}'(1)$ are shown making angles θ_0 and θ_1 with the line $\boldsymbol{P}_0\boldsymbol{P}_1$, and $l=\overline{\boldsymbol{P}_0\boldsymbol{P}_1}$. According to the definition by Manning, the magnitudes of the tangent vectors should be

$$\begin{aligned} |\boldsymbol{P}'(0)| &= \frac{2l}{1+\sigma\cos\theta_1+(1-\sigma)\cos\theta_0}, \\ |\boldsymbol{P}'(1)| &= \frac{2l}{1+\sigma\cos\theta_0+(1-\sigma)\cos\theta_1}, \end{aligned} \tag{7.13}$$

in which σ is an appropriate constant between 0 and 1. In a previous paper the value $\sigma=1$ was suggested by Manning, but in 1974 he considered that $\sigma=\frac{2}{3}$ should be a better choice after a series of plane curves had been plotted for various combinations of θ_0, θ_1 and σ. The tangent vectors, and then the cubic segments, are now said to be normalized.

Let $n+1$ data points $\boldsymbol{P}_i$ $(i=0, 1, \ldots, n)$ be given in the plane. We have shown that (7.7) is a necessary and sufficient condition for GC^2-continuity of the ith and $(i+1)^{\text{th}}$ segments at the data point $\boldsymbol{P}_i$. Figure 3-27 illustrates their conjunction.

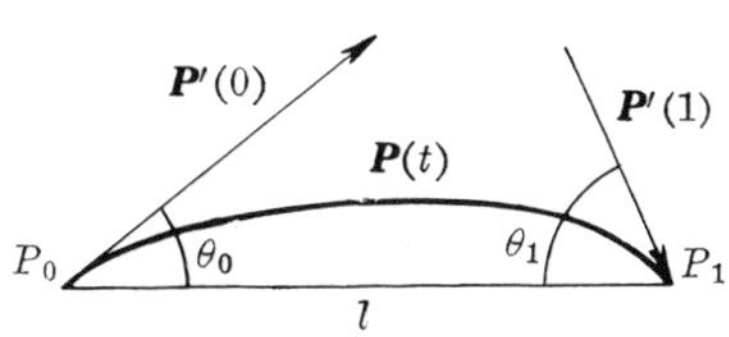

Figure 3-26

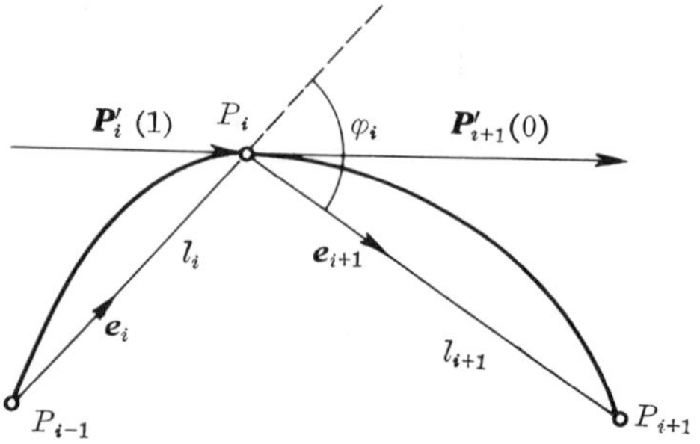

Figure 3-27

Let $s_i = |\boldsymbol{P}_i'(1)|$, $r_i = |\boldsymbol{P}_{i+1}'(0)|$. Write $\boldsymbol{T}_i$ for the unit vector in the tangent direction at $\boldsymbol{P}_i$, and $\boldsymbol{e}_i$ for the unit vector in the direction of $\boldsymbol{P}_{i-1}\boldsymbol{P}_i$. By using (7.13) with $\sigma = \frac{2}{3}$, the first equation in (7.7) can be written as

$$\boldsymbol{P}_i'(1) = s_i \boldsymbol{T}_i, \qquad \boldsymbol{P}_{i+1}'(0) = r_i \boldsymbol{T}_i, \tag{7.14}$$

in which

$$\begin{aligned} r_i &= \frac{2l_{i+1}}{1 + (\frac{2}{3}\boldsymbol{T}_{i+1} + \frac{1}{3}\boldsymbol{T}_i) \cdot \boldsymbol{e}_{i+1}}, \\ s_i &= \frac{2l_i}{1 + (\frac{2}{3}\boldsymbol{T}_{i-1} + \frac{1}{3}\boldsymbol{T}_i) \cdot \boldsymbol{e}_i}. \end{aligned} \tag{7.15}$$

Since each segment is a parametric cubic, equalities (7.8) hold. To ensure GC^2-continuity, (7.9) must be satisfied with $\xi_i = s_i/r_i$. By (7.14), (7.9) can be rewritten as

$$\kappa_i \boldsymbol{T}_i = 3(r_i^2 \boldsymbol{L}_i + s_i^2 \boldsymbol{L}_{i+1}) - r_{i-1} r_i^2 \boldsymbol{T}_{i-1} - s_i^2 s_{i+1} \boldsymbol{T}_{i+1} \qquad (i = 1, 2, \ldots, n-1), \tag{7.16}$$

where

$$\kappa_i = r_i s_i [2(r_i + s_i) + \tfrac{1}{2} r_i \eta_i].$$

There are continuity equations for Manning's spline curves. A complete system of continuity equations is obtained by (7.16) together with two appropriate end conditions. It is similar to the system of continuity equations for parametric splines in tension discussed in the last section. Obviously, the ith equation in (7.16) contains $\boldsymbol{T}_{i-1}$, $\boldsymbol{T}_i$ and $\boldsymbol{T}_{i+1}$, three unknown unit vectors. Since it is a system of nonlinear equations, difficulties arise in finding the solution. An iterative scheme has been designed by Manning as follows.

(1) Choose reasonable initial values for the unit tangents $\boldsymbol{T}_i$, e.g., set $\boldsymbol{T}_i$ parallel to $\boldsymbol{P}_{i-1}\boldsymbol{P}_{i+1}$.
(2) Calculate the tangent magnitudes r_i and s_i using equation (7.15).
(3) Insert these values of r_i, s_i and $\boldsymbol{T}_i$ in the right-hand side of equation (7.16) and calculate new values for the unit tangent $\boldsymbol{T}_i^*$.
(4) Replace $\boldsymbol{T}_i$ by $\boldsymbol{T}_i^*$.
(5) Repeat stages (2), (3) and (4) until the process converges.

Problems still exist, as Manning himself mentioned:

(1) There may be cases in which the iteration does not converge, but none has yet been found.
(2) The equations need not have a unique solution.

Since $\boldsymbol{T}_i$ is a unit vector, we are not interested in the magnitude of the coefficient κ_i in the left-hand side of (7.16), but we do need to know its sign. In the case of locally small deflection, it is possible to define κ_i as a positive scalar. Alternatively, we can define κ_i so as to make $\boldsymbol{T}_i \cdot \boldsymbol{T}_i^* \geqslant 0$, thus ensuring that the direction of $\boldsymbol{T}_i$ does not change by more than 90° with each iteration. Usually, both methods lead to the same result, but there are exceptions (e.g., see Fig. 3-28).

Both figures pass through the same eight (coplanar) knots, and both satisfy equations (7.15) and (7.16). The ambiguity is not a fault in the method, it is a consequence of the inadequacy of the data: the eight knots are insufficient to define where the curve is supposed to go.

Under the assumption of locally small deflection, we obtain by linearizing equations (7.15) and (7.16)

$$\begin{aligned} r_i &= l_{i+1}[1+\mathrm{O}(\phi^2)], \\ s_i &= l_i[1+\mathrm{O}(\phi^2)] \end{aligned} \tag{7.17}$$

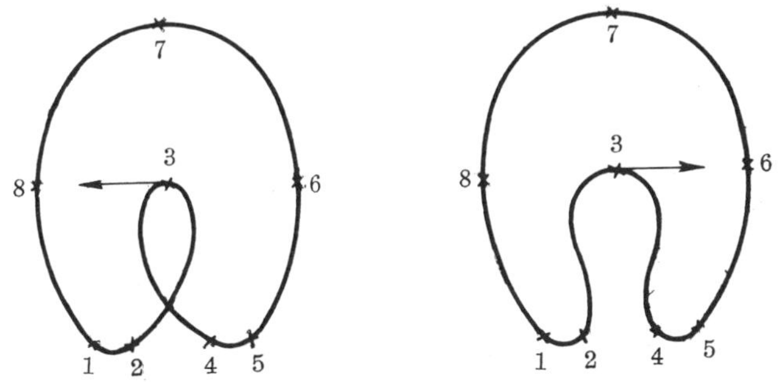

Figure 3-28

and

$$\lambda_i \boldsymbol{T}_{i-1} + \rho_i \boldsymbol{T}_i + \mu_i \boldsymbol{T}_{i+1} = 3\boldsymbol{E}_i + \boldsymbol{\varepsilon}_i \qquad (i = 1, 2, \ldots, n-1), \tag{7.18}$$

where we have set

$$\lambda_i = \frac{l_{i+1}}{l_i + l_{i+1}},$$
$$\mu_i = \frac{l_i}{l_i + l_{i+1}},$$
$$\rho_i = 2 + \tfrac{1}{2}\lambda_i \eta_i,$$
$$|\boldsymbol{\varepsilon}_i| = \mathrm{O}(\phi^3),$$
$$\boldsymbol{E}_i = \lambda_i \boldsymbol{e}_i + \mu_i \boldsymbol{e}_{i+1}.$$

Just as we have done in Section 6, projecting the continuity equation (7.18) on $\boldsymbol{e}_{i+1}$, we obtain

$$\lambda_i \cos(\theta_{i-1} - \phi_i) + \rho_i \cos\theta_i + \mu_i \cos(\theta_{i+1} + \phi_{i+1})$$
$$= 3(\lambda_i \cos\phi_i + \mu_i) + \mathrm{O}(\phi^3) \qquad (i = 1, 2, \ldots, n-1).$$

Linearizing these equations we get

$$\lambda_i + \rho_i + \mu_i = 3 + \mathrm{O}(\phi^2) \qquad (i = 1, 2, \ldots, n-1).$$

It follows that

$$\rho_i = 2 + \mathrm{O}(\phi^2) \qquad (i = 1, 2, \ldots, n-1), \tag{7.19}$$

in which $\phi = \max_i |\phi_i|$.

Substituting (7.19) into (7.18) and then comparing the resulting equations with equations (6.4), the continuity equations for the tangent vectors of the parametric cubic spline curve of cumulative chord length, it is easily seen that they have the same coefficient matrix and that at the right-hand sides the only difference is a vector $\boldsymbol{\varepsilon}_i^*$ with magnitude $\mathrm{O}(\phi^2)$.

We now discuss the difference between the curvature continuity equations of two such spline curves. Taking cross products of the two equations in (7.8) by vectors $\boldsymbol{P}_i'(1)$ and $\boldsymbol{P}_{i+1}'(0)$ respectively, using (7.14) and (7.17), writing $\boldsymbol{T}_{i-1}$, $\boldsymbol{T}_i$ and $\boldsymbol{T}_{i+1}$ for $\boldsymbol{m}_{i-1}$, $\boldsymbol{m}_i$ and $\boldsymbol{m}_{i+1}$, respectively, in Fig. 3-13 and taking care of directions of the signed angles θ_i and ϕ_i in the figure, we obtain

$$\left.\begin{aligned} l_i k_i &= 2(2\phi_i + \theta_{i-1} + 2\theta_i) + \mathrm{O}(\phi^3), \\ l_{i+1} k_i &= -2(\phi_{i+1} + 2\theta_i + \theta_{i+1}) + \mathrm{O}(\phi^3) \end{aligned}\right\} \qquad (i = 1, 2, \ldots, n-1),$$

where k_i denotes the curvature of Manning's spline at the data point $\boldsymbol{P}_i$. Solving for

$$\theta_{i-1} = -\frac{l_i}{6}(2k_{i-1} + k_i) + \mathrm{O}(\phi^3),$$

$$\theta_i = \frac{l_i}{6}(k_{i-1} + 2k_i) - \phi_i + \mathrm{O}(\phi^3),$$

then the curvature continuity equations of the spline curve are obtained:

$$\mu_i k_{i-1} + 2k_i + \lambda_i k_{i+1} = 3K_i + \mathrm{O}(\phi^2) \qquad (i = 1, 2, \ldots, n-1).$$

The equations and (6.12), the curvature continuity equations of the spline curve of cumulative chord length, have the same main part. The only difference occurs in the higher order term $\mathrm{O}(\phi^2)$.

Combining the discussions in Section 6 we conclude that for a given set of data points with locally small deflection, the order of approximation of curvatures at data points evaluated by the two splines is $\mathrm{O}(\phi^2)$; therefore the order of approximation of these two spline curves is $\mathrm{O}(\phi^4)$.

CHAPTER IV

Bézier Curves and *B*-Spline Curves

1 Background

So far we have discussed spline functions and parametric cubic spline curves that have been applied to interpolation. All these methods can certainly be used for geometric design. In design, the initial data points often are not precise and more consideration is given to aesthetics. Hence there is a considerable degree of freedom. It makes no sense to insist on using spline curves to interpolate the data points, which inevitably contain errors.

In this chapter, we study Bézier curves and their extension: *B*-spline curves. Such smooth curves are used to approximate (open) polygons.

Since 1962, parametric curves have been developed by Bézier, an engineer at Régie Renault, on the basis of approximation. These techniques became the mathematical foundation of UNISURF, a design system for curves and free-form surfaces, which has been established at Renault since 1972.

The designer himself need not know or care about these internal mathematical details. The Bézier system combines modern approximation theory and geometry in a way that provides the designer with computerized analogs of his conventional design and drafting tools.

Motivated by Bézier curves, Gordon and Riesenfeld extended *B*-spline functions to *B*-spline curves in parametric form. The so-called *B*-characteristic polygon still plays a role in controlling the shape of parametric

B-spline curves. The curves of degree two and three are most useful. Compared with the Bézier curves, the parametric B-spline curves have the following additional merits:

(1) Perturbing a single vertex of the polygon produces only a local perturbation of the curve in the vicinity of that vertex.
(2) The B-spline curve approximates the polygon more closely than the Bézier curve does.

2 Bézier Curves

2.1 Definition and Properties

Let $n+1$ vectors $\boldsymbol{b}_i$ $(i=0, 1, \ldots, n)$ be given in space. The parametric curve segment of degree n,

$$\boldsymbol{P}(t)=\sum_{i=0}^{n} \boldsymbol{b}_i B_{i,n}(t) \qquad 0 \leqslant t \leqslant 1, \tag{2.1}$$

is called the *Bézier curve*, in which

$$B_{i,n}(t)=C_n^i t^i(1-t)^{n-i}, \qquad C_n^i=\frac{n!}{i!(n-i)!} \qquad (i=0, 1, \ldots, n). \tag{2.2}$$

The functions $B_{i,n}(t)$ are density functions of the binomial distributions.

Joining the end-points of successive vectors $\boldsymbol{b}_{i-1}$ and $\boldsymbol{b}_i$ by line segments $(i=1, 2, \ldots, n)$, an open polygon, called the *Bézier polygon* or the *characteristic polygon*, is obtained.

It is well known that all algebraic polynomials of degree $\leqslant n$ constitute a linear space $\mathscr{P}_n$ of dimension $n+1$. Since the $n+1$ functions $B_{i,n}(t)$ in (2.2) are linearly independent, they form a basis for the space $\mathscr{P}_n$. Each $B_{i,n}(t)$ is called a *Bernstein basis function.* For $n=5$, the six Bernstein basis functions are illustrated in Fig. 4-1.

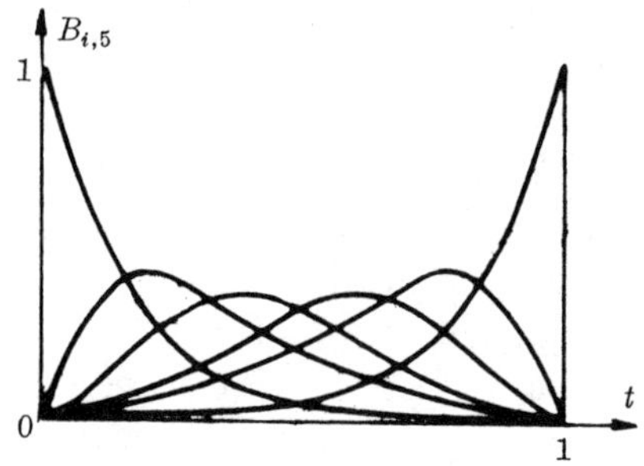

Figure 4-1

It is easy to show that Bernstein basis functions have the following properties:

(1) $$B_{i,n}(t)\begin{cases}=0, & \text{if} \quad t=0,1, \\ >0, & \text{if} \quad t\in(0,1),\end{cases} \qquad (i=1,2,\ldots,n-1);$$

$$B_{0,n}(0)=B_{n,n}(1)=1,$$

$$B_{0,n}(1)=B_{n,n}(0)=0,$$

$$0<B_{0,n}(t), \qquad B_{n,n}(t)<1, \qquad t\in(0,1).$$

(2) $\sum_{i=0}^{n} B_{i,n}(t)\equiv 1, \qquad t\in[0,1].$

(3) $B_{i,n}(t)=B_{n-1,n}(1-t) \qquad (i=0,1,\ldots,n).$

(4) $B'_{i,n}(t)=n\{B_{i-1,n-1}(t)-B_{i,n-1}(t)\} \qquad (i=0,1,\ldots,n).$ (2.3)

(5) The function $B_{i,n}(t)$ assumes its maximum at $t=i/n$.

(6) We have the recurssive relations

$$B_{i,n}(t)=(1-t)B_{i,n-1}(t)+tB_{i-1,n-1}(t) \qquad (i=0,1,\ldots,n).$$

Geometric properties of Bézier curves come from the properties of the Bernstein basis functions just mentioned.

(1) Equalities $\boldsymbol{P}(0)=\boldsymbol{b}_0$ and $\boldsymbol{P}(1)=\boldsymbol{b}_n$ indicate that the Bézier curve has $\boldsymbol{b}_0$ as its starting point and $\boldsymbol{b}_n$ as its ending point.

Differentiating both sides of (2.1) with respect to t, we have by (4)

$$\boldsymbol{P}'(t)=n\sum_{i=0}^{n}\boldsymbol{b}_i\{B_{i-1,n-1}(t)-B_{i,n-1}(t)\}$$

$$=n\sum_{i=1}^{n}\boldsymbol{a}_iB_{i-1,n-1}(t), \tag{2.4}$$

where $\boldsymbol{a}_i=\boldsymbol{b}_i-\boldsymbol{b}_{i-1}$ $(i=1,2,\ldots,n)$, representing the side vectors of the Bézier polygon.

In particular we have from (2.4)

$$\boldsymbol{P}'(0)=n\boldsymbol{a}_1, \qquad \boldsymbol{P}'(1)=n\boldsymbol{a}_n.$$

This shows that the Bézier curve is tangential to $\boldsymbol{a}_1$ and $\boldsymbol{a}_n$ at starting and ending points, respectively.

Analogously we get

$$\boldsymbol{P}''(0)=n(n-1)(\boldsymbol{a}_2-\boldsymbol{a}_1),$$

$$\boldsymbol{P}''(1)=n(n-1)(\boldsymbol{a}_n-\boldsymbol{a}_{n-1}).$$

Hence the binormal vectors at the end points of the curve are

$$\gamma(0) \equiv P'(0) \times P''(0) = n^2(n-1)a_1 \times a_2,$$

$$\gamma(1) \equiv P'(1) \times P''(1) = n^2(n-1)a_{n-1} \times a_n.$$

Generally, the derivative vector of degree r at the starting point, $P^{(r)}(0)$, is only dependent on the first r sides a_i ($i = 0, 1, \ldots, r$) of the Bézier polygon. A similar conclusion is valid for the ending point by symmetry.

(2) Keeping vertices b_i of the Bézier polygon fixed but reversing their order by setting $b_i^* = b_{n-i}$ ($i = 0, 1, \ldots, n$), the Bézier curve $P^*(t)$ defined by $b_0^*, b_1^*, \ldots, b_n^*$ coincides with the old one but has opposite orientation (see Fig. 4-2) as we have

$$P^*(t) = \sum_{i=0}^{n} b_i^* B_{i,n}(t) = \sum_{i=0}^{n} b_{n-i} B_{i,n}(t) = \sum_{i=n}^{0} b_i B_{n-i,n}(t)$$

$$= \sum_{i=0}^{n} b_i B_{i,n}(1-t) = P(1-t).$$

This property tells us that the two end-points of the Bézier curve are algebraically (rather than geometrically) symmetric in the sense that if a Bézier curve has some properties at the starting point, then it has the same properties at the ending point.

(3) From properties (1) and (2) of Bernstein basis functions we know that $B_{i,n}(t)$ ($i = 0, 1, \ldots, n$) constitute a set of weight functions. For any fixed $t \in (0, 1)$, $P(t)$ is a weighted mean of b_i ($i = 0, 1, \ldots, n$), the vertices of the Bézier polygon. This fact shows geometrically that all points on a Bézier curve must lie within the convex hull of the corresponding Bézier polygon (Fig. 4-3).

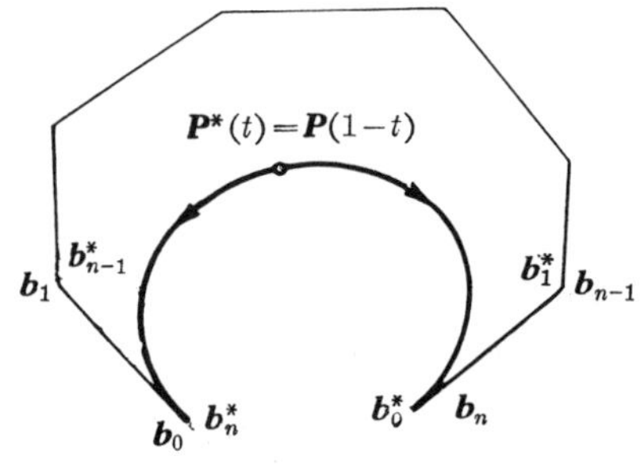

Figure 4-2

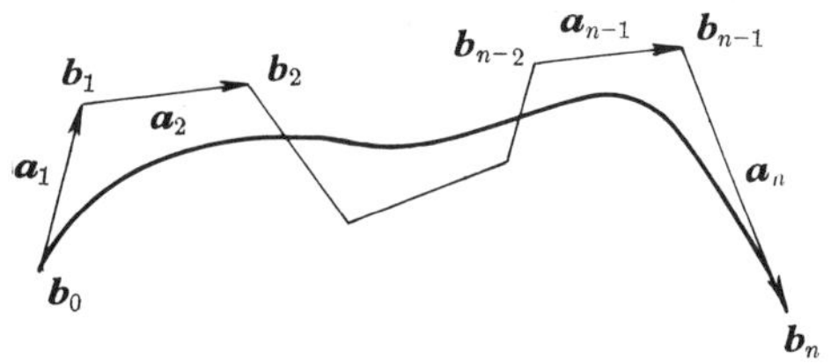

Figure 4-3

(4) Since the Bézier curve (2.1) is expressed in terms of vectors, the shape of the curve is dependent only on the vertices $\boldsymbol{b}_i$ $(i = 0, 1, \ldots, n)$ of the characteristic polygon and thus is not dependent on the choice of coordinate system.

Let us consider a few examples of Bézier curves of lower degree. When $n = 1$, (2.1) becomes

$$\boldsymbol{P}(t) = (1-t)\boldsymbol{b}_0 + t\boldsymbol{b}_1, \qquad 0 \leq t \leq 1.$$

This is a line segment joining $\boldsymbol{b}_0$ and $\boldsymbol{b}_1$.

For $n = 2$, (2.1) is a parametric quadratic curve. Hence the quadratic Bézier curve is a segment of the parabola whose equation can be written in matrix form

$$\boldsymbol{P}(t) = [t^2 \quad t \quad 1]\begin{bmatrix} 1 & -2 & 1 \\ -2 & 2 & 0 \\ 1 & 0 & 0 \end{bmatrix}\begin{bmatrix} \boldsymbol{b}_0 \\ \boldsymbol{b}_1 \\ \boldsymbol{b}_2 \end{bmatrix}, \qquad 0 \leq t \leq 1.$$

The parabolic segments has $\boldsymbol{b}_0$ and $\boldsymbol{b}_2$ as its end-points, and $2\boldsymbol{a}_1$ and $2\boldsymbol{a}_2$ as its tangent vectors at $\boldsymbol{b}_0$ and $\boldsymbol{b}_2$, respectively. We have $\boldsymbol{P}(\frac{1}{2}) = (\boldsymbol{b}^* + \boldsymbol{b}_1)/2$, where $\boldsymbol{b}^* = (\boldsymbol{b}_0 + \boldsymbol{b}_2)/2$. This shows that $\boldsymbol{P}(\frac{1}{2})$ is the midpoint on the median $\boldsymbol{b}_1\boldsymbol{b}^*$ of the triangle $\boldsymbol{b}_0\boldsymbol{b}_1\boldsymbol{b}_2$ (Fig. 4-4).

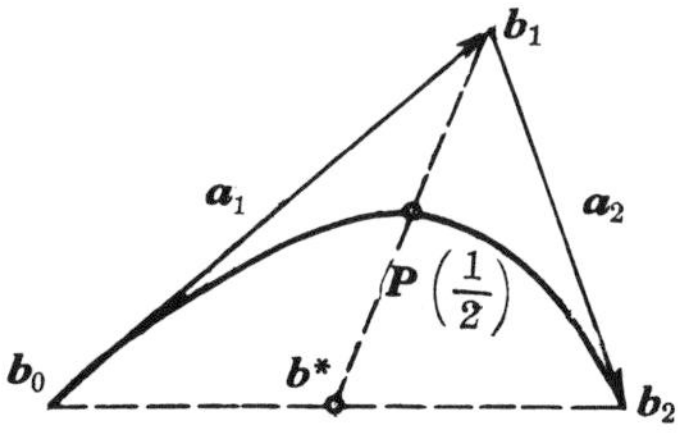

Figure 4-4

Inserting $n=3$ into (2.1), we obtain the cubic Bézier curve which is a special representation of parametric cubic segments. The cubic Bézier curve has the matrix equation

$$\boldsymbol{P}(t)=[t^3 \quad t^2 \quad t \quad 1]\begin{bmatrix}-1 & 3 & -3 & 1\\ 3 & -6 & 3 & 0\\ -3 & 3 & 0 & 0\\ 1 & 0 & 0 & 0\end{bmatrix}\begin{bmatrix}\boldsymbol{b}_0\\ \boldsymbol{b}_1\\ \boldsymbol{b}_2\\ \boldsymbol{b}_3\end{bmatrix}, \qquad 0\leqslant t\leqslant 1.$$

By using results obtained in the previous chapter, we can explain the relationship between the shape of the plane cubic Bézier curve and its characteristic polygon. For details the reader is referred to Section 2.4 below.

Bézier curves of degree greater than three are rather complicated. In these cases, many theoretical questions remain to be answered. For instance, given the characteristic polygon illustrated by Fig. 4-5, it is very difficult to answer the question: How many singularities and inflection-points are there on the Bézier curve?

What we can do at present is to examine relationships between the Bézier curve and its characteristic polygon in the view of approximation. Let us recall some properties of the univariant Bernstein polynomials from the approximation theory of functions.

Let $f(t)$ be a continuous function defined on [0, 1]. Then

$$\mathbb{B}_n(f, t)\equiv\sum_{i=0}^{n} f\left(\frac{i}{n}\right) B_{i,n}(t) \qquad (0\leqslant t\leqslant 1)$$

is called the nth Bernstein polynomial of $f(t)$. It is well known that the sequence of $\mathscr{B}_n(f, t)$ converges to $f(t)$ uniformly on [0, 1] as $n\to\infty$. Furthermore, if $f(t)\in C^r[0, 1]$ then $\mathbb{B}_n^{(r)}(f, t)$ converges to $f^{(r)}(t)$ in the same manner.

However, the convergence is very slow. This fact seems to have precluded any numerical application of Bernstein polynomials for a long time.

Just like B-spline functions, Bernstein polynomials possess a variation diminishing property. It has been shown that the Bernstein basis functions

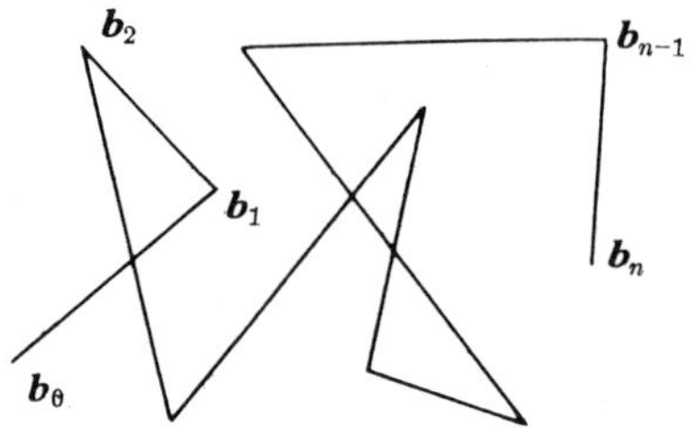

Figure 4-5

are special cases of the B-spline functions with multiple knots. Consequently, Bernstein polynomials are certainly of good fairness in the sense that the number of inflection points of $\mathbb{B}_n(f, t)$ does not exceed that of the approximated function $f(t)$. If $f(t)$ is a convex function on $[0, 1]$ then so is $\mathbb{B}_n(f, t)$. The Bernstein polynomial assumes the geometric properties of its approximated function. This fact makes Bernstein polynomials quite suitable for geometric design, since in this field the geometric properties of the approximant in the large are of more importance than the closeness of the approximation.

Each component of the curve (2.1) is a Bernstein polynomial. This shows that (2.1) is a vector-valued Bernstein polynomial. It is expected that Bézier curves still possess nice properties of geometric approximation when they are regarded as approximants of the corresponding characteristic polygon. Hence we could control the shape of the Bézier curve by adjusting the vertices of the corresponding polygon. Practice has shown that this idea is feasible and effective. But it is not necessarily true that plane Bézier curves have variation diminishing properties. Parametric curves are much more complicated than curves represented by scalar functions. For instance, a polynomial function of degree n has at most $n-2$ inflection points, but a plane parametric curve of degree n may have $2n-4$ inflection points as well as $(n-1)(n-2)/2$ singularities. The authors have established a theorem concerning the convexity preserving property of plane Bézier curves, more precisely, a convex plane Bézier polygon produces a convex Bézier curve, i.e., a curve without singularity and inflection point (Liu Dingyuan, 1982). By convexity of a Bézier polygon we mean that after joining the end points of the polygon a convex plane region is obtained.

Expression (2.1) given at the beginning of this section is referred to as the Bernstein form of Bézier curves and was developed by Forrest and other authors around 1972 (see Forrest [5], Gordon and Riesenfeld [1]). Since then many well known properties of Bernstein polynomials have been invoked to explore and understand the behavior of Bézier curves.

Originally, side vectors $\boldsymbol{a}_i$ $(i=1, 2, \ldots, n)$ of the characteristic polygon together with the position vector of its first vertex $\boldsymbol{a}_0=\boldsymbol{b}_0$ were used by Bézier to define the curve

$$\boldsymbol{P}(t)=\sum_{i=0}^{n} \boldsymbol{a}_i f_{i,n}(t), \qquad 0 \leqslant t \leqslant 1, \tag{2.5}$$

in which

$$f_{0,n}(t)=1,$$

$$f_{i,n}(t)=\frac{(-t)^i}{(i-1)!}\frac{d^{i-1}}{dt^{i-1}}\frac{(1-t)^n-1}{t} \qquad (i=1, 2, \ldots, n).$$

Straightforward calculation shows that there are relations between the functions $f_{i,n}(t)$ $(i=0, 1, \ldots, n)$ and the Bernstein basis functions $B_{i,n}(t)$ $(i=0, 1, \ldots, n)$:

$$f_{i,n}(t)=1-\sum_{j=0}^{i-1} B_{j,n}(t) \qquad (i=1, 2, \ldots, n), \tag{2.6}$$

$$f_{i,n}(t)-f_{i+1,n}(t)=B_{i,n}(t) \qquad (i=0, 1, \ldots, n), \tag{2.7}$$

$$f'_{i,n}(t)=nB_{i-1,n-1}(t) \qquad (i=1, 2, \ldots, n). \tag{2.8}$$

These equalities imply the following three corresponding facts:

(1) $f_{i,n}(t)$ $(i=1, 2, \ldots, n)$ are polynomials of degree n in t with $f_{i,n}(0)=0$ and $f_{i,n}(1)=1$ $(i=1, 2, \ldots, n)$.
(2) For fixed $t \in (0, 1)$, $f_{i,n}(t)$ is strictly decreasing with respect to $i=0, 1, \ldots, n$.
(3) For fixed $i \in \{1, 2, \ldots, n\}$, $f_{i,n}(t)$ is strictly increasing on the interval $[0, 1]$.

The functions $f_{i,n}(t)$ $(i=0, 1, \ldots, n)$ are illustrated in Fig. 4-6.

The equivalence of expressions (2.1) and (2.5) can be shown immediately by using (2.7) and $\boldsymbol{a}_i=\boldsymbol{b}_i-\boldsymbol{b}_{i-1}$ $(i=0, 1, \ldots, n)$, in which we assume that $\boldsymbol{b}_{-1}=0$.

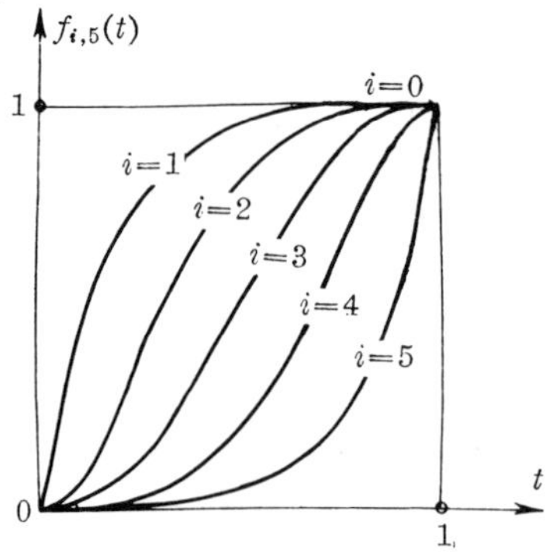

Figure 4-6

2.2 Geometric Construction

For given vertices $\boldsymbol{b}_i$ $(i=0, 1, \ldots, n)$ of the characteristic polygon, an interesting geometric construction of the corresponding Bézier curve was suggested by Bézier himself. The scheme is as follows. For arbitrarily fixed $t \in [0, 1]$, we define

$$\boldsymbol{P}_{i,1}(t) = (1-t)\boldsymbol{b}_i + t\boldsymbol{b}_{i+1} \qquad (i=0, 1, \ldots, n-1). \tag{2.9}$$

This means geometrically that the point $\boldsymbol{P}_{i,1}(t)$ divides the line segment determined by the two points $\boldsymbol{b}_i$ and $\boldsymbol{b}_{i+1}$ by the ratio $t:(1-t)$. A polygon with $n-1$ sides is formed with the points $\boldsymbol{P}_{i,1}(t)$ as its vertices. Repeating the same procedure to this polygon, a polygon with $n-1$ vertices $\boldsymbol{P}_{i,2}(t)$ $(i=0, 1, \ldots, n-2)$ is then obtained and so on. On the final polygon, composed of the vector $\overrightarrow{\boldsymbol{P}_{0,n-1}(t)\boldsymbol{P}_{1,n-1}(t)}$, there is a point $\boldsymbol{P}_{0,n}(t)$ such that

$$\boldsymbol{P}_{0,n}(t) = (1-t)\boldsymbol{P}_{0,n-1}(t) + t\boldsymbol{P}_{1,n-1}(t).$$

It may readily be proved that $\boldsymbol{P}_{0,n}(t)$ is the point $\boldsymbol{P}(t)$ on the curve for which $\boldsymbol{b}_0\boldsymbol{b}_1 \cdots \boldsymbol{b}_n$ is the characteristic polygon and that the vector $\overrightarrow{\boldsymbol{P}_{0,n-1}\boldsymbol{P}_{1,n-1}}$ is tangential to the curve at this point. Figure 4-7 illustrates the construction for $n=4$ and $t=\frac{1}{3}$.

The geometric construction is described algebraically by the recursive formula

$$\boldsymbol{P}_{i,l}(t) = (1-t)\boldsymbol{P}_{i,l-1}(t) + t\boldsymbol{P}_{i+1,l-1}(t), \qquad 0 \leq t \leq 1 \qquad \begin{pmatrix} l=1, 2, \ldots, n \\ i=0, 1, \ldots, n-l \end{pmatrix}, \tag{2.10}$$

in which $\boldsymbol{P}_{i,0}(t) = \boldsymbol{b}_i$ $(i=0, 1, \ldots, n)$. An induction on n shows that the final

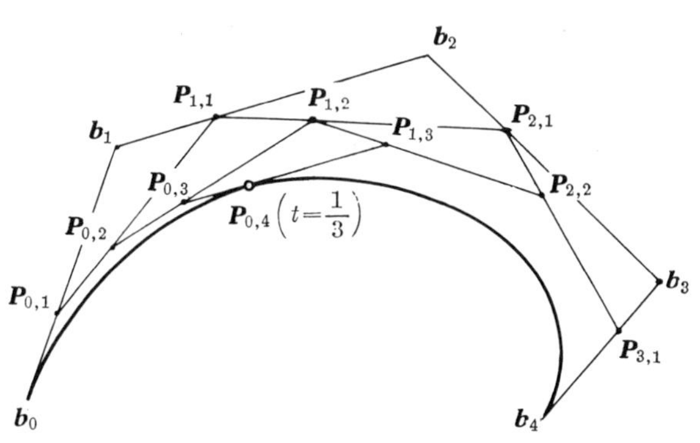

Figure 4-7

result $\boldsymbol{P}_{0,n}(t)$ in (2.10) is the point $\boldsymbol{P}(t)$ on Bézier curve (2.1), i.e.,

$$\boldsymbol{P}_{0,n}(t)=\sum_{i=0}^{n} B_{i,n}(t)\boldsymbol{b}_i. \tag{2.11}$$

It is obvious that (2.11) holds for $n=1$.

Assume that

$$\boldsymbol{P}_{0,n-1}(t)=\sum_{i=0}^{n-1} B_{i,n-1}(t)\boldsymbol{b}_i,$$

$$\boldsymbol{P}_{1,n-1}(t)=\sum_{i=0}^{n-1} B_{i,n-1}(t)\boldsymbol{b}_{i+1},$$

are points on the curves associated with the $(n-1)$-polygons $\boldsymbol{b}_0\boldsymbol{b}_1\cdots\boldsymbol{b}_{n-1}$ and $\boldsymbol{b}_1\boldsymbol{b}_2\cdots\boldsymbol{b}_n$, respectively. By the definition (2.10) we have

$$\begin{aligned}\boldsymbol{P}_{0,n}(t)&=(1-t)\boldsymbol{P}_{0,n-1}(t)+t\boldsymbol{P}_{1,n-1}(t)\\&=(1-t)\sum_{i=0}^{n-1} B_{i,n-1}(t)\boldsymbol{b}_i+t\sum_{i=1}^{n} B_{i-1,n-1}(t)\boldsymbol{b}_i\\&=\sum_{i=0}^{n}\{(1-t)B_{i,n-1}(t)+tB_{i-1,n-1}(t)\}\boldsymbol{b}_i\\&=\sum_{i=0}^{n} B_{i,n}(t)\boldsymbol{b}_i.\end{aligned}$$

This shows that for any n-polygon $\boldsymbol{b}_0\boldsymbol{b}_1\cdots\boldsymbol{b}_n$, the last point $\boldsymbol{P}_{0,n}(t)$ in the recursion (2.10) is just the point $\boldsymbol{P}(t)$ on (2.1).

On the other hand

$$\begin{aligned}\boldsymbol{P}'_{0,n}(t)&=\sum_{i=0}^{n} B'_{i,n}(t)\boldsymbol{b}_i=n\sum_{i=0}^{n}\{B_{i-1,n-1}(t)-B_{i,n-1}(t)\}\boldsymbol{b}_i\\&=n\{\boldsymbol{P}_{i,n-1}(t)-\boldsymbol{P}_{0,n-1}(t)\}=n\overrightarrow{\boldsymbol{P}_{0,n-1}\boldsymbol{P}}_{1,n-1},\end{aligned}$$

which is a tangent vector at the point $\boldsymbol{P}(t)$ on the curve (2.1).

2.3 Hodographs

Given a beginning point $\boldsymbol{a}_0$ and n side vectors $\boldsymbol{a}_i$ $(i=1,2,\ldots,n)$, there is an associated Bézier curve L given by

$$\boldsymbol{P}(t)=\sum_{i=0}^{n} \boldsymbol{a}_i f_{i,n}(t), \qquad 0\leqslant t\leqslant 1.$$

Putting the beginning points of all vectors $\boldsymbol{a}_i$ $(i=1,2,\ldots,n)$ on the origin $\boldsymbol{O}$ and then joining the ending points successively by line segments, a new polygon with $n-1$ sides will be obtained, which determines a Bézier curve of degree $n-1$, denoted by H. H has the equation

$$\boldsymbol{Q}(t)=\sum_{i=1}^{n}\boldsymbol{a}_iB_{i-1,n-1}(t), \qquad 0\leq t\leq 1,$$

by (2.8) which can be written as

$$\boldsymbol{Q}(t)=\frac{1}{n}\sum_{i=1}^{n}\boldsymbol{a}_if'_{i,n}(t)=\frac{1}{n}\boldsymbol{P}'(t). \tag{2.12}$$

This shows that up to the constant factor $1/n$, H is the curve formed by the tangent vectors of L. The Bézier curve H of degree $n-1$ is then called the *hodograph* of the Bézier curve of degree n. More precisely H is called the *hodograph of the first order* of L.

We can also consider the hodograph of H, which is said to be the hodograph of the second order of L. If t is considered as a time parameter, then the curve L represents the motion of a particle, and the hodographs of the first and second order represent velocity and acceleration of the particle, respectively.

Generally we can consider the hodograph of order s, especially hodographs of order $n-2$, $n-1$ and n, which are a parabolic segment, a line segment and a point different from the origin. Hodographs with order higher than n coincide with the origin.

The degree of the hodograph H is one less than that of the curve L, hence H might be simpler than L. It is reasonable to expect that properties of L may be discovered by studying characteristics of H.

When we study a space curve and its properties, generally the curve is projected into two coordinate planes. If the curve L and its hodograph H

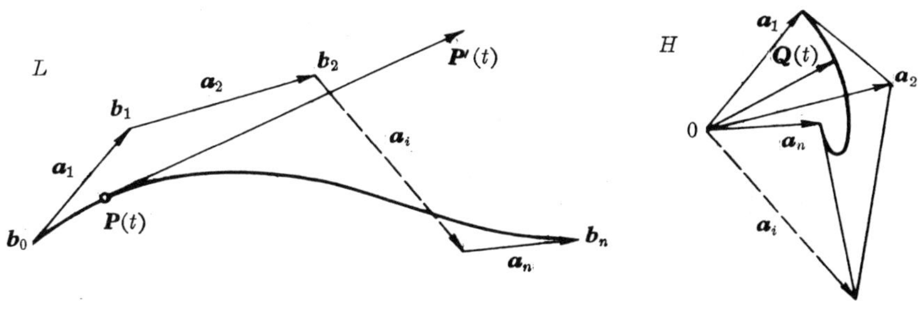

Figure 4-8

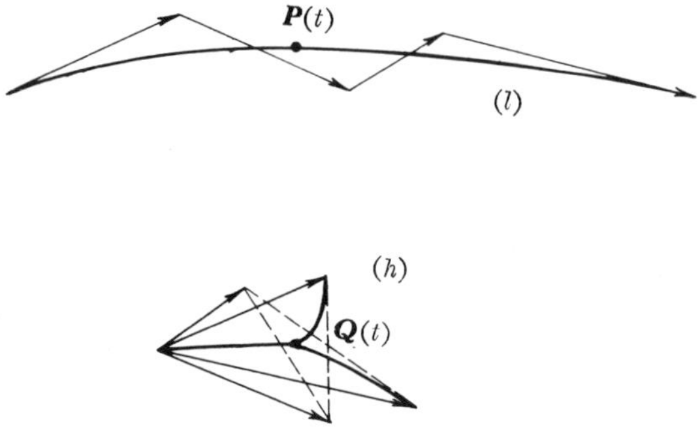

Figure 4-9

are projected into the same plane passing through the origin, the notations $\boldsymbol{P}(t)$ and $\boldsymbol{Q}(t)$ will still be used for the projected points of the corresponding curves. Curves (l) and (h) obtained by the projection have the following properties:

(1) If $\overrightarrow{\boldsymbol{OQ}(t)}$ is tangential to (h), then $\boldsymbol{P}(t)$ is a point of inflection of (l).

(2) If $\overrightarrow{\boldsymbol{OQ}(t)}$ is tangential to (h) and $\boldsymbol{Q}(t)$ is a point of inflection or a cusp of (h), then $\boldsymbol{P}(t)$ is a point at which (l) has zero curvature, but $\boldsymbol{P}(t)$ is not a point of inflection of (l) (see Fig. 4-9 and Fig. 4-10).

(3) If $\overrightarrow{\boldsymbol{OQ}(t)}$ coincides with the origin, then $\boldsymbol{P}(t)$ is a cusp of (l) and the tangent lines at $\boldsymbol{P}(t)$ and $\boldsymbol{Q}(t)$ are parallel (Fig. 4-11).

Proofs of these properties are left to the reader.

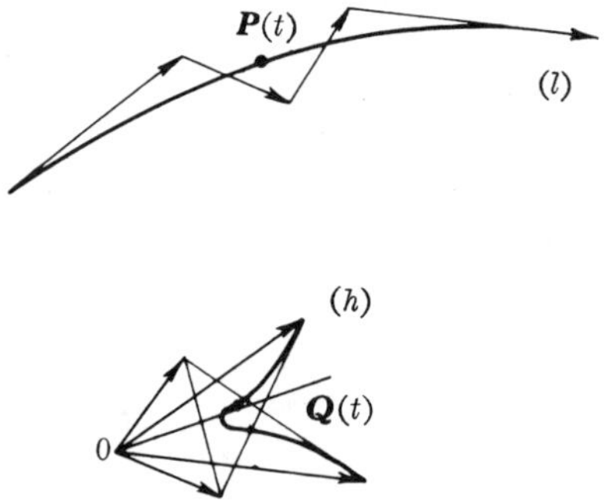

Figure 4-10

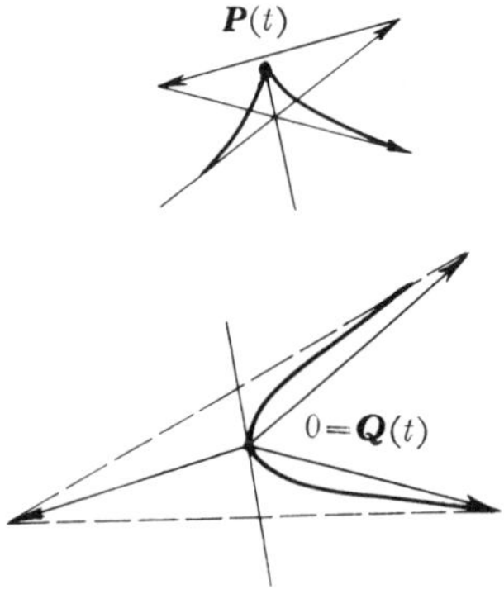

Figure 4-11

Taking $n = 3$, (h) is now a quadratic Bézier curve, i.e., a parabolic segment. A careful study of (h) helps us to get a better understanding of the cubic Bézier curve (l).

(1) If the origin $\boldsymbol{O}$ is in the exterior of the parabola but inside the triangle $\boldsymbol{Q}(0)\boldsymbol{Q}\boldsymbol{Q}(1)$, then there are two points of inflection on the curve (l). Their relative positions with respect to $\boldsymbol{P}(0)$ and $\boldsymbol{P}(1)$, are just like that of their corresponding points on (h) with respect to $\boldsymbol{Q}(0)$ and $\boldsymbol{Q}(1)$ (Fig. 4-12).

(2) If the origin is inside the parabola, there is no point of inflection on (l). If $\boldsymbol{O}$ falls in the region bounded by the parabolic segment

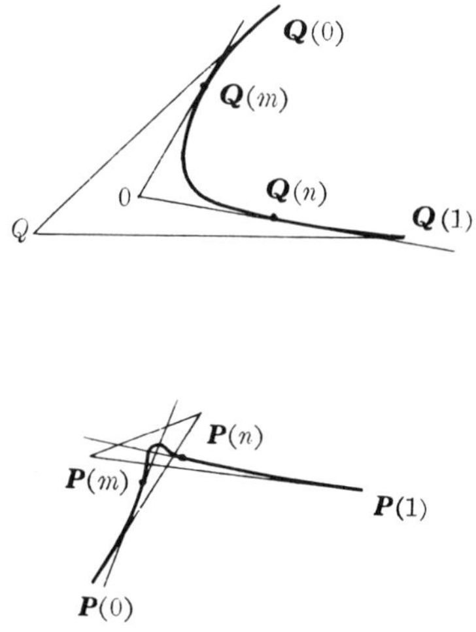

Figure 4-12

and the chord $\overline{\boldsymbol{Q}(0)\boldsymbol{Q}(1)}$, then there are two pairs of conjugate points on (l), namely $\boldsymbol{P}(0)$, $\boldsymbol{P}(n)$ and $\boldsymbol{P}(1)$, $\boldsymbol{P}(m)$. By a pair of conjugate points we mean two points on a curve whose tangent vectors are parallel but have opposite directions (Fig. 4-13).

(3) At infinity, the tangent line of (l) is parallel to the axis of the parabola.

2.4 Shape Control of Planar Cubic Bézier Curves

In the previous section we analyzed points of inflection and cusps of planar cubic Bézier curves by using hodographs, but few positive results were obtained. The technique is rather indirect and does not include a discussion of loops. We now raise such a question: Is it possible to control the number of points of inflection and singularities on a cubic Bézier curve by simply adjusting the positions of the vertices of the characteristic polygon with three sides? (See Liu Dingyuan [4], 1981).

Suppose that we are given the polygon $\boldsymbol{b}_0\boldsymbol{b}_1\boldsymbol{b}_2\boldsymbol{b}_3$. An affine coordinate system $\{\boldsymbol{O}, \overrightarrow{\boldsymbol{Ob}}_3, \overrightarrow{\boldsymbol{Ob}}_0\}$ is then established such that $\overrightarrow{\boldsymbol{Ob}}_3 \parallel \overrightarrow{\boldsymbol{b}_0\boldsymbol{b}_1}$, $\overrightarrow{\boldsymbol{Ob}}_0 \parallel \overrightarrow{\boldsymbol{b}_3\boldsymbol{b}_2}$. Assume that $\overrightarrow{\boldsymbol{b}_0\boldsymbol{b}_1} = x\overrightarrow{\boldsymbol{Ob}}_3$, $\overrightarrow{\boldsymbol{b}_3\boldsymbol{b}_2} = y\overrightarrow{\boldsymbol{Ob}}_0$, hence $\boldsymbol{b}_1$ and $\boldsymbol{b}_2$ have the coordinates $(x, 1)$ and $(1, y)$, respectively (Fig. 4-14). The point $\boldsymbol{R}$ with coordinates (x, y) is called the characteristic point of the polygon $\boldsymbol{b}_0\boldsymbol{b}_1\boldsymbol{b}_2\boldsymbol{b}_3$.

The cubic Bézier curve associated with the polygon $\boldsymbol{b}_0\boldsymbol{b}_1\boldsymbol{b}_2\boldsymbol{b}_3$ is denoted by L. Hence we have the following theorem.

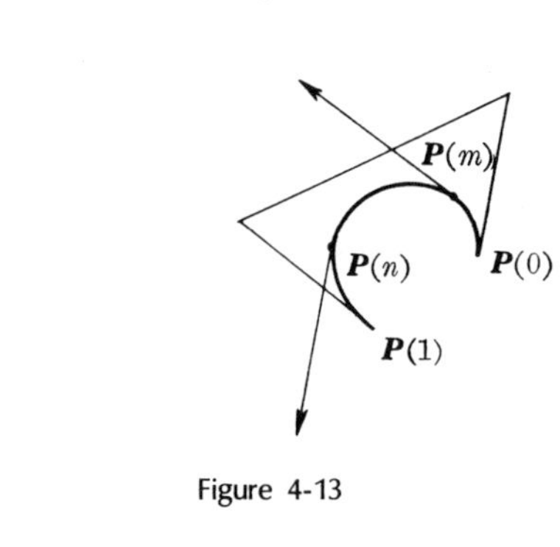

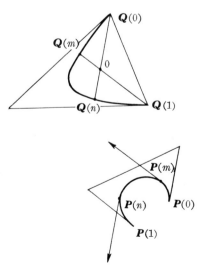

Figure 4-13

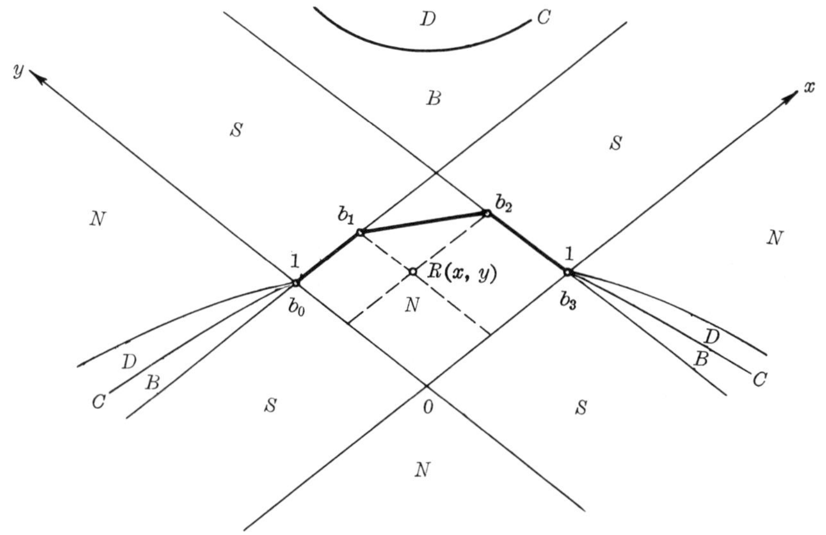

Figure 4-14

Theorem. *If the characteristic point*

$$R \in \begin{cases} N, \text{ then } L \text{ has no point of inflection or singularity;} \\ S, \text{ then } L \text{ has one point of inflection;} \\ B, \text{ then } L \text{ has two points of inflection;} \\ C, \text{ then } L \text{ has a cusp;} \\ D, \text{ then } L \text{ has a loop,} \end{cases}$$

where C represents the two branches of the hyperbola $(x-\frac{4}{3})(y-\frac{4}{3})=\frac{4}{9}$, *and the curve C and the parabolas* $3y^2-3y+x=0$ *and* $3x^2-3x+y=0$ *form the boundary of the region D.*

Proof. By basic properties of Bézier curves, we have $\boldsymbol{P}'(0)=3\overrightarrow{\boldsymbol{b}_0\boldsymbol{b}_1}$ and $\boldsymbol{P}'(1)=3\overrightarrow{\boldsymbol{b}_2\boldsymbol{b}_3}$. If L is considered as a cubic parametric segment, then the relative magnitudes of the tangent vectors at the end-points are $\lambda=3x$ and $\mu=3y$, respectively. Note that $\{\boldsymbol{O};\ \lambda,\ \mu\}$ is an affine coordinate system. The present theorem comes directly from the conclusions of Section 5 in the last chapter.

Several typical cases of cubic Bézier curves are illustrated in Fig. 4-15. In particular, it can be seen that if the Bézier polygon is convex then the characteristic point $\boldsymbol{R}$ certainly falls into the region N, which is associated with no point of inflection and singularity. Hence the cubic Bézier planar curves are convexity preserving.

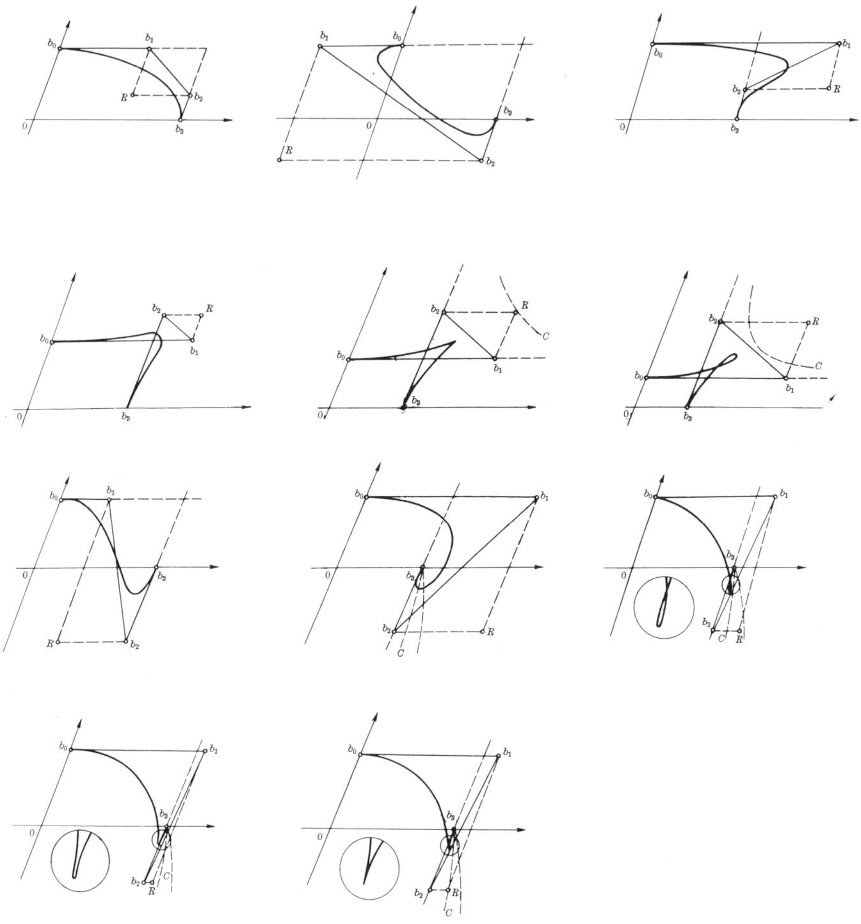

Figure 4-15

2.5 Bézier Spline Curves

A spline curve can be constructed by joining several Bézier curve segments together in a smooth manner, in order to get more flexibility and easier shape control.

Let L and L^* be two given Bézier curves, of degree n and degree m, respectively. Side vectors of the Bézier polygons are denoted by $\boldsymbol{a}_1 \cdots \boldsymbol{a}_{n-1}\boldsymbol{a}_n$ *and* $\boldsymbol{a}_1^*\boldsymbol{a}_2^* \cdots \boldsymbol{a}_m^*$. Assume that the last point of L and the first point of L^* coincide. It is simple to describe GC^1-continuity at their joint: There exists a real number α such that

$$\boldsymbol{a}_1^* = \alpha \boldsymbol{a}_n \qquad (\alpha > 0). \tag{2.13}$$

The two curves L and L^* in space reach GC^2-continuity at the joint, if the following two additional conditions are satisfied:

(1) the osculating planes coincide at the joint and the binormal vectors have the same direction;
(2) the two curves have the same curvature at the joint.

The binormal vector of L at the last point is

$$\boldsymbol{\gamma}(1) = n^2(n-1)(\boldsymbol{a}_{n-1} \times \boldsymbol{a}_n), \tag{2.14}$$

and the binormal vector of L^* at the first point is

$$\boldsymbol{\gamma}^*(0) = m^2(m-1)(\boldsymbol{a}_1^* \times \boldsymbol{a}_2^*). \tag{2.15}$$

Condition (1) says that four vectors $\boldsymbol{a}_{n-1}$, $\boldsymbol{a}_n$, $\boldsymbol{a}_1^*$, $\boldsymbol{a}_2^*$ are coplanar (Fig. 4-16). By virtue of (2.13) we have

$$\boldsymbol{a}_2^* = -\beta \boldsymbol{a}_{n-1} + \eta \boldsymbol{a}_n, \tag{2.16}$$

in which the scalars $\beta > 0$ and η are arbitrary.

By relations (2.13)-(2.16), the curvatures of L and L^* at the joint are, respectively,

$$\begin{aligned} k(1) &= \frac{|\boldsymbol{\gamma}(1)|}{|\boldsymbol{P}'(1)|^3} = \frac{n^2(n-1)|\boldsymbol{a}_{n-1} \times \boldsymbol{a}_n|}{n^3|\boldsymbol{a}_n|^3} \\ &= \frac{(n-1)|\boldsymbol{a}_{n-1} \times \boldsymbol{a}_n|}{n|\boldsymbol{a}_n|^3}, \end{aligned}$$

$$\begin{aligned} k^*(0) &= \frac{|\boldsymbol{\gamma}^*(0)|}{|\boldsymbol{P}^{*\prime}(0)|^3} = \frac{m^2(m-1)|\boldsymbol{a}_1^* \times \boldsymbol{a}_2^*|}{m^3|\boldsymbol{a}_1^*|^3} \\ &= \frac{(m-1)|\boldsymbol{a}_1^* \times \boldsymbol{a}_2^*|}{m|\boldsymbol{a}_1^*|^3} = \frac{(m-1)|\alpha \boldsymbol{a}_n \times (-\beta \boldsymbol{a}_{n-1} + \eta \boldsymbol{a}_n)|}{m\alpha^3|\alpha_n|^3} \\ &= \frac{(m-1)\beta|\boldsymbol{a}_{n-1} \times \boldsymbol{a}_n|}{m\alpha^2|\boldsymbol{a}_n|^3}. \end{aligned}$$

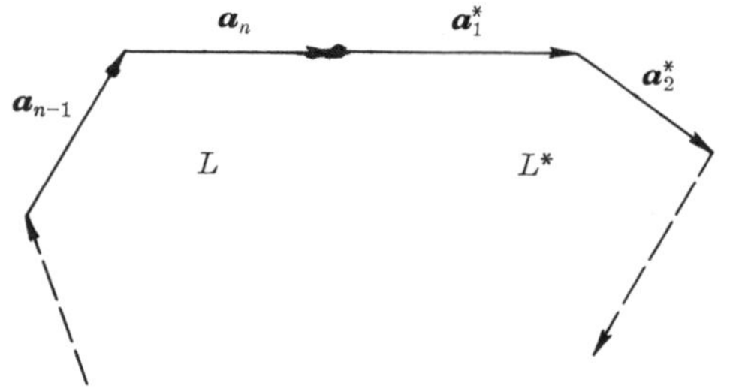

Figure 4-16

Setting $k(1)=k^*(0)$, we obtain

$$\beta=\frac{m(n-1)}{n(m-1)}\alpha^2. \tag{2.17}$$

In summary, we conclude that two space Bézier curves L (of degree n) and L^* (of degree m) are GC^1-continuous at the joint iff (2.13) holds, and GC^2-continuous iff (2.13), (2.16) and (2.17) hold simultaneously.

We now turn our discussion to the construction of GC^2-continuous Bézier spline curves by using quadratic and cubic Bézier segments.

(1) A convex polygon $\boldsymbol{b}_0\boldsymbol{b}_1\cdots\boldsymbol{b}_n$ is given in the plane. The problem is to construct a GC^2-continuous Bézier spline curve, formed by quadratic Bézier segments, such that each knot of the spline curve lies on the sides of the polygon and such that the spline curve is tangential to the polygon at those knots.

Let θ_i $(i=1,2,\ldots,n-1)$ be the oriented angles at the vertices of the convex polygon. The magnitude of the side vector $\boldsymbol{a}_i$ will be denoted by a_i $(i=1,2,\ldots,n)$. The knot on the ith side is denoted by $\boldsymbol{P}_i$, which divides the side by the ratio $x_i/(1-x_i)$ $(i=1,2,\ldots,n)$ (Fig. 4-17).

To ensure the two adjacent quadratic Bézier curves are GC^2-continuous at $\boldsymbol{P}_i$, it is necessary and sufficient that (2.13), (2.16) and (2.17) hold. In (2.13),

$$\alpha=\frac{1-x_i}{x_i},$$

and in (2.16)

$$\begin{aligned}\beta&=\frac{|\overrightarrow{\boldsymbol{b}_i\boldsymbol{P}}_{i+1}\times\overrightarrow{\boldsymbol{b}_{i-1}\boldsymbol{P}}_i|}{|\overrightarrow{\boldsymbol{P}_{i-1}\boldsymbol{b}}_{i-1}\times\overrightarrow{\boldsymbol{b}_{i-1}\boldsymbol{P}}_i|}=\frac{|x_{i+1}\boldsymbol{a}_{i+1}\times x_i\boldsymbol{a}_i|}{|(1-x_{i-1})\boldsymbol{a}_{i-1}\times x_i\boldsymbol{a}_i|}\\&=\frac{x_{i+1}a_{i+1}\sin\theta_i}{(1-x_{i-1})a_{i-1}\sin\theta_{i-1}}.\end{aligned}$$

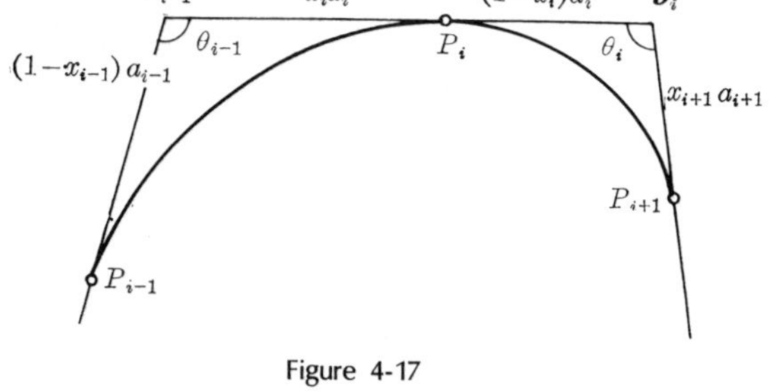

Figure 4-17

Equation (2.17) becomes $\beta = \alpha^2$, that is,

$$\left(\frac{1-x_i}{x_i}\right)^2 \frac{1-x_{i-1}}{x_{i+1}} = B_i \qquad (i = 2, 3, \ldots, n-1), \tag{2.18}$$

in which

$$B_i = \frac{a_{i+1} \sin \theta_i}{a_{i-1} \sin \theta_{i-1}} \,(>0)$$

is known.

In this way, the original problem reduces to solving a system of nonlinear equations, i.e., (2.18). Given two end conditions (for instance, given x_1 and x_n), simple iteration may be used to find the solution, and

$$x_i^{(0)} = \frac{1}{1+\sqrt{B_i}} \qquad (i = 2, 3, \ldots, n-1)$$

may be chosen as the initial approximation.

(2) The problem becomes simpler if we use cubic Bézier curve segments to construct a GC^2-continuous Bézier spline curve.

Assume that the given polygon has $2n-1$ sides, and that the knots $\boldsymbol{P}_i$ lie on the sides of odd index $(i = 1, 3, \ldots, 2n-1)$ (see Fig. 4-18). By using the same method, we obtain

$$\alpha = \frac{1-x_i}{x_i},$$

$$\beta = \frac{|\boldsymbol{a}_{i+1} \times x_i \boldsymbol{a}_i|}{|\boldsymbol{a}_{i-1} \times x_i \boldsymbol{a}_i|} = \frac{a_{i+1} \sin \theta_i}{a_{i-1} \sin \theta_{i-1}} \equiv B_i.$$

Then (2.17) becomes

$$\left(\frac{1-x_i}{x_i}\right)^2 = B_i \qquad (i = 3, 5, \ldots, 2n-3)$$

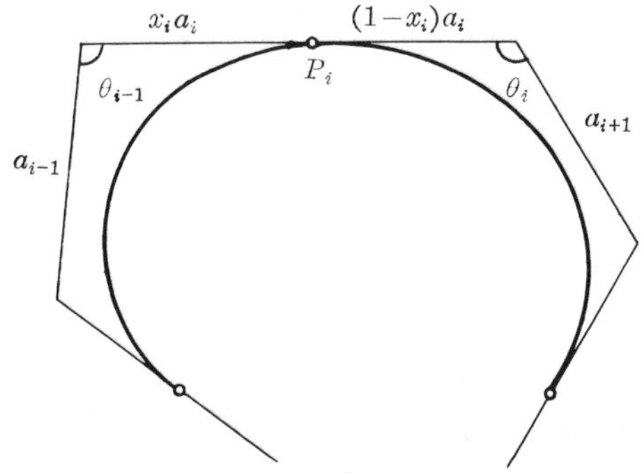

Figure 4-18

hence

$$x_i = \frac{1}{1+\sqrt{B_i}} \qquad (i = 3, 5, \ldots, 2n-3).$$

End conditions x_1 and x_{2n-1} can be arbitrarily specified. To ensure $B_i > 0$, additional conditions

$$\theta_{i-1}\theta_i > 0 \qquad (i = 3, 5, \ldots, 2n-3),$$

may be imposed.

3 *B*-Spline Curves

3.1 Definitions

Bézier curves, which we discussed in the previous section, are essentially the vector-valued Bernstein approximation with the given points $\boldsymbol{b}_i$ ($i = 0, 1, \ldots, n$) as coefficients and the family of functions $\{B_{i,n}(t)\}$ as the basis functions.

In 1972–1974, Gordon, Riesenfeld and other authors extended Bézier curves. The key point is that the basis functions $\{B_{i,n}(t)\}$ are replaced by the *B*-spline basis of degree *n*, and then we get vector-valued *B*-spline approximations instead of the Bernstein approximation. In this way they constructed *B*-spline curves.

Here we only discuss the case in which the partition of the axis of the parameter is equally spaced.

From Chapter II we know that the *B*-spline function of degree *n* has the analytical expression

$$M_n(x) = \frac{1}{n!}\sum_{j=0}^{n+1}(-1)^j C_{n+1}^j \left(x + \frac{n+1}{2} - j\right)_+^n.$$

It can also be expressed in piecewise manner

$$M_n(x) = \frac{1}{n!}\sum_{j=0}^{l}(-1)^j C_{n+1}^j \left(x + \frac{n+1}{2} - j\right)^n, \tag{3.1}$$

for

$$l - \frac{n+1}{2} \leqslant x \leqslant l - \frac{n+1}{2} + 1 \qquad (l = 0, 1, \ldots, n).$$

There are $n+1$ pieces in the interval $(-(n+1)/2, (n+1)/2)$, and all of them have positive function values. The function is identically zero if x is out of this interval.

The parameter for the Bézier curve runs from 0 to 1. It is desirable to take the parameter t from the interval [0, 1] for the vector-valued B-spline approximation. To do this, set $t = x - (l - (n+1)/2)$ in (3.1). Assume that

$$F_{n-1,n}(t) \equiv M_n\left(t + l - \frac{n-1}{2}\right) = \frac{1}{n!}\sum_{j=0}^{l}(-1)^j C_{n+1}^j (t+l-j)^n,$$

$$0 \leqslant t \leqslant 1 \qquad (l = 0, 1, \ldots, n).$$

We have

$$F_{l,n}(t) = \frac{1}{n!}\sum_{j=0}^{n-l}(-1)^j C_{n+1}^j (t+n-l-j)^n,$$

$$0 \leqslant t \leqslant 1 \qquad (l = 0, 1, \ldots, n). \tag{3.2}$$

The B-spline function $M_n(x)$ can be illustrated in terms of graphs of the $n+1$ functions $F_{l,n}(t)$ $(l = 0, 1, \ldots, n)$, as shown in Fig. 4-19.

Definition Let the $m+n+1$ vectors $\boldsymbol{b}_k$ $(k = 0, 1, \ldots, m+n)$ be given in space. Then the parametric curve of degree n

$$\boldsymbol{P}_{i,n}(t) = \sum_{l=0}^{n} \boldsymbol{b}_{i+l} F_{l,n}(t), \qquad 0 \leqslant t \leqslant 1 \tag{3.3}$$

is called the ith *span* $(i = 0, 1, \ldots, n)$ *of a B-spline of degree n.* All of them constitute the *B-spline curve of degree n.* Accordingly, if the end-points of two successive vectors from $\boldsymbol{b}_{i+l}$ $(l = 0, 1, \ldots, n)$ are joined by straight lines, the resulting polygon is said to be the *B-characteristic polygon* for the ith span of the spline.

Since the B-spline function $M_n(x)$ is of C^{n-1}-continuity, and the basis functions $\{F_{l,n}(t)\}$ are piecewise representations obtained by normalization of the variable in $M_n(x)$, the whole B-spline curve of degree n belongs to C^{n-1}.

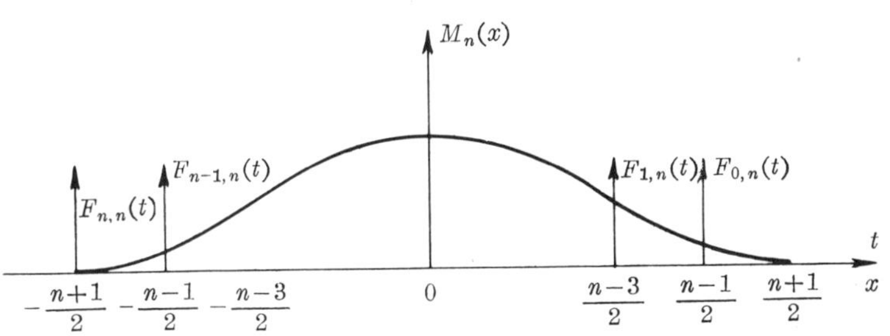

Figure 4-19

Hosaka and Kurota (1976) gave an alternate definition of the *B*-spline curve of degree n in terms of a recursive algorithm. Let $\boldsymbol{b}_k$ $(k=0, 1, \ldots, m+n)$ be $m+n+1$ given vectors. Define

$$\boldsymbol{R}_{k,0}(t) \equiv \boldsymbol{b}_k \qquad (k=0, 1, \ldots, m+n),$$

and, recursively on l, define

$$\boldsymbol{R}_{i,l}(t) = \int_t^1 \omega_l(\tau)\boldsymbol{R}_{i,l-1}(\tau)\, d\tau + \int_0^t \omega_l(\tau)\boldsymbol{R}_{i+1,l-1}(\tau)\, d\tau,$$

$$0 \leqslant t \leqslant 1 \qquad (l=1, 2, \ldots, n;\ i=0, 1, \ldots, m), \tag{3.4}$$

where the weight function

$$\omega_l(t) \geqslant 0, \qquad \text{and} \qquad \int_0^1 \omega_l(\tau)\, d\tau = 1 \qquad (l=1, 2, \ldots, n).$$

The curve consisting of segments represented by $\boldsymbol{R}_{i,l}(t)$, $i=0, 1, \ldots, n$, is said to be an *MA* curve of degree l.

Formula (3.4) has the following physical meaning: if $\omega_l(t)$ is regarded as a linear density function, then $\int_0^1 \omega_l(\tau)\, d\tau = 1$ means that the weight of each curve segment is equal to 1; for fixed t, $\boldsymbol{R}_{i,l}(t)$ is the center of gravity of the arc $\widehat{AB}$ in Fig. 4-20. When the parameter t varies in $[0, 1]$, $\boldsymbol{R}_{i,l}(t)$ represents the ith span of the *MA* curve.

For $l=1$, (3.4) becomes

$$\boldsymbol{R}_{i,1}(t) = \boldsymbol{b}_i G_{0,1}(t) + \boldsymbol{b}_{i+1} G_{1,1}(t), \qquad 0 \leqslant t \leqslant 1, \tag{3.5}$$

in which

$$G_{0,1}(t) = \int_t^1 \omega_1(\tau)\, d\tau \geqslant 0, \qquad G_{1,1}(t) = \int_0^t \omega_1(\tau)\, d\tau \geqslant 0.$$

Since

$$G_{0,1}(t) + G_{1,1}(t) = \int_0^1 \omega_1(\tau)\, d\tau = 1,$$

(3.5) represents the line segment joining $\boldsymbol{b}_i$ and $\boldsymbol{b}_{i+1}$.

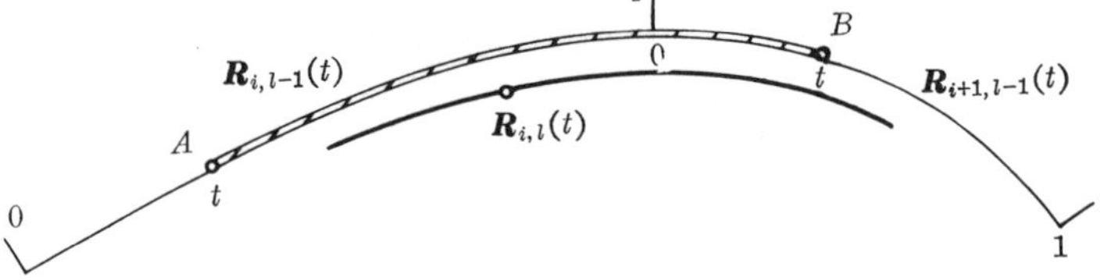

Figure 4-20

In general, the ith span of the MA curve of degree l depends only on $l+1$ points $\boldsymbol{b}_{i+k}$ $(k=0, 1, \ldots, l)$. In fact

$$\boldsymbol{R}_{i,l}(t)=\sum_{k=0}^{l} \boldsymbol{b}_{i+k}G_{k,l}(t), \qquad 0\leqslant t\leqslant 1 \qquad (l=1, 2, \ldots, n). \tag{3.6}$$

Substituting (3.6) into both sides of (3.4), we can derive the recursive formula for the function $G_{k,l}(t)$:

$$G_{k,l}(t)=\int_t^1 \omega_l(\tau)G_{k,l-1}(\tau)\, d\tau+\int_0^t \omega_l(\tau)G_{k-1,l-1}(\tau)\, d\tau,$$

$$0\leqslant t\leqslant 1 \qquad (l=1, 2, \ldots, n;\ k=0, 1, \ldots, l).$$

It is easy to see that $G_{k,l}(t)\geqslant 0$, and by induction we have

$$\sum_{k=0}^{l} G_{k,l}(t)=\int_0^1 \omega_l(\tau)\left(\sum_{k=0}^{l-1} G_{k,l-1}(\tau)\right) d\tau=1. \tag{3.7}$$

This shows that the curve segment $\boldsymbol{R}_{i,l}(t)$ expressed by (3.6) is a weighted mean of $l+1$ points $\boldsymbol{b}_{i+k}$ $(k=0, 1, \ldots, l)$, with weights $G_{k,l}(t)$ $(k=0, 1, \ldots, l)$.

If $\omega_l(t)\equiv 1$ $(l=1, 2, \ldots, n)$, then the corresponding MA curve of degree n reduces to the B-spline curve of degree n. In fact, induction on n shows that

$$G_{l,n}(t)=\frac{1}{n!}\sum_{j=0}^{n-l} (-1)^j C_{n+1}^{j}(t+n-l-j)^n, \qquad 0\leqslant t\leqslant 1 \qquad (l=0, 1, \ldots, n),$$

i.e., it is the same as $F_{l,n}(t)$ defined in (3.2).

From (3.7) we know that $F_{l,n}(t)$ $(l=0, 1, \ldots, n)$ constitute a set of weight functions, i.e.,

$$F_{l,n}(t)\geqslant 0, \qquad \sum_{l=0}^{n} F_{l,n}(t)=1.$$

3.2 Geometric Properties of Quadratic and Cubic B-Spline Curves

We stated previously that the B-spline curve of first degree is piecewise linear and coincides with its B-characteristic polygon. In applications, cubic B-spline curves are the most frequently used. We are mainly concerned here with quadratic and cubic B-spline curves and their properties. Since each piece of a B-spline curve is similar in its construction, for simplicity we can put $i=0$ in the definition (3.3).

We consider the quadratic B-spline curve. In this case $n=2$. We have from (3.2)

$$F_{0,2}(t)=\tfrac{1}{2}(t-1)^2,\qquad F_{1,2}(t)=\tfrac{1}{2}(-2t^2+2t+1),\qquad F_{2,2}(t)=\tfrac{1}{2}t^2.$$

Hence the quadratic B-spline curve can be written in matrix form

$$\boldsymbol{P}(t)=\sum_{l=0}^{2}\boldsymbol{b}_l F_{l,2}(t)=[t^2 \quad t \quad 1]\frac{1}{2}\begin{bmatrix}1 & -2 & 1\\ -2 & 2 & 0\\ 1 & 1 & 0\end{bmatrix}\begin{bmatrix}\boldsymbol{b}_0\\ \boldsymbol{b}_1\\ \boldsymbol{b}_2\end{bmatrix},\qquad 0\leqslant t\leqslant 1. \tag{3.8}$$

Each piece of the quadratic B-spline is a parabolic segment with end-point properties

$$\boldsymbol{P}(0)=\tfrac{1}{2}(\boldsymbol{b}_0+\boldsymbol{b}_1),\qquad \boldsymbol{P}'(0)=\boldsymbol{b}_1-\boldsymbol{b}_0,$$

$$\boldsymbol{P}(1)=\tfrac{1}{2}(\boldsymbol{b}_1+\boldsymbol{b}_2);\qquad \boldsymbol{P}'(1)=\boldsymbol{b}_2-\boldsymbol{b}_1.$$

These relations show that the end points of the quadratic B-spline curve are the midpoint of two sides of the B-characteristic polygon (Fig. 4-21).

The matrix representation of the cubic B-spline curve (3.3) is (Coons [3], 1974)

$$\boldsymbol{P}(t)=[t^3 \quad t^2 \quad t \quad 1]\frac{1}{6}\begin{bmatrix}-1 & 3 & -3 & 1\\ 3 & -6 & 3 & 0\\ -3 & 0 & 3 & 0\\ 1 & 4 & 1 & 0\end{bmatrix}\begin{bmatrix}\boldsymbol{b}_0\\ \boldsymbol{b}_1\\ \boldsymbol{b}_2\\ \boldsymbol{b}_3\end{bmatrix},\qquad 0\leqslant t\leqslant 1. \tag{3.9}$$

It is clear that

$$\boldsymbol{P}(0)=\tfrac{1}{6}(\boldsymbol{b}_0+4\boldsymbol{b}_1+\boldsymbol{b}_2)=\frac{1}{3}\left(\frac{\boldsymbol{b}_0+\boldsymbol{b}_2}{2}\right)+\tfrac{2}{3}\boldsymbol{b}_1,$$

$$\boldsymbol{P}(1)=\tfrac{1}{6}(\boldsymbol{b}_1+4\boldsymbol{b}_2+\boldsymbol{b}_3)=\frac{1}{3}\left(\frac{\boldsymbol{b}_1+\boldsymbol{b}_3}{2}\right)+\tfrac{2}{3}\boldsymbol{b}_2;$$

$$\begin{aligned}&\boldsymbol{P}'(0)=\tfrac{1}{2}(\boldsymbol{b}_2-\boldsymbol{b}_0),\\ &\boldsymbol{P}'(1)=\tfrac{1}{2}(\boldsymbol{b}_3-\boldsymbol{b}_1);\\ &\boldsymbol{P}''(0)=(\boldsymbol{b}_2-\boldsymbol{b}_1)+(\boldsymbol{b}_0-\boldsymbol{b}_1),\\ &\boldsymbol{P}''(1)=(\boldsymbol{b}_3-\boldsymbol{b}_2)+(\boldsymbol{b}_1-\boldsymbol{b}_2).\end{aligned} \tag{3.10}$$

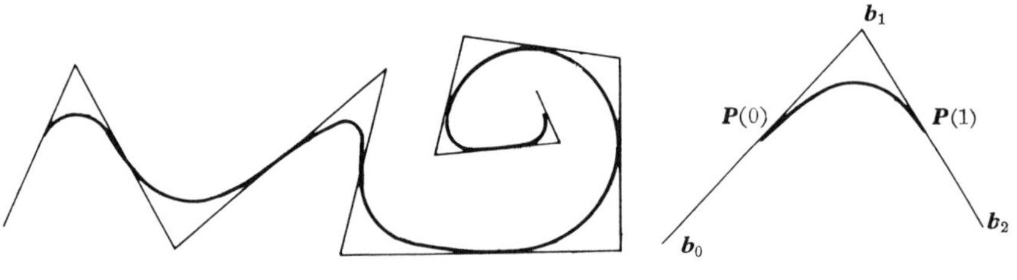

Figure 4-21

Thus the beginning point $\boldsymbol{P}(0)$ of the cubic B-spline segment (3.9) is on the median $\boldsymbol{b}_1\boldsymbol{b}_1^*$ of the triangle $\boldsymbol{b}_0\boldsymbol{b}_1\boldsymbol{b}_2$, and the distance from $\boldsymbol{P}(0)$ to $\boldsymbol{b}_1$ is one-third the distance between $\boldsymbol{b}_1$ and $\boldsymbol{b}_1^*$. The tangent vector $\boldsymbol{P}'(0)$ at this point is parallel to the side $\boldsymbol{b}_0\boldsymbol{b}_2$ of the triangle, and the magnitude of $\boldsymbol{b}_0\boldsymbol{b}_2$ is twice that of $\boldsymbol{P}'(0)$. The derivative vector of second order, $\boldsymbol{P}''(0)$, equals twice the median vector $\overrightarrow{\boldsymbol{b}_1\boldsymbol{b}_1^*}$. Statements about the ending point $\boldsymbol{P}(1)$ can be symmetrically described. With all the above information in mind, the cubic B-spline curve segment can be roughly determined (Fig. 4-22).

If one more vertex $\boldsymbol{b}_4$ is added to the B-characteristic polygon, then $\boldsymbol{b}_1\boldsymbol{b}_2\boldsymbol{b}_3\boldsymbol{b}_4$ determines the next piece of the cubic B-spline curve. Since information about the last point on the last segment and the first point on the new segment depends only on the triangle $\boldsymbol{b}_1\boldsymbol{b}_2\boldsymbol{b}_3$, and furthermore, since the position vectors, tangent vectors and the derivative vectors of second order of both segments are equal, respectively, we again have a proof of C^2-continuity of the cubic B-spline curve.

Adding one more vertex to the B-characteristic polygon adds one more segment of the B-spline curve. Figure 4-23 illustrates a closed B-characteristic polygon and the corresponding cubic B-spline curve.

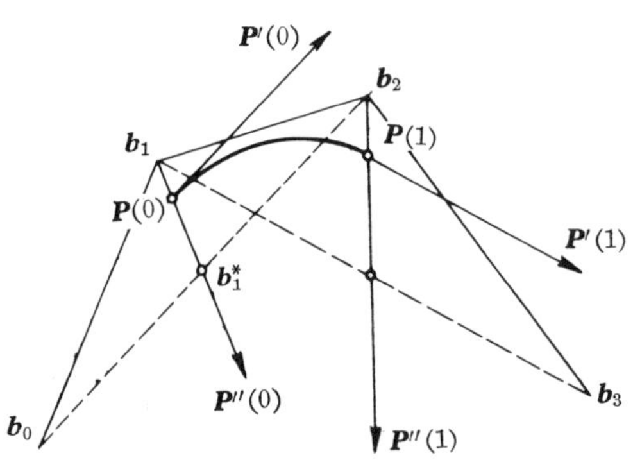

Figure 4-22

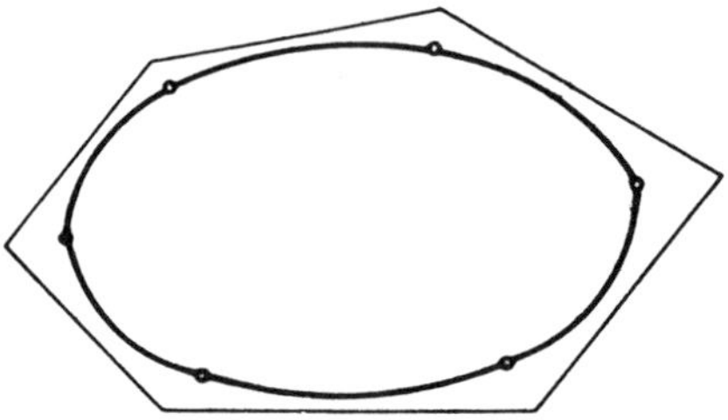

Figure 4-23

B-spline curves have further properties mentioned below:

(1) Approximation. The shape of the *B*-spline curve is determined by that of its *B*-characteristic polygon, and the curve provides a good approximation to the polygon.

(2) Convex hull property. Since $F_{l,n}(t)$ $(l=0, 1, \ldots, n)$ in (3.3) constitutes a set of weight functions, the ith span of the *B*-spline curve lies within the convex hull of the corresponding i^{th} polygon.

(3) Local control. Perturbing a single vertex of the polygon produces only a local perturbation of the curve in the vicinity of that vertex. For example, for $n=2$, only $n+1=3$ pieces of curves will be perturbed (Fig. 4-24).

(4) Convexity preserving. Since *B*-spline functions have the variation diminishing property, they are convexity preserving. It has been proved that the parametric *B*-spline curve whose components are *B*-spline functions also possesses the convexity preserving property.

In Section 3.6, we will give a proof for the convexity preserving property of cubic *B*-spline curves.

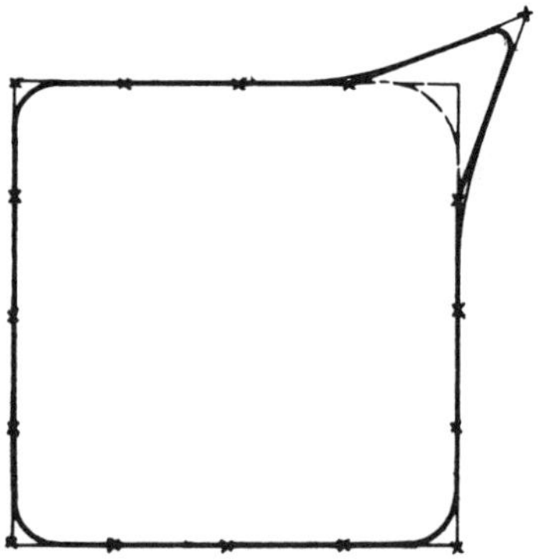

Figure 4-24

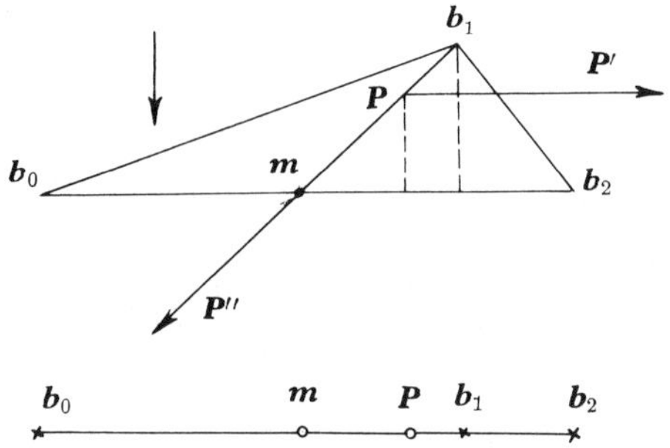

Figure 4-25

The following special cases of cubic B-spline curves are very useful in geometric design.

(1) ***Vertices b_0, b_1, b_2 are collinear.*** This case can be viewed as a degenerate triangle $b_0b_1b_2$, as if the vertex b_1 falls down vertically to the side b_0b_2 (Fig. 4-25). An end-point P of the corresponding cubic B-spline curve satisfies $\overrightarrow{Pb_1} = \frac{1}{3}\overrightarrow{mb_1}$, in which m is the midpoint of the segment b_0b_2. In this case we have $P' \| P''$, thus the curvature $k = 0$ at the point P, which may be a point of inflection.

Conversely, in order that $k = 0$ at the point P, it is necessary that the three vertices b_0, b_1, b_2 be collinear.

Making three vertices collinear is a technique for producing a point of inflection at knots of cubic B-spline curves.

(2) ***Four vertices b_0, b_1, b_2, b_3 are collinear.*** By the convex hull property of the B-spline curve, the cubic curve segment determined by these vertices is a line segment. Determination of two end-points $P(0)$ and $P(1)$ follows from the previous discussion (Fig. 4-26).

(3) ***Vertices b_1 and b_2 are coincident.*** This can also be regarded as the degenerate triangle $b_0b_1b_2$ when b_0 tends to b_2. It is easy to see that the end point P of the cubic B-spline curve segment satisfies $\overrightarrow{Pb_1} = \frac{1}{6}\overrightarrow{b_0b_1}$ and $k = 0$ (Fig. 4-27).

The curve segment associated with $b_0b_1b_2b_3$ is illustrated in Fig. 4-28.

(4) ***Vertices b_2, b_3, b_4 are coincident.*** We know from (2) and (3) immediately that four pieces of the cubic B-spline curve determined by seven vertices b_i $(i = 0, 1, \ldots, 6)$ are as in Fig. 4-29: At the triple vertex $b_2b_3b_4$, there is a cusp on the compound curve which is slope discontinuous. But

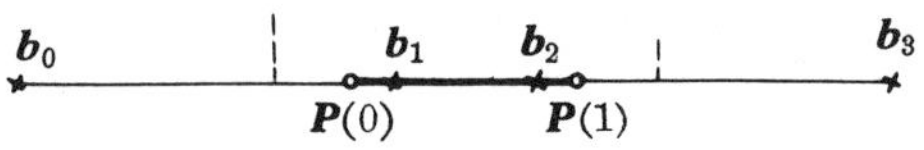

Figure 4-26

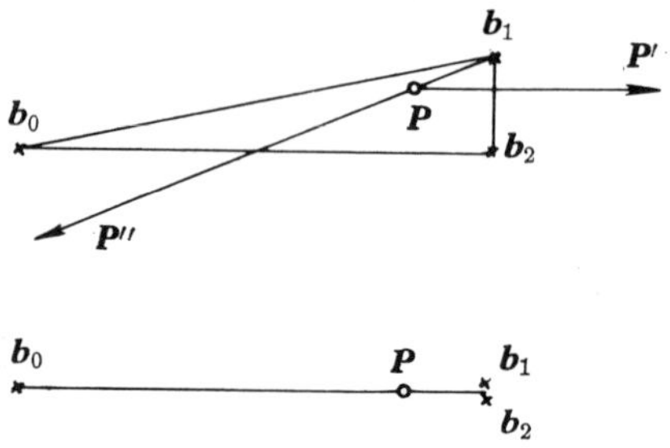

Figure 4-27

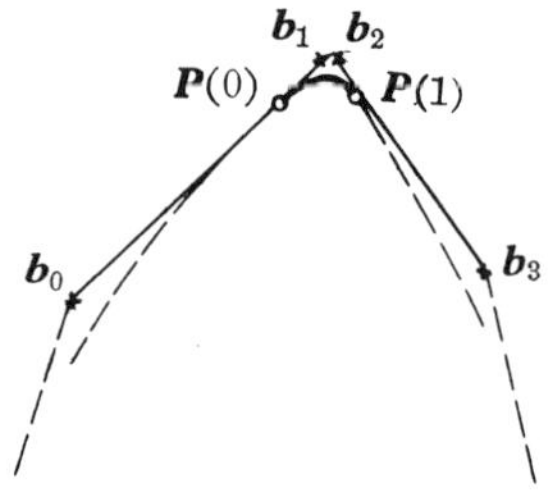

Figure 4-28

the compound curve is really C^2-continuous, as the tangent vector and the second derivative vector are continuous there (both the first and second derivatives simultaneously vanish at such a point). The point is a singularity of the curve.

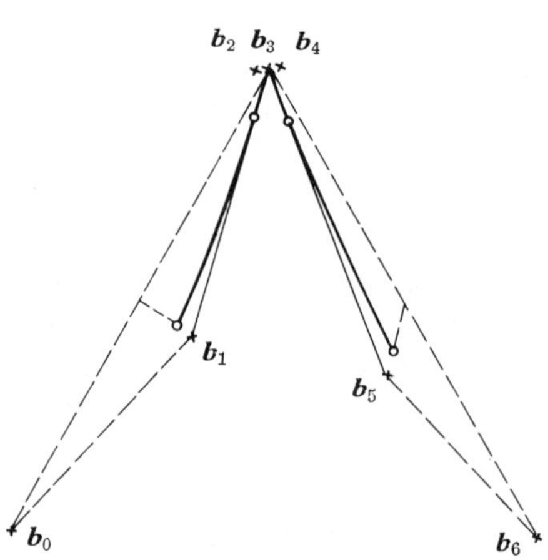

Figure 4-29

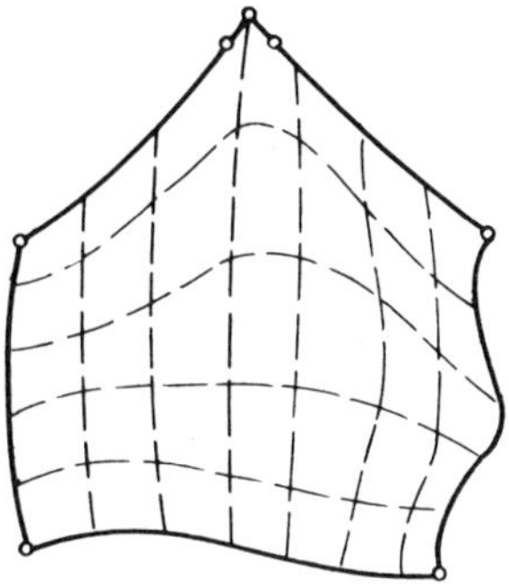

Figure 4-30

In summary, we conclude:

(1) To make a straight line segment on the spline curve, we may take four collinear vertices.
(2) To make a piece of the spline tangential to the B-characteristic polygon, the technique of three collinear vertices or a double vertex may be used.
(3) To make a spline passing through a certain vertex or to produce a cusp on the spline, the triple vertex technique works.

If one wants to produce a cusp on the boundary of a Coons patch, one can use a cubic B-spline curve with triple vertex as the boundary. In this case, the central part of the patch is still smooth (Fig. 4-30).

Note that the multi-vertex technique for the B-spline curve is different from multi-knot technique for the B-spline function, but both have similar effects.

A combination of collinear vertices and multi-vertices produces curves such as the one shown in Fig. 4-31.

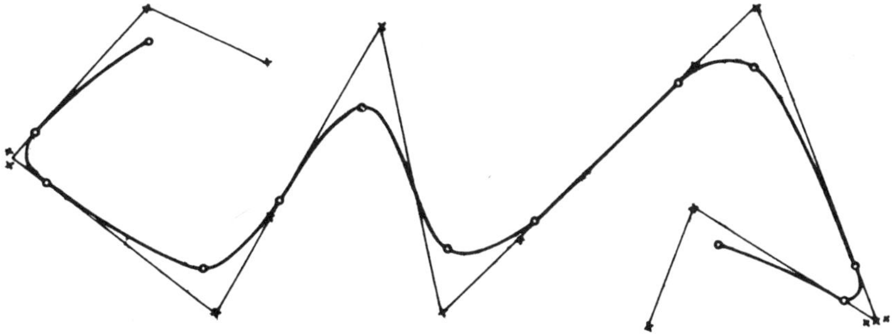

Figure 4-31

3.3 Fairness of Planar Cubic *B*-Spline Curves

In geometric design in the car, ship and plane industry, designers always insist that designed curves should be fair. When planar cubic *B*-spline curves are used for geometric design, the following problem naturally arises: What kinds of *B*-characteristic polygons ensure fair cubic *B*-spline curves?

A detailed discussion of the notion and techniques of fairness appears in Chapter VII. Here we content ourselves with such an understanding: A spline curve is said to be fair if the following conditions are satisfied:

(1) The deviation of the spline curve from the wooden spline curve is small.

(2) The curvature k_i $(i=0, 1, \ldots, n)$ at knot $\boldsymbol{P}_i$ of the spline forms a uniform sequence (also called a *fair* sequence).

For example, if the sequence of curvature at the knots is 1, 2, 4, 3, 3, 2, 1, and the interpolatory curve is chosen to be the cubic parametric spline of cumulative chord length, then it is fair. But the curvature sequence 1, −2, 10, 1, −3, 2, 1 is not fair.

Let $\boldsymbol{b}_i$ $(i=0, 1, \ldots, n)$ be given vertices of a *B*-characteristic polygon. Passing through three neighboring vertices $\boldsymbol{b}_{i-1}$, $\boldsymbol{b}_i$, $\boldsymbol{b}_{i+1}$, a circle could be drawn. Let K_i $(i=1, 2, \ldots, n-1)$ be the curvature of the circle. K_i is said to be the discrete curvature of these three points. It is easy to show that

$$K_i = \frac{4\Delta_i}{L_i L_{i+1} L_i^*} = \frac{[\boldsymbol{P}_i' \, \boldsymbol{P}_i'']}{L_i L_{i+1} |\boldsymbol{P}_i'|} \qquad (i=1, 2, \ldots, n-1),$$

where Δ_i denotes the signed area of the triangle $\boldsymbol{b}_{i-1}\boldsymbol{b}_i\boldsymbol{b}_{i+1}$. Let $L_i = |\overrightarrow{\boldsymbol{b}_{i-1}\boldsymbol{b}_i}|$, $L_{i+1} = |\overrightarrow{\boldsymbol{b}_i\boldsymbol{b}_{i+1}}|$, $L_i^* = |\overrightarrow{\boldsymbol{b}_{i-1}\boldsymbol{b}_{i+1}}|$, and let $\boldsymbol{P}_i'$ and $\boldsymbol{P}_i''$ denote the derivative vectors of the first and second order of the cubic *B*-spline curve at the knot $\boldsymbol{P}_i$ (Fig. 4-32). The curvature at $\boldsymbol{P}_i$ is

$$k_i = \frac{[\boldsymbol{P}_i' \, \boldsymbol{P}_i'']}{|\boldsymbol{P}_i'|^3},$$

$$\frac{k_i}{K_i} = \frac{L_i L_{i+1}}{|\boldsymbol{P}_i'|^2} = \frac{4L_i L_{i+1}}{L_i^{*2}} = \frac{4L_i L_{i+1}}{L_i^2 + L_{i+1}^2 + 2L_i L_{i+1} \cos \phi_i}$$

$$\frac{k_i}{K_i} = \frac{L_i L_{i+1}}{|\boldsymbol{P}_i'|^2} = \frac{4L_i L_{i+1}}{L_i^{*2}} = \frac{4L_i L_{i+1}}{L_i^2 + L_{i+1}^2 + 2L_i L_{i+1} \cos \phi_i}$$

$$= \frac{4L_i L_{i+1}}{(L_i + L_{i+1})^2 - L_i L_{i+1} \phi_i^2 + O(\phi_i^4)}$$

$$= \frac{4L_i L_{i+1}}{(L_i + L_{i+1})^2} + O(\phi_i^2)$$

$$= 4\lambda_i \mu_i + O(\phi_i^2) \qquad (i=1, 2, \ldots, n-1),$$

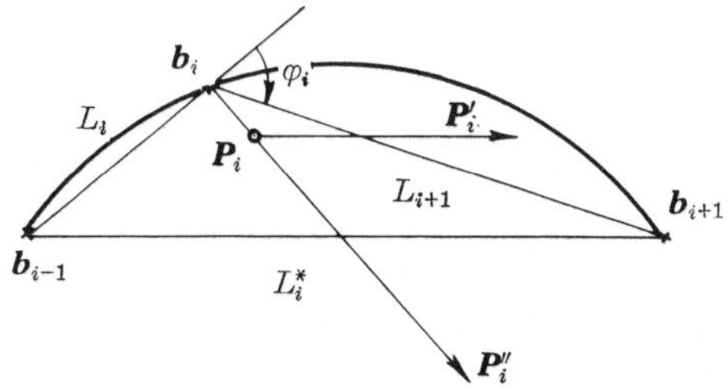

Figure 4-32

where

$$\lambda_i = \frac{L_{i+1}}{L_i + L_{i+1}}, \qquad \mu_i = \frac{L_i}{L_i + L_{i+1}}.$$

The above expression can be rewritten as

$$k_i = 4\lambda_i\mu_i K_i + O(\phi_i^2) \qquad (i = 1, 2, \ldots, n-1). \tag{3.11}$$

If necessary, the main part of the higher-order term may be calculated as

$$O(\phi_i^2) = 4K_i\lambda_i^2\mu_i^2\phi_i^2 + O(\phi_i^4).$$

If the given vertices $\boldsymbol{b}_i$ $(i = 0, 1, \ldots, n)$ of the B-characteristic polygon are equally spaced, i.e., if all L_i are equal to the same quantity L, the $\lambda_i = \mu_i = \frac{1}{2}$ and (3.11) becomes

$$k_i = K_i + O(\phi_i^2) \qquad (i = 1, 2, \ldots, n-1).$$

If the B-characteristic polygon is of small local deflection, i.e., $|\phi_i| \leq 30°$, then $O(\phi_i^2)$ may be omitted. This shows that the fairness of the sequence of curvatures k_i $(i = 1, 2, \ldots, n-1)$ at the knots of the cubic B-spline curve is equivalent to that of the sequence of discrete curvatures K_i $(i = 1, 2, \ldots, n-1)$ at the vertices of the B-characteristic polygon.

The magnitude of the tangent vector at a knot of the spline is

$$|\boldsymbol{P}_i'| = \tfrac{1}{2}L_i^* = L + O(\phi_i^2).$$

Just like the cubic parametric spline of cumulative chord length, the cubic B-spline has order of approximation $O(\phi^4)$. The discussion of the Manning normalized spline in the previous chapter shows that the deviation between the wooden spline and the cubic B-spline curve is not much.

In summary we conclude that if the given B-characteristic polygon satisfies the conditions,

(1) distances between any two neighboring vertices are equal,

(2) there is locally small deflection,
(3) the sequence of discrete curvatures K_i $(i = 1, 2, \ldots, n-1)$ is fair,

then the corresponding cubic B-spline curve must be fair (Liu Dingyuan [3], 1979).

We mention that in applications, condition (1) may be replaced by "vertices are uniformly spaced." In this case condition (3) should be replaced, according to (3.11), by "the sequence $\bar{K}_i \equiv \lambda_i \mu_i K_i$ $(i = 1, 2, \ldots, n-1)$ is fair."

3.4 End Conditions and the Inverse Problem for Cubic *B*-Spline Curves

In some practical problems, it is desirable to design a cubic B-spline curve having given end-points and specified tangent vectors at these two points. In other words, interpolation conditions should be satisfied at the two end-points.

Assume that internal vertices $\boldsymbol{b}_2, \boldsymbol{b}_3, \boldsymbol{b}_4, \ldots$ are given. We extend two extreme vertices $\boldsymbol{b}_0$ and $\boldsymbol{b}_1$ such that the spline begins with $\boldsymbol{P}_0$ and has tangent vector $\boldsymbol{P}_0'$ at this point. The construction consists of three steps:

(1) $\boldsymbol{P} = \boldsymbol{P}_0 + \frac{1}{3}\boldsymbol{P}_0'$, i.e., $\overrightarrow{\boldsymbol{P}_0\boldsymbol{P}} = \frac{1}{3}\boldsymbol{P}_0'$;
(2) $\boldsymbol{b}_1 = \frac{1}{2}(3\boldsymbol{P} - \boldsymbol{b}_2)$, i.e., $\overrightarrow{\boldsymbol{b}_1\boldsymbol{P}} = \frac{1}{3}\overrightarrow{\boldsymbol{b}_1\boldsymbol{b}_2}$;
(3) $\boldsymbol{b}_0 = \boldsymbol{b}_2 - 2\boldsymbol{P}_0'$, i.e., $\overrightarrow{\boldsymbol{b}_0\boldsymbol{b}_2} = 2\boldsymbol{P}_0'$.

The construction is shown in Fig. 4-33.

A similar construction applies to interpolation at the ending point.

Here is another method to determine end conditions which is very useful for applications.

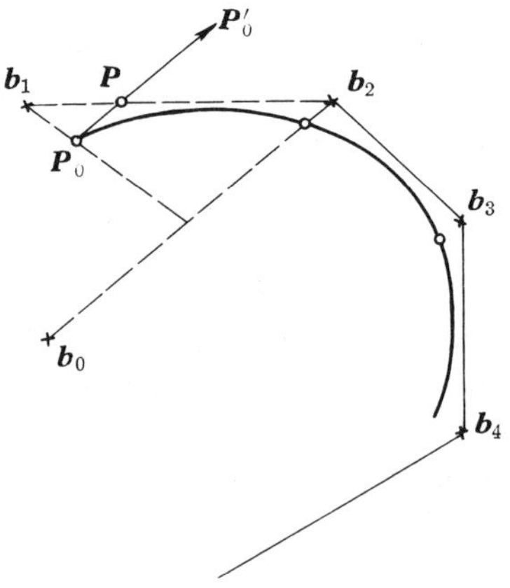

Figure 4-33

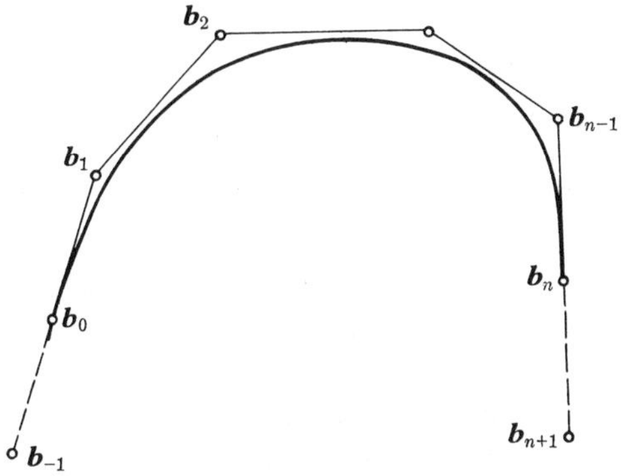

Figure 4-34

Suppose that we are given vertices $\boldsymbol{b}_i$ $(i=0,\ldots,n)$ of the polygon. We assume that the resulting *B*-spline curve has the first point at $\boldsymbol{b}_0$ and the last point at $\boldsymbol{b}_n$, and is tangential to $\overrightarrow{\boldsymbol{b}_0\boldsymbol{b}_1}$ and $\overrightarrow{\boldsymbol{b}_{n-1}\boldsymbol{b}_n}$, respectively, at these two points. The construction is quite simple: Choose two additional vertices $\boldsymbol{b}_{-1}$ and $\boldsymbol{b}_{n-1}$ such that

$$\overrightarrow{\boldsymbol{b}_{-1}\boldsymbol{b}_0}=\overrightarrow{\boldsymbol{b}_0\boldsymbol{b}_1}, \qquad \overrightarrow{\boldsymbol{b}_{n-1}\boldsymbol{b}_n}=\overrightarrow{\boldsymbol{b}_n\boldsymbol{b}_{n+1}}.$$

Then take $\boldsymbol{b}_j$ $(j=-1,0,\ldots,n+1)$ as vertices of a new *B*-characteristic polygon. The *B*-spline curve generated by the new polygon satisfies the required end conditions (Fig. 4-34).

B-spline curves obtained in such a way and Bézier curves have the same relations with their characteristic polygons at the end points, except that the curvature is equal to zero at these points for such *B*-spline curves.

The so-called inverse problem is that for given points $\boldsymbol{P}_i$ $(i=1,2,\ldots,n-1)$, we want to find a cubic *B*-spline curve *L* with $\{\boldsymbol{P}_i\}$ as its knots. Hence the inverse problem is equivalent to interpolation. By "to find a spline *L*" we mean that we must determine the vertices $\boldsymbol{b}_i$ $(i=0,1,\ldots,n)$ of its *B*-characteristic polygon (Fig. 4-35).

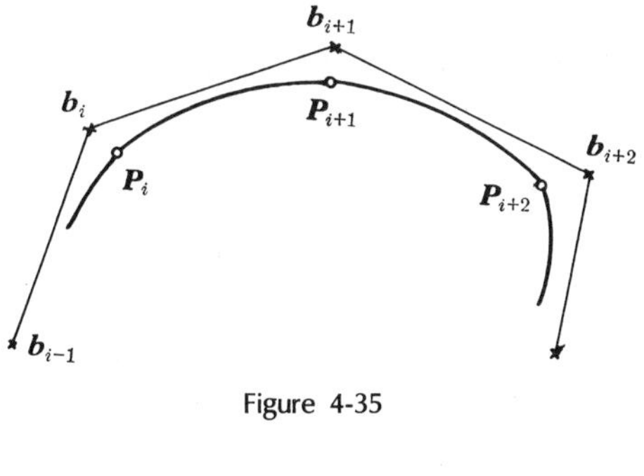

Figure 4-35

From the first two equalities of (3.10) we see that the inverse problem reduces to solving the following system of linear algebraic equations:

$$\boldsymbol{b}_{i-1}+4\boldsymbol{b}_i+\boldsymbol{b}_{i+1}=6\boldsymbol{P}_i \qquad (i=1,2,\ldots,n-1). \tag{3.12}$$

If two suitable end conditions are provided, then the system may have a unique solution.

Recall that a tridiagonal system of linear equations appeared when cubic spline functions were used for interpolation in Chapter II. Here (3.12) is merely a tridiagonal system in vector-valued form.

Now we discuss the interdependence of vertices $\{\boldsymbol{b}_i\}$ and knots $\{\boldsymbol{P}_i\}$. The influence upon knots $\{\boldsymbol{P}_i\}$ caused by perturbation of vertices $\{\boldsymbol{b}_i\}$ can be formulated explicitly from (3.10). On the other hand, how is the influence upon vertices $\{\boldsymbol{b}_i\}$ caused by perturbed knots $\{\boldsymbol{P}_i\}$?

Fix an index k. Let a single knot $\boldsymbol{P}_k$ be perturbed. Assume that the terms on the right-hand side of the system (3.12) are all zero except $\boldsymbol{P}_k$. We only consider the case in which the number of knots is so big that the end conditions need not be taken into account. In this case, the solution of (3.12) can be expressed by

$$\boldsymbol{b}_{k+j}=\sqrt{3}\lambda^{|j|}\boldsymbol{P}_k \qquad (j=0,\pm 1,\pm 2,\ldots),$$

where $\lambda=\sqrt{3}-2\approx -0.268$. This implies that the influence upon the vertex $\boldsymbol{b}_{k+j}$ caused by knot $\boldsymbol{P}_k$ decays rapidly with increasing $|j|$. We have seen that the cardinal cubic spline with equally spaced knots, discussed in Chapter II, possesses the same property. We also see that the computations for cubic B-spline curves, either in approximation or in interpolation, are very stable.

Direct computation yields $\lambda^2\approx 0.0718$, $\lambda^3\approx -0.0192$, $\lambda^4\approx 0.00515$. For $j=\pm 4$, the influence upon $\boldsymbol{b}_{k\pm 4}$ caused by $\boldsymbol{P}_k$ reduces to 10^{-3}. When all knots are given, vertices $\boldsymbol{b}_i$ in (3.12) far from the end-points can be expressed approximately by

$$\boldsymbol{b}_i=\sqrt{3}\left\{\boldsymbol{P}_i+\sum_{j=1}^{4}(\boldsymbol{P}_{i+j}+\boldsymbol{P}_{i-j})\lambda^j\right\}. \tag{3.13}$$

This expression is independent of the coordinate system. This without loss of generality $\boldsymbol{P}_i$ can be taken as the origin. Letting $\boldsymbol{Q}_j$ denote the midpoint of $\boldsymbol{P}_{i+j}$ and $\boldsymbol{P}_{i-j}$, we have

$$\boldsymbol{b}_i=2\sqrt{3}\sum_{j=1}^{4}\boldsymbol{Q}_j\lambda^j.$$

Just like B-spline functions, B-spline curves are very convenient tools for approximation, i.e., by designing vertices of the B-characteristic polygon to realize the shape control of the B-spline curve. Such a technique provides a designer with the very desirable geometric properties we previously mentioned.

3.5 Relations Between B-Spline Curves and Bézier Curves

It is well known that Bézier curves of degree n are special cases of B-spline curves of degree n. For the proof one uses the following fact: B-spline functions with multi-knots produce a degenerate spline basis, i.e., Bernstein basis functions. We begin with the recursive algorithm (3.4) to derive the relations between these two curves.

Put $\omega_l(t) \equiv l \ (l = 1, 2, \ldots, n)$. In this case the integral condition should be replaced by $\int_0^1 \omega_l(\tau)\, d\tau = l$. After translating a constant vector $-\sum_{j=1}^{n-1} \boldsymbol{b}_j$, the resulting MA curve segment of degree n will be denoted again by $\boldsymbol{R}_{0,n}(t)$.

Inserting $l = n$, $i = 0$ into (3.4), we have

$$\boldsymbol{R}_{0,n}(t) = n \int_t^1 \boldsymbol{R}_{0,n-1}(\tau)\, d\tau + n \int_0^t \boldsymbol{R}_{1,n-1}(\tau)\, d\tau - \sum_{j=1}^{n-1} \boldsymbol{b}_j.$$

Differentiating with respect to t, we have

$$\begin{aligned} \boldsymbol{R}'_{0,n}(t) &= n\{\boldsymbol{R}_{1,n-1}(t) - \boldsymbol{R}_{0,n-1}(t)\} \\ &= n(E-1)\boldsymbol{R}_{0,n-1}(t), \end{aligned}$$

where E represents the shifting operator $E\boldsymbol{b}_i = \boldsymbol{b}_{i+1}$.

It is clear that the initial condition for the above differential equation is $\boldsymbol{R}_{0,n}(0) = \boldsymbol{b}_0$. Thus we have the solution

$$\boldsymbol{R}_{0,n}(t) = (1 - t + tE)^n \boldsymbol{b}_0.$$

By binomial expansion, we obtain

$$\boldsymbol{R}_{0,n}(t) = \sum_{i=0}^{n} C_n^i t^i (1-t)^{n-i} \boldsymbol{b}_i, \qquad 0 \leqslant t \leqslant 1.$$

This is the Bernstein representation of the Bézier curve of degree n.

We conclude that Bézier curves of degree n and B-spline curve segments can be incorporated by MA curves, if we choose

$$\omega_l(t) \equiv l, \qquad \omega_l(t) \equiv 1 \qquad (l = 1, 2, \ldots, n),$$

respectively.

3.6 Three Equivalent Representations of Parametric Cubic Curve Segments

The cubic Bézier curve, the cubic *B*-spline curve segment and the cubic Ferguson curve are different representations of the parametric cubic curve segment. From an algebraic point of view, these representations can be written as unified matrix forms:

$$\boldsymbol{P}(t)=[t][B]_j[\boldsymbol{b}]^{(j)}, \qquad 0\leqslant t\leqslant 1 \qquad (j=1,2,3), \tag{3.14}$$

where $[t]=[t^3\ t^2\ t\ 1]$, $[\boldsymbol{b}]^{(j)}=[\boldsymbol{b}_0^{(j)}\ \boldsymbol{b}_1^{(j)}\ \boldsymbol{b}_2^{(j)}\ \boldsymbol{b}_3^{(j)}]^T$ $(j=1,2,3)$, and T denotes the transpose operation of matrices. The matrices $[B]_j$ $(j=1,2,3)$ are, respectively,

$$\begin{bmatrix} 1 & & & 0 \\ & 1 & & \\ & & 1 & \\ 0 & & & 1 \end{bmatrix}, \quad \begin{bmatrix} -1 & 3 & -3 & 1 \\ 3 & -6 & 3 & 0 \\ -3 & 3 & 0 & 0 \\ 1 & 0 & 0 & 0 \end{bmatrix},$$

and

$$\frac{1}{6}\begin{bmatrix} -1 & 3 & -3 & 1 \\ 3 & -6 & 3 & 0 \\ -3 & 0 & 3 & 0 \\ 1 & 4 & 1 & 0 \end{bmatrix}.$$

For $j=1$, (3.14) represents the Ferguson form of the parametric cubic curve segment. Being a polynomial expanded in powers of the parameter t, the Ferguson representation is suitable for numerical computation.

For $j=2$, (3.14) is a Bézier curve, and $[\boldsymbol{b}]^{(2)}$ represents the sequence of vertices of the corresponding characteristic polygon.

For $j=3$, (3.14) is a segment of the cubic *B*-spline curve, and $[\boldsymbol{b}]^{(3)}$ forms the sequence of vertices of the corresponding *B*-characteristic polygon. For each j, the first and second matrices are fixed. The shape of the curve is completely determined by information in the matrix $[\boldsymbol{b}]^{(j)}$. The matrix $[\boldsymbol{b}]^{(1)}$ is only related to the first derivative vectors of the curve at the beginning point. A simple consideration of $[\boldsymbol{b}]^{(1)}$ does not tell us the shape of the curve. The situation is different for $j=2$ and 3. Since the Bézier curve and the *B*-spline curve are good approximations of their characteristic polygons, the matrices $[\boldsymbol{b}]^{(j)}$ $(j=2,3)$ formed by the polygonal vertices provide us with shape control ability. This is an advantage of Bézier curves and *B*-spline curves.

For a parametric cubic curve segment L, any one of the three representations can be transformed into another. Each two matrices are connected by a nonsingular matrix

$$[\boldsymbol{b}]^{(2)} = [B]_2^{-1}[\boldsymbol{b}]^{(1)},$$

$$[\boldsymbol{b}]^{(3)} = [B]_3^{-1}[\boldsymbol{b}]^{(1)},$$

$$[\boldsymbol{b}]^{(3)} = [B]_3^{-1}[B]_2[\boldsymbol{b}]^{(2)}.$$

If one has obtained geometric properties of a general parametric curve segment, then by a linear transformation one can obtain the corresponding properties of Bézier or B-spline representations of the same segment. For the planar cubic curve segment, the problem has been completely solved. For the parametric curve segment of degree n, if we can find its affine invariants and the distribution of real singularities and points of inflection, then shape control of the Bézier curve and B-spline curve of degree n can be realized. This is a significant task both in theory and practice.

Different representations of curve (3.14) come from different choices of basis functions. The basis $\{t^3, t^2, t, 1\}$, the cubic Bernstein basis, and the cubic B-spline basis are used for $j = 1$, 2 and 3, respectively.

Geometric information of the Bézier polygon and B-characteristic polygon of the same parametric cubic curve segment L can also be transformed into each other. For simplicity of notation, let $[\boldsymbol{b}]^{(2)} \equiv [\boldsymbol{b}_0, \boldsymbol{b}_1, \boldsymbol{b}_2, \boldsymbol{b}_3]$ be vertices of the Bézier polygon and $[\boldsymbol{b}]^{(3)} \equiv [\boldsymbol{c}_0, \boldsymbol{c}_1, \boldsymbol{c}_2, \boldsymbol{c}_3]$ be vertices of the B-characteristic polygon.

(1) ***Given*** $[\boldsymbol{b}]^{(3)}$**.** From properties of the cubic B-spline segment and the cubic Bézier curve at end points, we know that $\boldsymbol{b}_0$ and $\boldsymbol{b}_3$ are the end points of the curve, and that $\boldsymbol{b}_1$ and $\boldsymbol{b}_2$ are coincident with the two trisection points of the line segment $\boldsymbol{c}_1\boldsymbol{c}_2$ (Fig. 4-36).

It is clear from the figure that if the cubic B-characteristic polygon is convex, then so is the cubic Bézier polygon. Hence the corresponding curve L is convex. This proves that the cubic B-spline curve is convexity preserving.

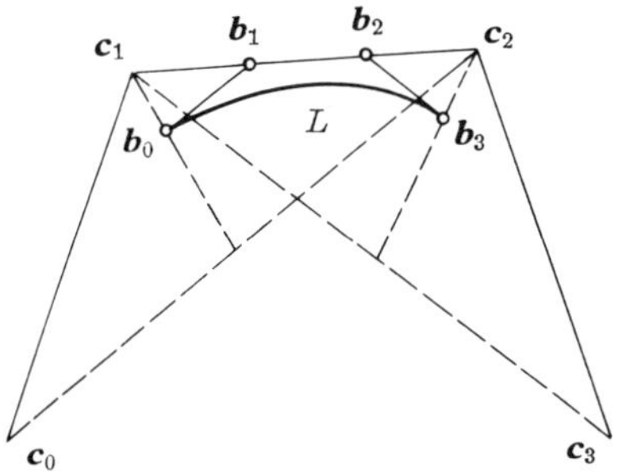

Figure 4-36

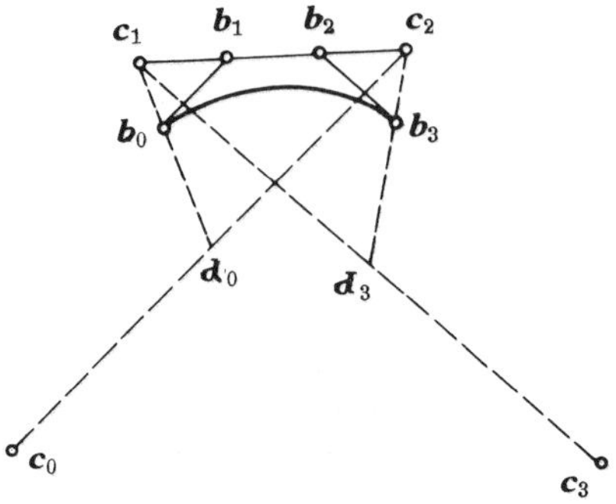

Figure 4-37

(2) ***Given*** $[b]^{(2)}$**.** Extend b_2b_1 to get c_1 such that $b_1c_1 = b_2b_1$. Then extend c_1b_0 to get d_0 such that $b_0d_0 = 2c_1b_0$. Finally extend c_2d_0 to get c_0 such that $d_0c_0 = c_2d_0$. c_2 and c_3 can be obtained by similar construction (Fig. 4-37).

It is seen from Fig. 4-36 and Fig. 4-37 that the cubic *B*-spline curve approximates more closely to its characteristic polygon than the Bézier curve does.

Figure 4-38 illustrates that for the same characteristic polygon, the corresponding *B*-spline curve (solid line) approximates the polygon more closely than the Bézier curve (broken line) does.

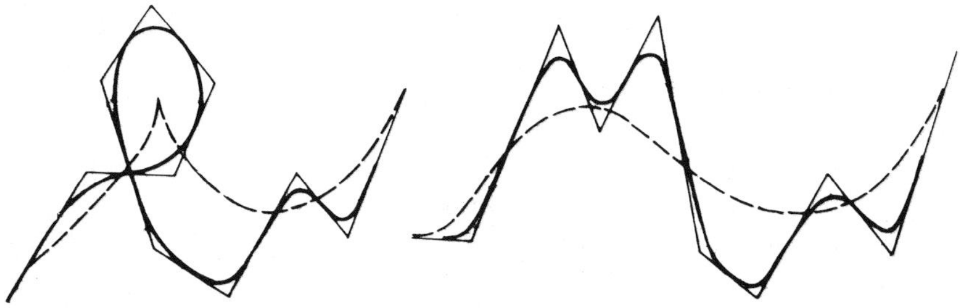

Figure 4-38

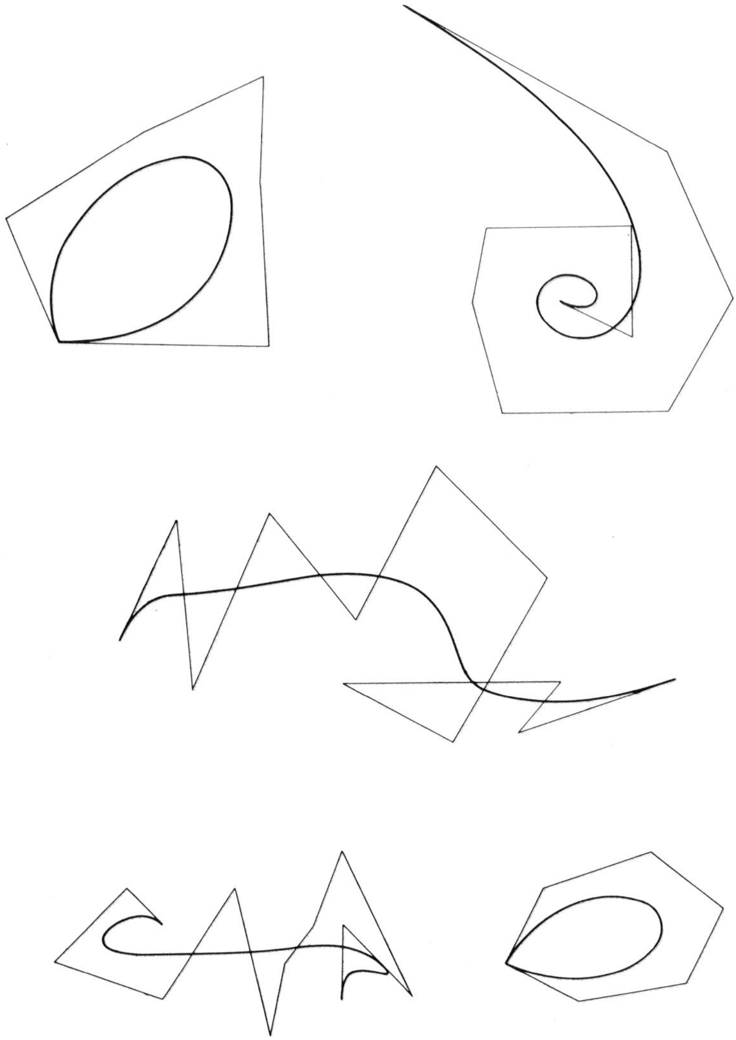

Figure 4-39

Bézier Curves and Their Characteristic Polygons.

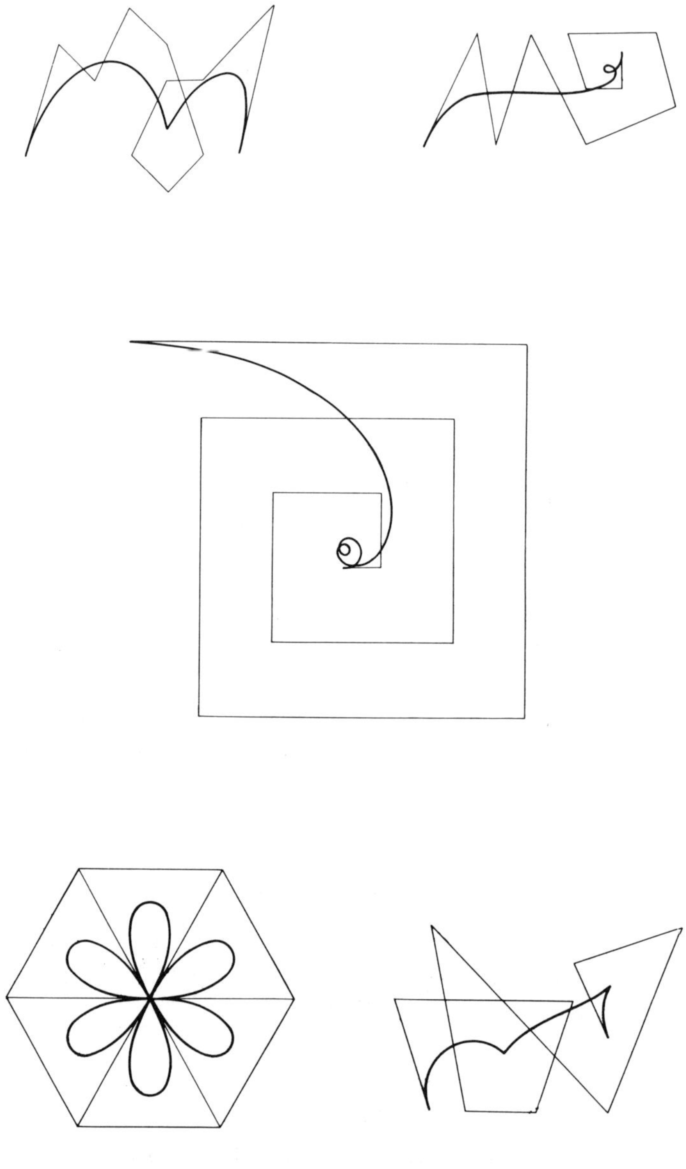

Figure 4-39 *continued*

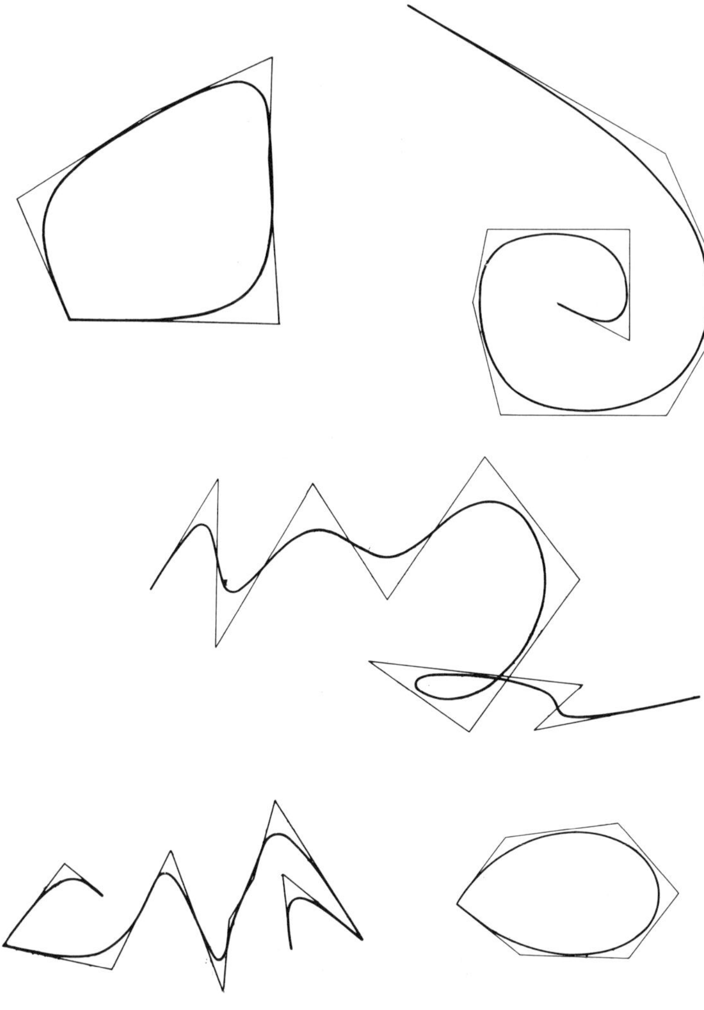

Figure 4-40

Cubic *B*-Spline Curves and Their *B*-Characteristic Polygons. A comparison between Fig. 4-39 and 4-40 shows that for the same characteristic polygon, the cubic *B*-spline curve has a better approximation than the Bézier curve has.

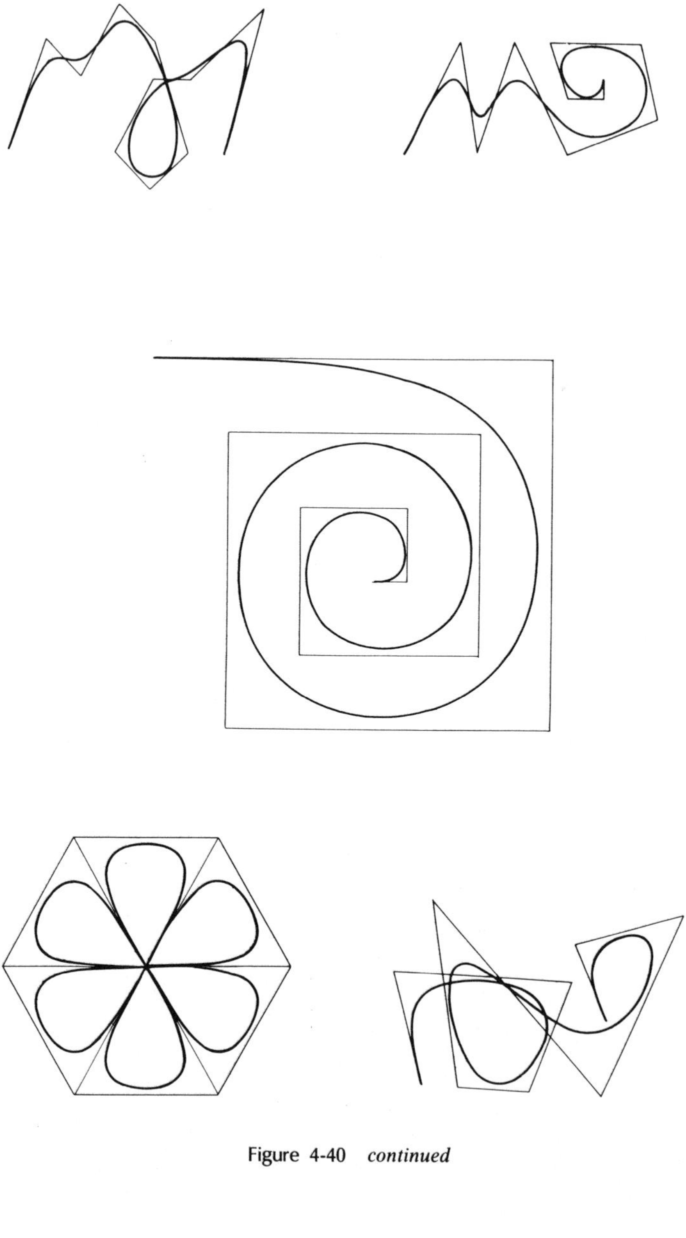

Figure 4-40 *continued*

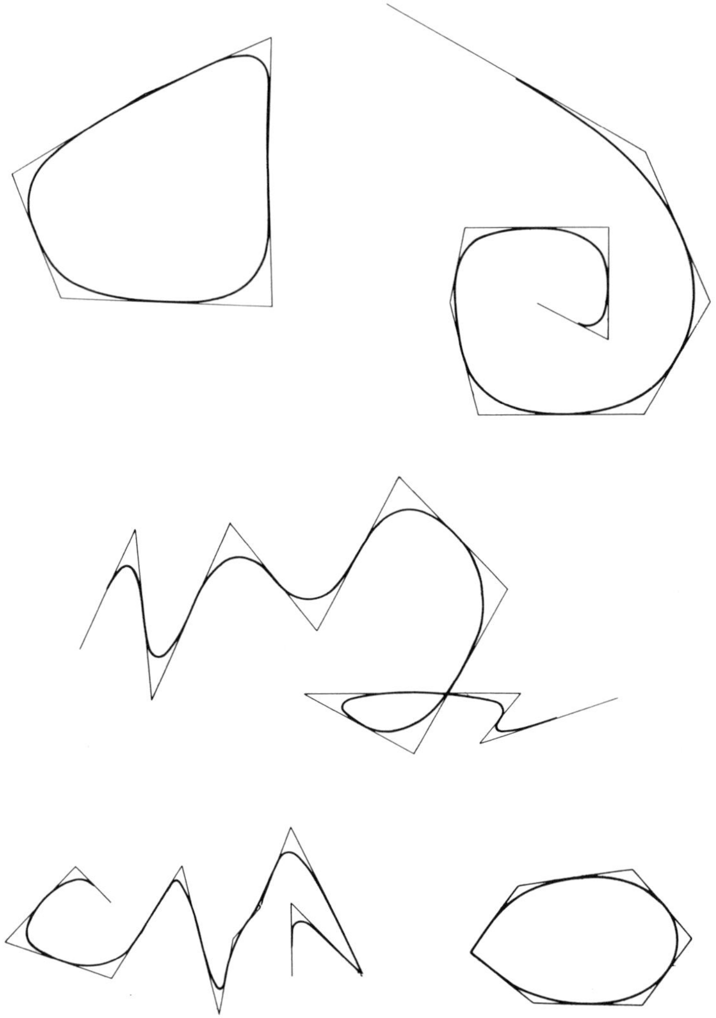

Figure 4-41

Quadratic *B*-Spline Curves and Their *B*-Characteristic Polygons. Generally, the quadratic *B*-spline curve approximates the same *B*-characteristic polygon more closely than the cubic does. Probably the quadratic *B*-spline curve is not as fair as the cubic.

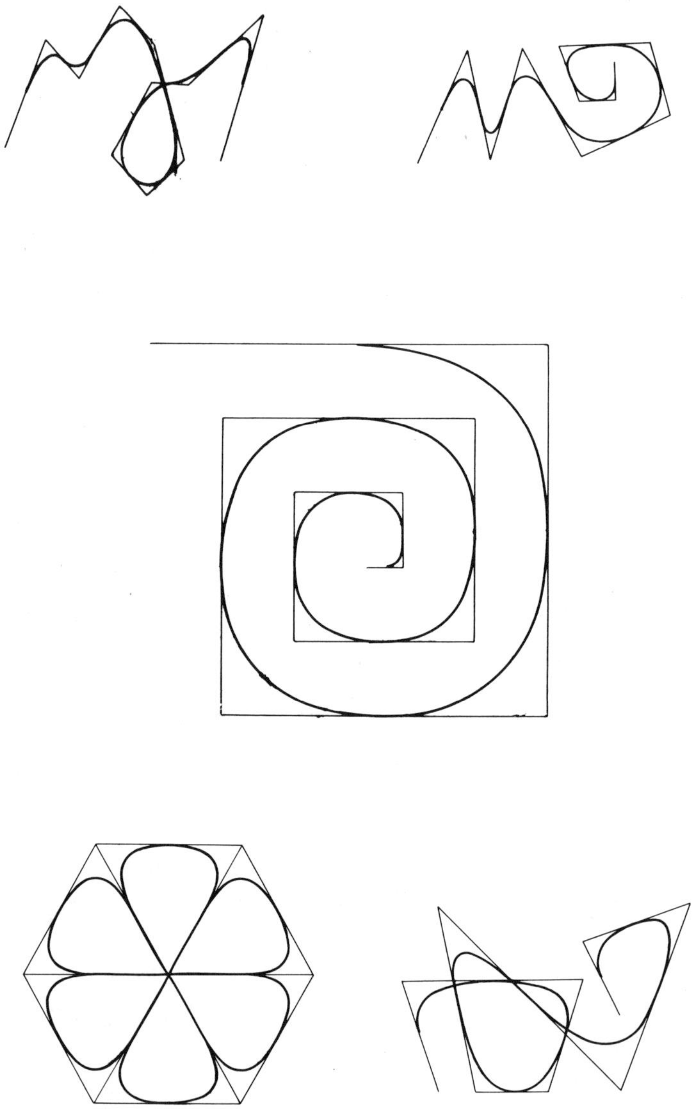

Figure 4-41 *continued*

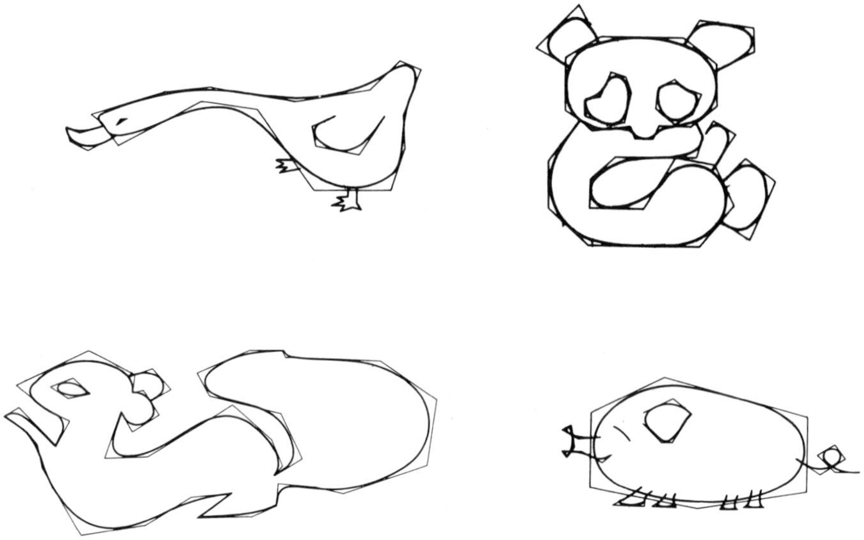

Figure 4-42

Animals Drawn Using Cubic *B*-Spline Curves.

CHAPTER V

Spline Surfaces

In geometric lofting and the design of cars, ships and planes, the objects involved are mainly surfaces. To represent surfaces, spline functions of one variable should be extended to bivariate spline functions, and spline curves should be extended to spline surfaces.

In 1962, deBoor did the first part of this work. The second part was done by Coons from 1964 to 1967. Their techniques are suitable for surface interpolation and have wide application to mathematical lofting in geometric design.

Two-dimensional extensions of Bézier curves and *B*-spline curves are Bézier surfaces and *B*-spline surfaces, which are tools mainly for approximation.

1 Bicubic Spline Functions

In 1962, an interpolatory scheme of bicubic spline functions defined over rectangles with rectangular partitions was suggested by deBoor. He proved the existence and the uniqueness of the interpolatory bicubic spline function and established an efficient algorithm. His work is of great importance in the history of the development of two-dimensional spline functions.

1.1 Definitions

Univariate spline functions have been discussed in Chapter II. For a given partition of the closed interval $[a, b]$, $\Delta_x: a = x_0 < x_1 < \cdots < x_n = b$, all cubic spline functions with respect to Δ_x constitute a linear space, denoted by $S(x; \Delta_x)$, of dimension $n+3$.

Now we extend univariate cubic spline functions to bivariate cases. Let $R: [a, b]\otimes[c, d]$ be a rectangular region in the uw-plane. A rectangular partition of R is the tensor product of two partitions in one dimension. More precisely, the partitions

$$\Delta_u: \qquad a = u_0 < u_1 < \cdots < u_n = b,$$

$$\Delta_w: \qquad c = w_0 < w_1 < \cdots < w_m = d,$$

of the u-axis and w-axis, respectively, induce a rectangular partition of $R: \Delta \equiv \Delta_u \otimes \Delta_w$, consisting of mn subrectangles

$$R_{ij}: \qquad [u_{i-1}, u_i]\otimes[w_{j-1}, w_j]$$

with side length

$$h_i = u_i - u_{i-1} \qquad (i = 1, 2, \ldots, n),$$

$$g_j = w_j - w_{j-1} \qquad (j = 1, 2, \ldots, m).$$

Straight lines $u = u_i$ $(i = 0, 1, \ldots, n)$ and $w = w_j$ $(j = 0, 1, \ldots, m)$ are called the *grid lines* of the partition Δ. Intersections of grid lines, (u_i, w_j) $(i = 0, 1, \ldots, n; j = 0, 1, \ldots, m)$ are said to be the *nodes* of the partition Δ. There are altogether $(m+1)(n+1)$ nodes (Fig. 5-1).

Definition Let $R: [a, b]\otimes[c, d]$ be a rectangular region in the uw-plane. Let a partition $\Delta = \Delta_u \otimes \Delta_w$ of R be given, in which

$$\Delta_u: \qquad a = u_0 < u_1 < \cdots < u_n = b,$$

$$\Delta_w: \qquad c = w_0 < w_1 < \cdots < w_m = d.$$

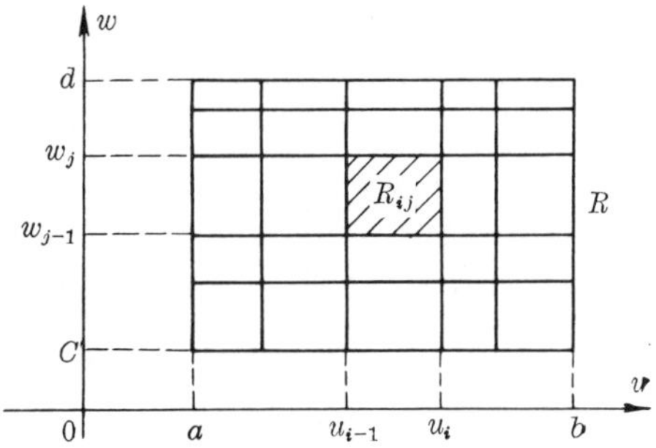

Figure 5-1

A function $x(u, w)$ is called a *bicubic spline function* with respect to the partition Δ of R, if the following conditions are satisfied:

(1) In each subrectangle $R_{ij}: [u_{i-1}, u_i]\otimes[w_{j-1}, w_j]$ $(i=1, 2, \ldots, n;$ $j=1, 2, \ldots, m)$, $x(u, w)$ is a cubic polynomial with respect to either u or to w, i.e.,

$$x(u, w)=\sum_{e,f=0}^{3} B_{ef}^{ij}(u-u_{i-1})^e(w-w_{j-1})^f. \tag{1.1}$$

(2) In the region R, the partial derivatives $\partial^{(\alpha+\beta)}x(u, w)/\partial u^\alpha\, \partial w^\beta$, $(\alpha, \beta=0, 1, 2)$ are continuous. The fact is abbreviated by the notation $x(u, w)\in C_2^4(R)$.

In addition, if for a set of given numbers $\{x_{ij}\}$ $(i=0, 1, \ldots, n; j=0, 1, \ldots, m)$, we have

$$x(u_i, w_j)=x_{ij} \qquad (i=0, 1, \ldots, n; j=0, 1, \ldots, m), \tag{1.2}$$

then $x(u, w)$ is called the *interpolatory* bicubic spline function.

The bicubic spline function restricted to the subtriangle of Δ is a bicubic polynomial which is the tensor product of two univariate cubic polynomials. In some engineering problems, the designer needs the continuity of partial derivatives of second order across grid lines to ensure that the surface represented by the bicubic spline function has continuous Gaussian curvature and mean curvature.

1.2 Cardinal Representation

We have already seen that all univariate cubic spline functions with respect to the partition Δ_u constitute the linear space $S(u; \Delta_u)$ of dimension $n+3$. Its cardinal splines $\{\phi_s(u)\}$ $(s=0, 1, \ldots, n+2)$ satisfy

$$\phi_s(u_i)=\delta_{si}, \qquad \phi_s'(u_0)=\phi_s'(u_n)=0 \qquad (i, s=0, 1, \ldots, n);$$

$$\phi_{n+1}(u_i)=\phi_{n+2}(u_i)=0 \qquad (i=0, 1, \ldots, n);$$

$$\phi'_{n+1}(u_0)=\phi'_{n+2}(u_n)=1, \qquad \phi'_{n+1}(u_n)=\phi'_{n+2}(u_0)=0.$$

Similarly, for the $(m+3)$-dimensional linear space $S(w; \Delta_w)$, the cardinal splines $\{\psi_t(w)\}$ $(t=0, 1, \ldots, m+2)$ satisfy

$$\psi_t(w_j)=\delta_{tj}, \qquad \psi_t'(w_0)=\psi_t'(w_m)=0 \qquad (t, j=0, 1, \ldots, m);$$

$$\psi_{m+1}(w_j)=\psi_{m+2}(w_j)=0 \qquad (j=0, 1, \ldots, m);$$

$$\psi'_{m+1}(w_0)=\psi'_{m+2}(w_m)=1, \qquad \psi'_{m+1}(w_m)=\psi'_{m+2}(w_0)=0.$$

All bicubic spline functions with respect to the partition $\Delta=\Delta_u\otimes\Delta_w$ of R form a linear space $S(u, w; \Delta)$. Since a bicubic spline function is the tensor product of two univariate cubic spline functions, i.e.,

$$S(u, w; \Delta)=S(u; \Delta_u)\otimes S(w; \Delta_w),$$

$S(u, w; \Delta)$ is a linear space of dimension $(m+3)(n+3)$, and the products $\{\phi_s(u)\psi_t(w)\}$ $(s=0, 1, \ldots, n+2;\ t=0, 1, \ldots, m+2)$ form a basis. The basis functions are called *bicubic cardinal splines.* Any bicubic spline function of $S(u, w; \Delta)$ can be expressed by

$$x(u, w)=\sum_{s=0}^{n+2}\sum_{t=0}^{m+2} a_{st}\phi_s(u)\psi_t(w), \qquad (u, w)\in R. \tag{1.3}$$

There are $(m+3)$ $(n+3)$ coefficients $\{a_{st}\}$ in (1.3) to be determined. For an interpolatory bicubic spline function, there are $(m+1)(n+1)$ data points for interpolation. Hence $2(m+1)+2(n+1)+4$ degrees of freedom remain, which can be determined by boundary conditions. A commonly used boundary condition is given by

(1) normal partial derivatives of the first order at the nodes on the boundary of R:

$$\begin{aligned} p_{\alpha j}&=x'_u(u_\alpha, w_j) \qquad (j=0, 1, \ldots, m;\ \alpha=0, n),\\ q_{i\beta}&=x'_w(u_i, w_\beta) \qquad (i=0, 1, \ldots, n;\ \beta=0, m); \end{aligned} \tag{1.4}$$

(2) cross partial derivatives of the second order at the four vertices of R:

$$S_{\alpha\beta}=x''_{uw}(u_\alpha, w_\beta) \qquad (\alpha=0, n;\ \beta=0, m). \tag{1.5}$$

1.3 Existence and Uniqueness

When we discussed interpolatory cubic spline functions in Chapter II, we showed that for a given partition, the cubic interpolatory spline function with end conditions of type I exists uniquely. The proof of this fact comes simply from the diagonally dominant property of the coefficient matrix. The statement has the following bivariate generalization.

Theorem *Let Δ be a rectangular partition of the rectangular region R in the uw-plane. For arbitrarily given $(m+3)(n+3)$ scalars*

$$x_{ij}, p_{\alpha j}, q_{i\beta}, s_{\alpha\beta}, \qquad (i=0, 1, \ldots, n; j=0, 1, \ldots, m;\ \alpha=0, n;\ \beta=0, m),$$

there exists a unique bicubic spline function $x(u, w)$ such that the interpolatory condition (1.2) and the boundary conditions (1.4) and (1.5) are satisfied.

Proof Any bicubic spline function $x(u, w)$ with respect to the partition Δ can always be expressed by the cardinal form (1.3). Inserting it into the interpolatory condition (1.2) and then boundary conditions (1.4) and (1.5), we obtain by cardinal properties

$$x_{ij} = x(u_i, w_j) = a_{ij} \qquad (i=0,1,\dots,n;\, j=0,1,\dots,m);$$

$$p_{\alpha j} = x'_u(u_\alpha, w_j) = \begin{cases} a_{n+1,j}, & \alpha=0, \\ a_{n+2,j}, & \alpha=n, \end{cases} \qquad (j=0,1,\dots,m);$$

$$q_{i\beta} = x'_w(u_i, w_\beta) = \begin{cases} a_{i,m+1}, & \beta=0, \\ a_{i,m+2}, & \beta=m, \end{cases} \qquad (i=0,1,\dots,n);$$

$$S_{\alpha\beta} = x''_{uw}(u_\alpha, w_\beta) = \begin{cases} a_{n+1,m+1}, & \alpha=0,\ \beta=0, \\ a_{n+1,m+2}, & \alpha=0,\ \beta=m, \\ a_{n+2,m+1}, & \alpha=n,\ \beta=0, \\ a_{n+2,m+2}, & \alpha=n,\ \beta=m. \end{cases}$$

Each coefficient a_{st} $(s=0,1,\dots,n+2;\ t=0,1,\dots,m+2)$ in (1.3) appears on the right-hand sides of the above equalities once and only once. The continuity of partial derivatives $\partial^{(\alpha+\beta)}x(u,w)/\partial u^\alpha\,\partial w^\beta$ $(\alpha,\beta=0,1,2)$ comes from the C^2-continuity of each univariate cardinal spline in (1.3). This proves the statement.

Applying the theorem to a single subrectangle R_{ij}, we know that for given function values, first partial derivatives in each direction, and cross partial derivatives of second order at the four vertices, altogether 16 pieces of data in the matrix

$$[C]_{ij} = \left[\begin{array}{cc|cc} x_{i-1,j-1} & x_{i-1,j} & q_{i-1,j-1} & q_{i-1,j} \\ x_{i,j-1} & x_{ij} & q_{i,j-1} & q_{ij} \\ \hline p_{i-1,j-1} & p_{i-1,j} & s_{i-1,j-1} & s_{i-1,j} \\ p_{i,j-1} & p_{ij} & s_{i,j-1} & s_{ij} \end{array}\right], \tag{1.6}$$

the bicubic polynomial $x(u, w)$ over R_{ij} is completely determined. Elements in the matrix (1.6) are given by

$$x_{ij} = x(u_i, w_j), \qquad p_{ij} = x'_u(u_i, w_j), \qquad q_{ij} = x'_w(u_i, w_j), \qquad s_{ij} = x''_{uw}(u_i, w_j).$$

It is clear that the bicubic polynomial over R_{ij} can be uniquely written as

$$x(u, w) = [(u-u_{i-1})][A(h_i)][C]_{ij}[A(g_j)]^T[(\omega-\omega_{j-1})]^T,$$

$$(u, w) \in R_{ij}, \tag{1.7}$$

in which $[(u-u_{i-1})]=[(u-u_{i-1})^3, (u-u_{i-1})^2, (u-u_{i-1}), 1]$, and

$$[A(h_i)]=\begin{bmatrix} \frac{2}{h_i^3} & -\frac{2}{h_i^3} & \frac{1}{h_i^2} & \frac{1}{h_i^2} \\ -\frac{3}{h_i^2} & \frac{3}{h_i^2} & -\frac{2}{h_i} & -\frac{1}{h_i} \\ 0 & 0 & 1 & 0 \\ 1 & 0 & 0 & 0 \end{bmatrix}. \tag{1.8}$$

In fact, putting (u_{i-1}, w_{j-1}), (u_{i-1}, w_j), (u_i, w_{j-1}), and (u_i, w_j), the coordinates of the four vertices of R_{ij}, in turn into (1.7), (1.7)$'u$, (1.7)$'w$, and (1.7)$''uw$, we get expressions for 16 elements of the matrix $[C]_{ij}$, where (1.7)$'u$ represents the equality obtained by differentiating both sides of (1.7) with respect to u, etc.

The representation of the bicubic spline function $x(u, w)$ is entirely determined by the matrix $[C]_{ij}$. The four elements in the upper left-hand corner can be read directly from the interpolatory condition. The other 12 elements, namely p_{ij}, q_{ij} and s_{ij}, have to be solved from systems of continuity equations with boundary conditions (1.4) and (1.5).

First of all, if $w=w_j$ is fixed, then the function $x(u, w_j)\in S(u; \Delta_u)$. By the theory of univariate cubic spline functions in Chapter II, we have

$$\lambda_i p_{i-1,j}+2p_{ij}+\mu_i p_{i+1,j}=3\left[\lambda_i\frac{x_{ij}-x_{i-1,j}}{h_i}+\mu_i\frac{x_{i+1,j}-x_{ij}}{h_{i+1}}\right]$$

$$(i=1, 2, \ldots, n-1), \tag{1.9}$$

in which

$$\lambda_i=\frac{h_{i+1}}{h_i+h_{i+1}}, \qquad \mu_i=\frac{h_i}{h_i+h_{i+1}}.$$

End conditions p_{0j} and p_{nj} of (1.9) have been given by (1.4). Hence we can solve for p_{ij} $(i=0, 1, \ldots, n)$ where $j=0, 1, \ldots, m$. This means that the first partial derivatives of $x(u, w)$ with respect to u, evaluated at (u_i, w_j), i.e., p_{ij}, are already known $(i=0, 1, \ldots, n; j=0, 1, \ldots, m)$.

Symmetrically, for fixed u_i, $x(u_i, w)\in S(w; \Delta_w)$. The corresponding system is

$$\lambda_j^* q_{i,j-1}+2q_{ij}+\mu_j^* q_{i,j+1}=3\left[\lambda_j^*\frac{x_{ij}-x_{i,j-1}}{g_j}+\mu_j^*\frac{x_{i,j+1}-x_{ij}}{g_{j+1}}\right]$$

$$(j=1, 2, \ldots, m-1), \tag{1.10}$$

where

$$\lambda_j^* = \frac{g_{j+1}}{g_j + g_{j+1}}, \qquad \mu_j^* = \frac{g_j}{g_j + g_{j+1}}.$$

End conditions q_{i0} and q_{im} can be read also directly from (1.4). Hence we can solve for q_{ij} $(j=0, 1, \ldots, m)$. Note that i can be any of $(0, 1, \ldots, n)$. Thus all q_{ij} $(i=0, 1, \ldots, n; j=0, 1, \ldots, m)$ are determined.

Now we turn to the computation of s_{ij}, the cross partial derivative of the second order at the node (u_i, w_j). For fixed u_i, the function $x'_u(u_i, w) \in S(w; \Delta_w)$. The value of the function at w_j has been evaluated by (1.9), as $x'_u(u_i, w_j) = p_{ij}$. Hence we have the system of continuity equations of a cubic spline function in w,

$$\lambda_j^* s_{i,j-1} + 2s_{ij} + \mu_j^* s_{i,j+1} = 3\left[\lambda_j^* \frac{p_{ij} - p_{i,j-1}}{g_j} + \mu_j^* \frac{p_{i,j+1} - p_{ij}}{g_{j+1}}\right]$$
$$(j = 1, 2, \ldots, m-1). \qquad (1.11)$$

If end conditions s_{i0} and s_{im} are given for the system (1.11), then s_{ij} $(j=0, 1, \ldots, m)$ will be found. Thus all the cross partial derivatives of the second order s_{ij} $(i=0, 1, \ldots, n; j=0, 1, \ldots, m)$, at nodes (u_i, w_j), are completely determined.

In fact, the end conditions s_{i0} and s_{im} for (1.11) can be found in the following. Along two sides of R, namely $w = w_0$ and $w = w_m$, $x'_w(u, w_0)$ and $x'_w(u, w_m)$ belong to $S(u; \Delta_u)$. The values of these two functions at u_i, $x'_w(u_i, w_0) = q_{i0}$ and $x'_w(u_i, w_m) = q_{im}$, can be obtained from (1.10). Then we establish the following continuity equations:

$$\lambda_i s_{i-1,\beta} + 2s_{i\beta} + \mu_i s_{i+1,\beta} = 3\left[\lambda_i \frac{q_{i\beta} - q_{i-1,\beta}}{h_i} + \mu_i \frac{q_{i+1,\beta} - q_{i\beta}}{h_{i+1}}\right]$$
$$(i = 1, 2, \ldots, n-1), \qquad \beta = 0, m. \qquad (1.12)$$

The end conditions for (1.12) can be read from (1.5). Thus s_{i0} and s_{im} $(i=0, 1, \ldots, n)$ are determined.

So far all elements in matrix (1.6) are already known. This means that the bicubic spline function $x(u, w)$ on R is determined, and its representation on the subrectangle R_{ij} is given by (1.7).

One question still remains: Does $x(u, w)$ really belong to $C_2^4(R)$? The answer is yes. By existence and uniqueness of the interpolatory bicubic spline function we know that the bicubic spline function interpolating to (1.2) and satisfying the boundary conditions (1.4) and (1.5) is unique and belongs to $C_2^4(R)$.

A computational procedure for the interpolatory bicubic spline function with respect to the partition Δ of the rectangle R is given below.

(1) Specify the interpolatory condition (1.2) and the boundary conditions (1.4) and (1.5).
(2) Solve the tridiagonal systems of linear equations (1.9), (1.10), (1.12) and (1.11) for p_{ij}, q_{ij}, s_{ij} $(i=0,1,\ldots,n; j=0,1,\ldots,m)$. There are altogether $2n+m+5$ systems. However, their coefficient matrices are of only two types, characterized by the set of λ_i, μ_i $(i=1,2,\ldots,n-1)$ and the set of λ_j^*, μ_j^* $(j=1,2,\ldots,m-1)$, respectively.
(3) Evaluate $x(u^*, w^*)$ for a point $(u^*, w^*)\in R$. Find i and j such that $(u^*, w^*)\in R_{ij}$ and then insert into (1.7) for computation.

The problem of interpolatory bicubic spline functions with respect to the rectangular partition Δ of the rectangle R has been solved beautifully and completely by deBoor. The key to the success is probably that the rectangular partition Δ is a tensor product of two one-dimensional partitions and the bicubic function is a tensor product of two univariate cubic spline functions. Hence the two-dimensional problem has been reduced to the one-dimensional problem in two directions.

Investigations of bivariate spline functions with respect to arbitrary partition of general regions in the plane are much more difficult and remain a developing subject. The most significant two-dimensional partition is the triangulation. There are many ways to construct bivariate spline functions with continuous first partial derivatives with respect to the triangulation. However, the degree of the spline function will rapidly increase if continuity of partial derivatives higher than first order is required (see, for example, Wang Renhong, 1975). This precludes any numerical application of those spline functions.

Just like univariate cubic spline functions, when bicubic spline functions are used for geometric design, the small deflection of data should be assumed; otherwise the fairness of the resulting surface may not be guaranteed. Modifications to bicubic functions are needed in order to fit large deflection or multivalued surfaces. The most successful modification is that the bicubic functions are replaced by vector-valued functions which are bicubic with respect to two parameters. Coons's, Bézier's and B-spline forms of the bicubic parametric patches will be discussed in the next three sections.

2 Coons Patches

2.1 Blending Functions

Four cubic polynomials in [0, 1] are given by

$$\begin{aligned} F_0(u) &= 2u^3 - 3u^2 + 1, \\ F_1(u) &= -2u^3 + 3u^2, \\ G_0(u) &= u^3 - 2u^2 + u, \\ G_1(u) &= u^3 - u^2, \end{aligned} \qquad u \in [0, 1] \tag{2.1}$$

which are called the cubic blending functions. It is easy to verify that

$$\begin{aligned} &F_0(0) = 1,\ F_0(1) = 0, && F_1(0) = 0,\ F_1(1) = 1, \\ &F_0'(0) = 0,\ F_0'(1) = 0; && F_1'(0) = 0,\ F_1'(1) = 0; \\ &G_0(0) = 0,\ G_0(1) = 0, && G_1(0) = 0,\ G_1(1) = 0, \\ &G_0'(0) = 1,\ G_0'(1) = 0; && G_1'(0) = 0,\ G_1'(1) = 1. \end{aligned} \tag{2.2}$$

Conversely, four cubic polynomials satisfying (2.2) must have expressions in (2.1), as any cubic polynomial can be uniquely determined by given values and the first derivatives at the end points of [0, 1]. The functions F_0, F_1, G_0 and G_1 are illustrated in Fig. 5-2.

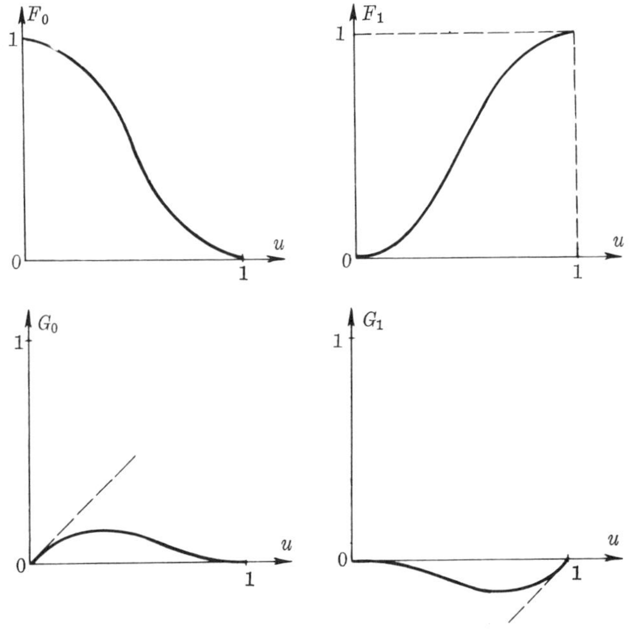

Figure 5-2

The property in (2.2) is called the cardinal property of blending functions. Any four functions that have the cardinal property, not necessarily cubic polynomials but with C^1-continuity, can be used as blending functions.

The role played by the blending functions can be demonstrated by the following example. Let four vectors $\boldsymbol{P}_0$, $\boldsymbol{P}_1$, $\boldsymbol{m}_0$, $\boldsymbol{m}_1$ be given. The cubic parametric curve segment

$$\boldsymbol{P}(u)=F_0(u)\boldsymbol{P}_0+F_1(u)\boldsymbol{P}_1+G_0(u)\boldsymbol{m}_0+G_1(u)\boldsymbol{m}_1, \qquad u\in[0,1] \quad (2.3)$$

has points $\boldsymbol{P}_0$ and $\boldsymbol{P}_1$ as its end-points and $\boldsymbol{m}_0$ and $\boldsymbol{m}_1$ as its first derivative vectors at these points, respectively. This fact is a direct consequence of the cardinal property (2.2). In fact, (2.3) represents the Hermite interpolation for the parametric curve segment. A similar role will be played by blending functions in the generation and representation of Coons patches.

2.2 Bicubic Patches

It is known that surfaces can be expressed by vector-valued functions

$$\boldsymbol{r}(u,w)=[x(u,w),y(u,w),z(u,w)] \qquad (u,w)\in D, \qquad (2.4)$$

of parameters u and w which vary on the region $D=[0,1]\otimes[0,1]$, a square on the parametric plane. $\boldsymbol{r}(u,0)$, $\boldsymbol{r}(u,1)$, $\boldsymbol{r}(0,w)$, $\boldsymbol{r}(1,w)$ represent four boundaries of the surface patch, while $\boldsymbol{r}(0,0)$, $\boldsymbol{r}(0,1)$, $\boldsymbol{r}(1,0)$, $\boldsymbol{r}(1,1)$ are the four vertices, or corners, of the patch.

In Coons's representation of surface patches, some simplified notations invented by Coons himself are widely used. These notations lead to very neat algebraic operations and no confusions will arise. If only one surface patch $\boldsymbol{r}(u,w)$ is involved at a time, the letter $\boldsymbol{r}$ together with the parentheses will be eliminated, i.e., the equation (2.4) would be expressed simply by

$$uw=[x(uw)y(uw)z(uw)].$$

Abbreviations $u0$, $u1$, $0w$, $1w$ represent the four boundary curves and 00, 01, 10, 11 are the four corners of the patch.

Now we agree upon the following simplified notation for partial derivatives

$$uw_u\equiv\frac{\partial(uw)}{\partial u}, \qquad uw_{wu}\equiv\frac{\partial(uw)}{\partial w\,\partial u}, \qquad u0_w\equiv\left.\frac{\partial(uw)}{\partial w}\right|_{w=0},$$

$$u0_u\equiv\left.\frac{\partial(uw)}{\partial u}\right|_{w=0}=\frac{d(u0)}{du}, \qquad 10_{uw}\equiv\left.\frac{\partial(uw)}{\partial u\,\partial w}\right|_{\substack{u=1\\w=0}},$$

etc.

The vector function $u0_w$ is called the *boundary slope* along the boundary $u0$. The other boundary slopes are $u1_w$, $0w_u$ and $1w_u$. Partial derivative vectors of the second order $0w_{uu}$, $1w_{uu}$, $u0_{ww}$, $u1_{ww}$ are called the *boundary curvatures* along the boundaries $0w$, $1w$, $u0$, $u1$, respectively. The vectors 00_{uw}, 01_{uw}, 10_{uw}, 11_{uw} are called the *twists* at the corresponding corners (Fig. 5-3).

In the sequel, the four blending functions will be written as a four-dimensional row vector:

$$[F_0 \quad F_1 \quad G_0 \quad G_1]=[U][M], \tag{2.5}$$

in which $[U]=[u^3 \quad u^2 \quad u \quad 1]$ and

$$[M]=\begin{bmatrix} 2 & -2 & 1 & 1 \\ -3 & 3 & -2 & -1 \\ 0 & 0 & 1 & 0 \\ 1 & 0 & 0 & 0 \end{bmatrix}.$$

If the blending functions are arranged in a column, we shall agree that the variable of these functions is w, namely

$$\begin{bmatrix} F_0 \\ F_1 \\ G_0 \\ G_1 \end{bmatrix}=[M]^T[W]^T, \tag{2.6}$$

where $[W]=[w^3 \quad w^2 \quad w \quad 1]$.

Now we proceed with the parametrization of the bicubic function (1.7) described in the last section to construct the vector-valued bicubic patch. Here u and w are regarded as two independent parameters. The left-hand

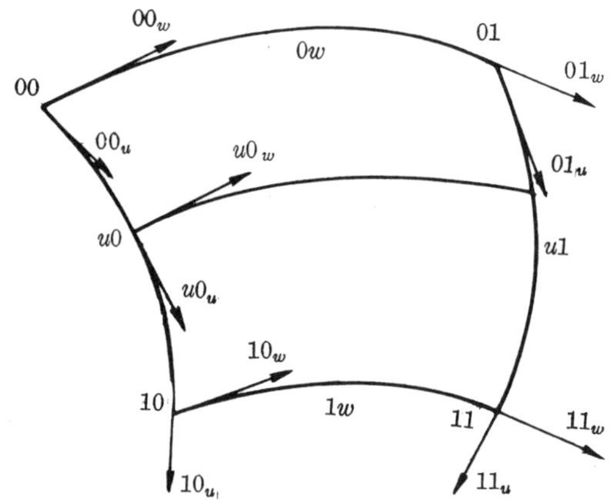

Figure 5-3

side of (1.7) is replaced by the position vector $\boldsymbol{r}(u, w)$ of the patch. Obviously the matrix $[C]$ in the right-hand side of (1.7) has its vector analogue

$$[C]=\left[\begin{array}{cc|cc} 00 & 01 & 00_w & 01_w \\ 10 & 11 & 10_w & 11_w \\ \hline 00_u & 01_u & 00_{uw} & 01_{uw} \\ 10_u & 11_u & 10_{uw} & 11_{uw} \end{array}\right],$$

which is called the matrix of corner information. Hence the bicubic patch has the following equation:

$$uw=[F_0 \quad F_1 \quad G_0 \quad G_1]\left[\begin{array}{cc|cc} 00 & 01 & 00_w & 01_w \\ 10 & 11 & 10_w & 11_w \\ \hline 00_u & 01_u & 00_{uw} & 01_{uw} \\ 10_u & 11_u & 10_{uw} & 11_{uw} \end{array}\right]\begin{bmatrix} F_0 \\ F_1 \\ G_0 \\ G_1 \end{bmatrix}, \qquad (u, w) \in D. \tag{2.7}$$

More compactly, by (2.5) and (2.6),

$$uw=[U][M][C][M]^T[W]^T. \tag{2.8}$$

The quantities in $[C]$ can be divided into four groups. The partition in the upper left-hand corner contains four corners of the patch. The partitions in the lower left-hand corner and in the upper right-hand corner consist of the tangent vectors of the boundaries at the corners. All these 12 quantities have definite meaning in geometry. Since the four boundary curves of the patch are parametric cubic curve segments, they are entirely determined by those three partitions just mentioned. The partition in the lower right-hand corner of $[C]$ contains the twists at the corners, which have nothing to do with the shape of the boundaries of the patch. Adjusting the twists causes changes only in the interior part of the patch. Substituting zero into all twists, (2.7) reduces to the so-called Ferguson patch which becomes rather flat around the four corners, a behavior not desirable for geometric modeling. Unfortunately, the dependence of the interior shape of a patch on twists is not geometrically clear, hence it has been difficult for a designer to choose proper twists in patches design. Bézier patches, which will be described in the next section, give us some help to overcome this difficulty.

2.3 Composite Bicubic Surfaces

We saw in Chapter III that there are many ways to construct GC^2-continuous spline curves in terms of cubic parametric curve segments. We can imagine that constructions may be more complicated if we form a spline surface in terms of bicubic patches.

Let us consider first the conjunction of two bicubic patches S and $\bar{S}$, both in the form of (2.7). The only difference is that there is a bar on the top of each element in the corner information matrix for $\bar{S}$.

(1) By C^0-continuity between S and $\bar{S}$, we mean that there is a boundary curve in common, say $0w \equiv \overline{1w}$. This is equivalent to

$$00 = \overline{10}, \qquad 01 = \overline{11}, \qquad 00_w = \overline{10}_w, \qquad 01_w = \overline{11}_w, \tag{2.9}$$

as a cubic parametric curve segment is completely determined by its end points and the tangent vectors at these points.

(2) By GC^1-continuity between S and $\bar{S}$, we mean that at each point of the common boundary curve of S and $\bar{S}$, the tangent planes of the two patches should be coincident. Obviously (2.9) must hold. From (2.7) we find

$$0w_u = [00_u \quad 01_u \quad 00_{uw} \quad 01_{uw}] \begin{bmatrix} F_0 \\ F_1 \\ G_0 \\ G_1 \end{bmatrix},$$

$$\overline{1w}_u = [\overline{10}_u \quad \overline{11}_u \quad \overline{10}_{uw} \quad \overline{11}_{uw}] \begin{bmatrix} F_0 \\ F_1 \\ G_0 \\ G_1 \end{bmatrix}.$$

If there exists a scalar $\lambda > 0$ such that

$$[00_u \quad 01_u \quad 00_{uw} \quad 01_{uw}] = \lambda [\overline{10}_u \quad \overline{11}_u \quad \overline{10}_{uw} \quad \overline{11}_{uw}], \tag{2.10}$$

then $0w_u = \lambda \overline{1w}_u$. This implies that the tangent planes of the two patches coincide at each point of the common boundary curve. Equations (2.9) and (2.10) provide a sufficient condition for GC^1-continuity (Fig. 5-4).

(3) Applying the algorithm for the bicubic spline function to each component of the surface $\boldsymbol{r}(uw)$, we obtain the parametric bicubic spline interpolant

$$\begin{aligned} \boldsymbol{r}(uw) &= [x(uw)y(uw)z(uw)] \\ &= [(u-u_{i-1})](A(h_i)][\boldsymbol{C}]_{ij}[A(g_j)]^T[(w-w_{j-1})]^T, \\ &\quad (u, w) \in R_{ij} \qquad (i = 0, 1, \ldots, n; j = 0, 1, \ldots, m), \end{aligned} \tag{2.11}$$

where the upper left-hand partition of the matrix $[C]_{ij}$ contains the given data points $\boldsymbol{r}_{ij}$ $(i = 0, 1, \ldots, n; j = 0, 1, \ldots, m)$. The other three partitions can be determined by solving systems of linear equations (1.9), (1.10), (1.11), (1.12), if the boundary conditions (1.4) and (1.5) and the rectangular region R in the parametric uw-plane with a partition are suitably given.

The key step is to determine the rectangle R, the domain of the parameters, and its partition. In general, we fix a suitable index j_0 and put $h_i = |\boldsymbol{r}_{i,j_0} - \boldsymbol{r}_{i-1,j_0}|$ $(i = 1, 2, \ldots, n)$. Again choose an appropriate index i_0 and put $g_j = |\boldsymbol{r}_{i_0,j} - \boldsymbol{r}_{i_0,j-1}|$ $(j = 1, 2, \ldots, m)$. Define the rectangle $R = [0, H] \otimes [0, G]$,

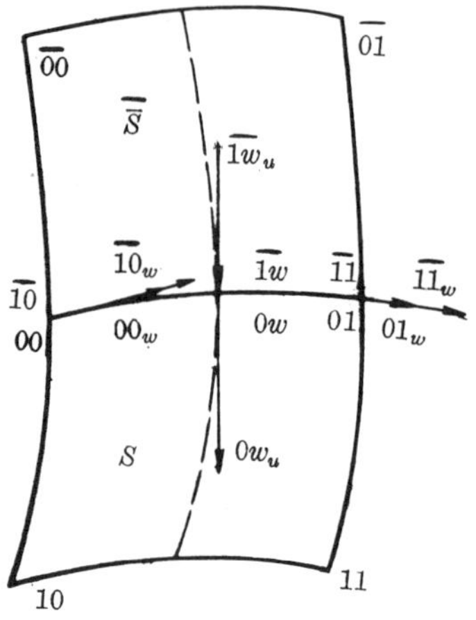

Figure 5-4

where

$$H = \sum_{i=1}^{n} h_i, \qquad G = \sum_{j=1}^{m} g_j.$$

Thus the domain R of parameters and its partition Δ have been defined. The parametric bicubic spline surface obtained can be regarded as a tensor product of two parametric cubic spline curves of cumulative chord length in two directions. We have mentioned that parametric cubic spline curves of cumulative chord length have good fairness, hence if the distribution of data points $\boldsymbol{r}_{ij}$ $(i=0, 1, \ldots, n; j=0, 1, \ldots, m)$ is relatively uniform, then the curve networks on the resulting spline surface will be fair. Otherwise the spline surface is most likely not satisfactory. By "fixing a suitable index j_0," we mean that the data points $\boldsymbol{r}_{i,j_0}$ $(i=0, 1, \ldots, n)$ are approximately equally spaced (Fig. 5-5).

Since each component belongs to $C_2^4(R)$, the parametric bicubic spline surface is really C^2-continuous.

The above method is one of the most useful techniques for interpolating a set of spatial data points, and hence is widely used for practical purposes.

The disadvantage of the interpolatory parametric cubic spline surfaces, besides the requirement that data points $\boldsymbol{r}_{ij}$ should be approximately equally spaced, is a lack of flexibility. More precisely, for specified boundary conditions each bicubic patch has been uniquely determined. Any local change is not possible.

2.4 General Coons Patches

Across the common boundary curve of two patches, sometimes the positions, slopes and curvatures, and even higher partial derivative vectors,

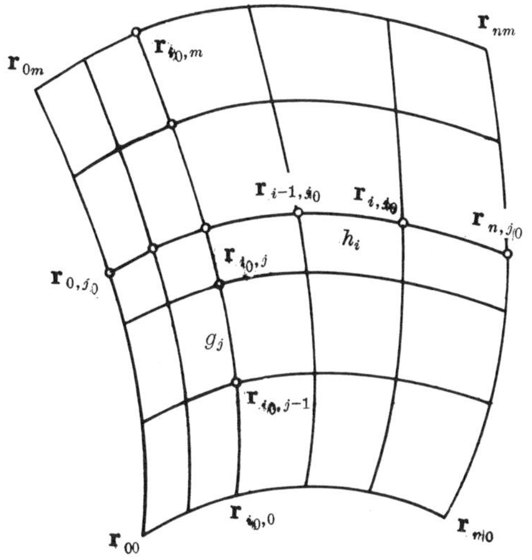

Figure 5-5

should be matched. These problems have been solved by general Coons patch schemes.

Formulas for these schemes will be presented below, without detailed derivations. Blending functions, not necessarily the cubic polynomials, are any functions satisfying the cardinal property (2.2). Trigonometric functions and B-spline functions were used as blending functions by Coons himself.

Let $u0$, $u1$, $0w$, $1w$ be four given boundary curves and let $u0_w$, $u1_w$, $0w_u$, $1w_u$ be the boundary slopes. It is easy to show, by the cardinal property (2.2), that the patch

$$uw = -[-1 \quad F_0 \quad F_1 \quad G_0 \quad G_1] \left[\begin{array}{c|cccc} 0 & u0 & u1 & u0_w & u1_w \\ \hline 0w & 00 & 01 & 00_w & 01_w \\ 1w & 10 & 11 & 10_w & 11_w \\ 0w_u & 00_u & 01_u & 00_{uw} & 01_{uw} \\ 1w_u & 10_u & 11_u & 10_{uw} & 11_{uw} \end{array}\right] \begin{bmatrix} -1 \\ F_0 \\ F_1 \\ G_0 \\ G_1 \end{bmatrix}. \tag{2.12}$$

interpolates to eight given vector functions. The structure of the 5×5 matrix in the right-hand side of (2.12) is simple and regular: Eight pieces of given boundary information are contained by the first row and the first column; 16 pieces of corner information, which can be evaluated from the corresponding elements on the first row or the first column, form the 4×4 partition in the lower right-hand corner of the matrix, which is the same as the corner information matrix $[C]$ of the bicubic patch.

If two patches expressed by (2.12) have a boundary curve in common and the same boundary slope across this boundary curve, the composite surface will be GC^1-continuous.

To realize C^2-continuity between two adjacent patches, the above expression is not sufficient. In this case, besides boundary curves and slopes, four boundary curvatures, $u0_{ww}$, $u1_{ww}$, $0w_{uu}$, $1w_{uu}$ are needed. In addition, three pairs of blending functions—F_0, F_1; G_0, G_1; H_0, H_1—with the cardinal property

$$\begin{aligned} &F_\alpha(\beta) = G'_\alpha(\beta) = H''_\alpha(\beta) = \delta_{\alpha\beta}, \\ &F'_\alpha(\beta) = F''_\alpha(\beta) = G_\alpha(\beta) = G''_\alpha(\beta) = H_\alpha(\beta) = H'_\alpha(\beta) = 0 \end{aligned} \qquad (\alpha, \beta = 0, 1),$$

are necessary.

Such blending functions can be uniquely constructed in terms of quintic polynomials. We omit the details.

The Coons patch interpolating to the boundary curves, slopes and curvatures can be written as

$$uw = -[-1 \quad F_0 \quad F_1 \quad G_0 \quad G_1 \quad H_0 \quad H_1]$$
$$\times \left[\begin{array}{c|cccc|cc} 0 & u0 & u1 & u0_w & u1_w & u0_{ww} & u1_{ww} \\ \hline 0w & 00 & 01 & 00_w & 01_w & 00_{ww} & 01_{ww} \\ 1w & 10 & 11 & 10_w & 11_w & 10_{ww} & 11_{ww} \\ 0w_u & 00_u & 01_u & 00_{uw} & 01_{uw} & 00_{uww} & 01_{uww} \\ 1w_u & 10_u & 11_u & 10_{uw} & 11_{uw} & 10_{uww} & 11_{uww} \\ \hline 0w_{uu} & 00_{uu} & 01_{uu} & 00_{uuw} & 01_{uuw} & 00_{uuww} & 01_{uuww} \\ 1w_{uu} & 10_{uu} & 11_{uu} & 10_{uuw} & 11_{uuw} & 10_{uuww} & 11_{uuww} \end{array}\right] \begin{bmatrix} -1 \\ F_0 \\ F_1 \\ G_0 \\ G_1 \\ H_0 \\ H_1 \end{bmatrix}. \qquad (2.13)$$

The distribution of elements in the 7×7 matrix on the right-hand side of (2.13) is similar to the 5×5 matrix in (2.12).

Flexibility for matching patches increases by using higher-order Coons patches. As a consequence, however, more boundary information should be prescribed, which is the price to be paid for higher-order continuity.

3 Bézier Patches

3.1 Definition

It is natural to extend Bézier curves to Bézier patches by again using the idea of tensor products, which helped us to extend the parametric cubic curve segments to parametric bicubic patches.

Definition Let the $(m+1)(n+1)$ points $\boldsymbol{b}_{ij}$ $(i=0, 1, \ldots, n; j=0, 1, \ldots, m)$ be given. The parametric surface patch

$$\boldsymbol{P}(u, w)=\sum_{i=0}^{n}\sum_{j=0}^{m} B_{i,n}(u)B_{j,m}(w)\boldsymbol{b}_{ij}, \qquad 0\leqslant u, w\leqslant 1, \tag{3.1}$$

is called the *Bézier patch of degree* $m\times n$, in which $\{B_{i,n}(u)\}$ are the nth Bernstein basis functions. Joining with a line segment each pair of points $\boldsymbol{b}_{ij}$ $(i=0, 1, \ldots, n; j=0, 1, \ldots, m)$ with neighboring subscripts, the resulting net is called the *characteristic net* of the patch.

The convex hull property, the interpolation property at end points and the property of approximation, which hold for Bézier curves, still hold for Bézier patches.

In most applications, m and n are in general both less than or equal to five. Otherwise—just as for Bézier curves—we cannot predict precisely the shape of the patch via the Bézier net. The most important case is $m=n=3$, i.e., bicubic Bézier patches, which will be fully discussed later. Now we give two simple examples.

(1) For $m=n=1$, we get the bilinear Bézier patch

$$\boldsymbol{P}(u, w)=(1-u)(1-w)\boldsymbol{b}_{00}+(1-u)w\boldsymbol{b}_{01}+u(1-w)\boldsymbol{b}_{10} + uw\boldsymbol{b}_{11}, \qquad 0\leqslant u, w\leqslant 1. \tag{3.2}$$

We can show that (3.2) represents a patch on a hyperbolic paraboloid, with four line segments as its boundary. Actually (3.2) can be rewritten as

$$\boldsymbol{P}(u, w)=uw\boldsymbol{a}_{11}+u\boldsymbol{a}_{10}+w\boldsymbol{a}_{01}+\boldsymbol{b}_{00}, \tag{3.3}$$

where

$$\boldsymbol{a}_{01}=\boldsymbol{b}_{01}-\boldsymbol{b}_{00}, \qquad \boldsymbol{a}_{10}=\boldsymbol{b}_{10}-\boldsymbol{b}_{00}, \qquad \boldsymbol{a}_{11}=\boldsymbol{b}_{11}-(\boldsymbol{b}_{00}+\boldsymbol{a}_{10}+\boldsymbol{a}_{01})$$

(see Fig. 5-6). Assume that

$$\boldsymbol{P}(u, w)=\begin{bmatrix} x\\ y\\ z \end{bmatrix}, \qquad \boldsymbol{b}_{00}=\begin{bmatrix} b_1\\ b_2\\ b_3 \end{bmatrix},$$

with respect to a certain affine coodinate system. Then (3.3) can be expressed in terms of vector components:

$$\begin{bmatrix} x\\ y\\ z \end{bmatrix}-\begin{bmatrix} b_1\\ b_2\\ b_3 \end{bmatrix}=[A]\begin{bmatrix} uw\\ u\\ w \end{bmatrix}, \tag{3.4}$$

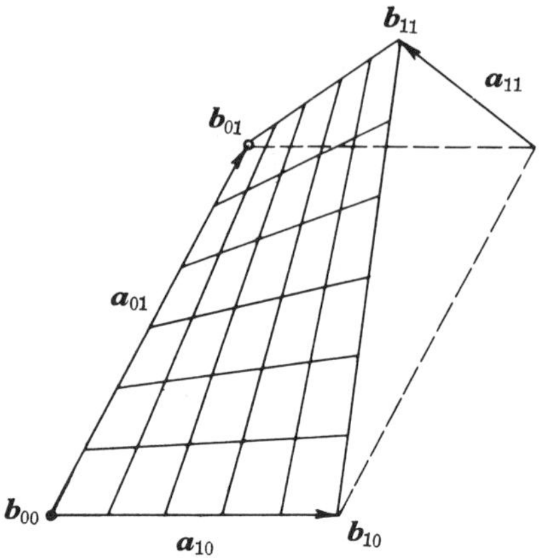

Figure 5-6

where elements in the first, second and third row of the 3×3 matrix $[A]$ are three components of the vectors $\boldsymbol{a}_{11}$, $\boldsymbol{a}_{10}$, $\boldsymbol{a}_{01}$, respectively.

If the four vertices $\boldsymbol{b}_{00}$, $\boldsymbol{b}_{10}$, $\boldsymbol{b}_{01}$, $\boldsymbol{b}_{11}$ are coplanar, then the bilinear Bézier patch (3.2) is a plane, as it is known by the convex hull property. We exclude this trival case and assume that the three vectors $\boldsymbol{a}_{11}$, $\boldsymbol{a}_{10}$, $\boldsymbol{a}_{01}$ are not coplanar. Hence $[A]^{-1}$ exists and (3.4) is equivalent to

$$\begin{bmatrix} uw \\ u \\ w \end{bmatrix} = [A]^{-1} \begin{bmatrix} x - b_1 \\ y - b_2 \\ z - b_3 \end{bmatrix}. \tag{3.5}$$

By the affine transformation

$$\begin{bmatrix} \bar{x} \\ \bar{y} \\ \bar{z} \end{bmatrix} = [A]^{-1} \begin{bmatrix} x - b_1 \\ y - b_2 \\ z - b_3 \end{bmatrix},$$

the bilinear Bézier patch (3.2) satisfies

$$\bar{x} = \bar{y}\bar{z},$$

which is well known as the equation of a hyperbolic paraboloid.

(2) For $m = n = 2$, we have the biquadratic Bézier patch

$$\boldsymbol{P}(u, w) = \sum_{i,j=0}^{2} B_{i,2}(u) B_{j,2}(w) \boldsymbol{b}_{ij}, \qquad 0 \leq u, w \leq 1. \tag{3.6}$$

Clearly its boundary curves and parametric coordinate curves are all parabolas. Eight vertices on the boundary of the Bézier net determine four boundary curves of the patch. The vertex $\boldsymbol{b}_{11}$ has an influence only on the internal shape of the patch, not on the boundary curves (Fig. 5-7). For given boundary curves, we can choose $\boldsymbol{b}_{11}$ suitably in a geometrically simple manner to get a desirable surface patch.

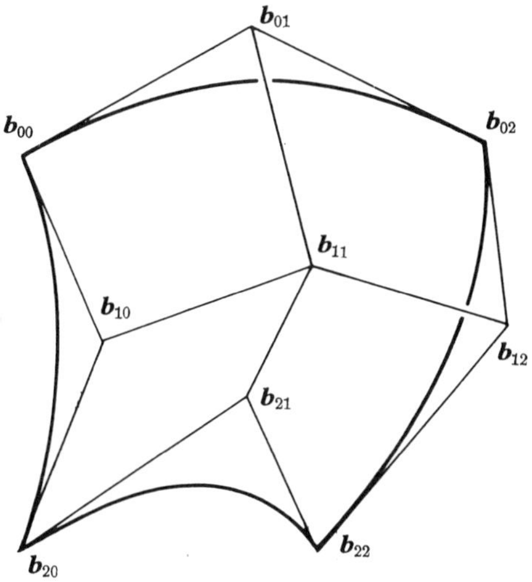

Figure 5-7

3.2 Bicubic Bézier Patches

For $m = n = 3$, the bicubic Bézier patch can be represented in matrix form:

$$\boldsymbol{P}_b(u, w) = [B_{0,3}(u), B_{1,3}(u), B_{2,3}(u), B_{3,3}(u)]$$

$$\times \begin{bmatrix} \boldsymbol{b}_{00} & \boldsymbol{b}_{01} & \boldsymbol{b}_{02} & \boldsymbol{b}_{03} & B_{0,3}(w) \\ \boldsymbol{b}_{10} & \boldsymbol{b}_{11} & \boldsymbol{b}_{12} & \boldsymbol{b}_{13} & B_{1,3}(w) \\ \boldsymbol{b}_{20} & \boldsymbol{b}_{21} & \boldsymbol{b}_{22} & \boldsymbol{b}_{23} & B_{2,3}(w) \\ \boldsymbol{b}_{30} & \boldsymbol{b}_{31} & \boldsymbol{b}_{32} & \boldsymbol{b}_{33} & B_{3,3}(w) \end{bmatrix}. \tag{3.7}$$

More compactly, as we did for the bicubic Coons patch,

$$\boldsymbol{P}_b(u, w) = [U][N][\boldsymbol{b}][N]^T[W]^T, \tag{3.8}$$

where the matrix $[\boldsymbol{b}]$ with vector elements is the 4×4 matrix in (3.7) formed by vertices of the characteristic net, and

$$[N] = \begin{bmatrix} -1 & 3 & -3 & 1 \\ 3 & -6 & 3 & 0 \\ -3 & 3 & 0 & 0 \\ 1 & 0 & 0 & 0 \end{bmatrix}.$$

The same bicubic patch can be expressed either in Bézier form (3.8) or in Coons form (2.8):

$$\boldsymbol{P}_c(u, w) = [U][M][C][M]^T[W]^T.$$

Hence for all $(u, w) \in [0, 1] \otimes [0, 1]$ we must have

$$\boldsymbol{P}_b(u, w) = \boldsymbol{P}_c(u, w),$$

so it follows that

$$[N][\boldsymbol{b}][N]^T = [M][\boldsymbol{C}][M]^T. \tag{3.9}$$

By introducing

$$[D] = [N]^{-1}[M] = \begin{bmatrix} 1 & 0 & 0 & 0 \\ 1 & 0 & \frac{1}{3} & 0 \\ 0 & 1 & 0 & -\frac{1}{3} \\ 0 & 1 & 0 & 0 \end{bmatrix},$$

we obtain

$$[\boldsymbol{b}] = [D][C][D]^T =$$

$$\begin{bmatrix} 00 & 00+\frac{1}{3}00_w & 01-\frac{1}{3}01_w & 01 \\ 00+\frac{1}{3}00_u & 00+\frac{1}{3}(00_u+00_w)+\frac{1}{9}00_{uw} & 01+\frac{1}{3}(01_u-01_w)-\frac{1}{9}01_{uw} & 01+\frac{1}{3}01_u \\ 10-\frac{1}{3}10_u & 10-\frac{1}{3}(10_u-10_w)-\frac{1}{9}10_{uw} & 11-\frac{1}{3}(11_u+11_w)+\frac{1}{9}11_{uw} & 11-\frac{1}{3}11_u \\ 10 & 10+\frac{1}{3}10_w & 11-\frac{1}{3}11_w & 11 \end{bmatrix}. \tag{3.10}$$

This matrix equality expresses the matrix $[\boldsymbol{b}]$ formed by vertices of the characteristic net of the bicubic Bézier patch in terms of elements in the corner information matrix $[C]$ of the bicubic Coons patch. Relationships of those vectors are shown by Fig. 5-8.

The expressions of the 12 elements in the first and last row and column of the matrix on the right-hand side of (3.10) can be derived directly from the properties of cubic Bézier curves. In fact, the four boundary curves are all cubic Bézier curves. Vertices of the corresponding Bézier polygons are in the first row and first column of the matrix $[\boldsymbol{b}]$. Properties at end-points of a cubic Bézier curve show immediately that

$$00 = \boldsymbol{b}_{00}, \qquad 01 = \boldsymbol{b}_{03}, \qquad 10 = \boldsymbol{b}_{30}, \qquad 11 = \boldsymbol{b}_{33};$$

$$\tfrac{1}{3}00_w = \overrightarrow{\boldsymbol{b}_{00}\boldsymbol{b}_{01}}, \qquad -\tfrac{1}{3}01_w = \overrightarrow{\boldsymbol{b}_{03}\boldsymbol{b}_{02}},$$

etc. These relations are reflected in the first and the last row and column in (3.10).

Consequently, the element on the four corners of the matrix $[\boldsymbol{b}]$ are identical with the four corners of the Coons patch. The other eight elements in the first and the last row and column are associated with the tangent vectors at the four corners in the Coons representation.

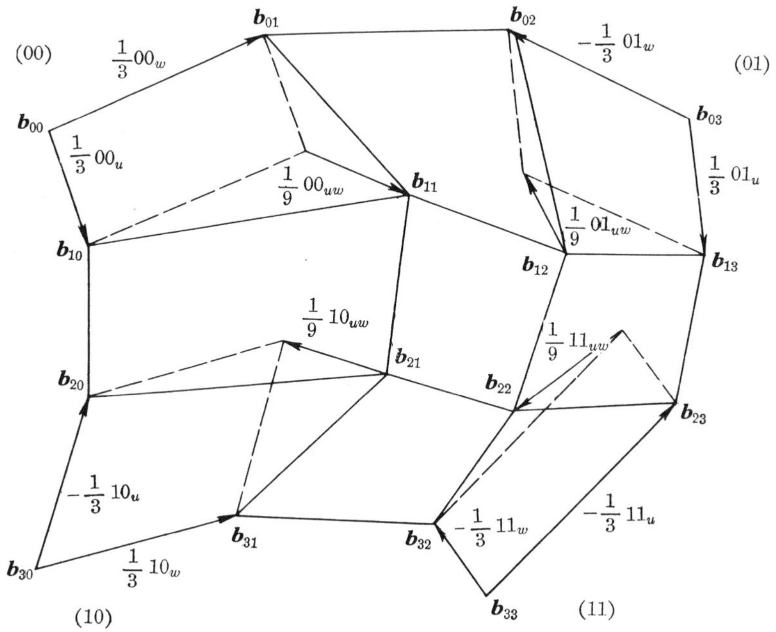

Figure 5-8

Consider the four elements in the center of the matrix on the right-hand side of (3.10). Note, for example, that

$$\boldsymbol{b}_{11} = \infty + \tfrac{1}{3}(00_u + 00_w) + \tfrac{1}{9}00_{uw},$$

which can be written as

$$\tfrac{1}{9}00_{uw} = \boldsymbol{b}_{00} + \boldsymbol{b}_{11} - \boldsymbol{b}_{01} - \boldsymbol{b}_{10}.$$

This shows that the vector which begins at the fourth vertex of the parallelogram with $\overrightarrow{\boldsymbol{b}_{00}\boldsymbol{b}_{01}}$ and $\overrightarrow{\boldsymbol{b}_{00}\boldsymbol{b}_{10}}$ as its neighboring sides and ends at point $\boldsymbol{b}_{11}$ is equal to $\frac{1}{9}00_{uw}$ (see Fig. 5-8). Similar relations hold for the other three corners.

An interesting fact has been observed, that the four corner twists in the Coons patch are explicitly related to the four central vertices $\boldsymbol{b}_{11}$, $\boldsymbol{b}_{12}$, $\boldsymbol{b}_{21}$, $\boldsymbol{b}_{22}$ of the characteristic net of the Bézier patch. Once four boundary curves of the bicubic Bézier patch are given, adjustment of the central vertices $\boldsymbol{b}_{11}$, $\boldsymbol{b}_{12}$, $\boldsymbol{b}_{21}$, $\boldsymbol{b}_{22}$ is equivalent to that of four corner twists in the Coons form (Sadeghi and Gould, 1974).

Even though parametric bicubic patches can be expressed equivalently by either the Coons form or the Bézier form, we prefer the latter to the former, since the approximation of a Bézier patch by its characteristic net tells us that the net sketches roughly the shape of the corresponding patch. The shape of the patch can be controlled by adjusting elements in the matrix $[\boldsymbol{b}]$, formed by vertices of the characteristic net.

By no means do we mean that details of the shape control of the bicubic Bézier patch via the characteristic net have been well understood. For planar cubic Bézier curves, the analogous problem has been completely solved. In case of parametric patches, however, the problem becomes much more difficult.

4 *B*-Spline Patches

The extension of *B*-spline curves to *B*-spline surfaces is similar to that of Bézier curves to Bézier surfaces. The *B*-spline surface can be regarded as the tensor product of *B*-spline curves in two directions.

Definition Let the $(m+1)(n+1)$ points $\boldsymbol{b}_{ij}$ $(i=0, 1, \ldots, n; j=0, 1, \ldots, m)$ be given in space. The parametric surface

$$\boldsymbol{P}(u, w)=\sum_{i=0}^{n}\sum_{j=0}^{m} F_{i,n}(u)F_{j,m}(w)\boldsymbol{b}_{ij}, \qquad 0\leqslant u, w\leqslant 1 \tag{4.1}$$

is called a *B-spline patch*, in which $\{F_{i,n}(u)\}$ are *B-spline basis functions*. The spatial net formed by $\boldsymbol{b}_{ij}$ $(i=0, 1, \ldots, n; j=0, 1, \ldots, m)$ is called the *B-characteristic net.*

(1) For $m=n=1$, we obtain the hyperbolic paraboloid, just as in the case of the bilinear Bézier patch.

(2) For $m=n=2$, we get the biquadratic patch whose parametric coordinate curves are all parabolas. Figure 5-9 shows the relation of the patch and its *B*-characteristic net.

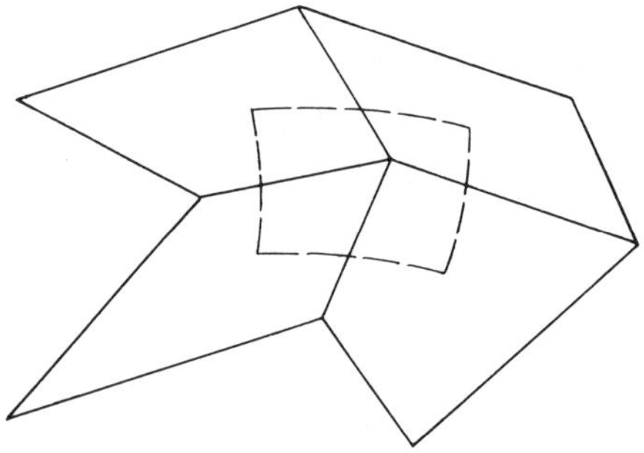

Figure 5-9

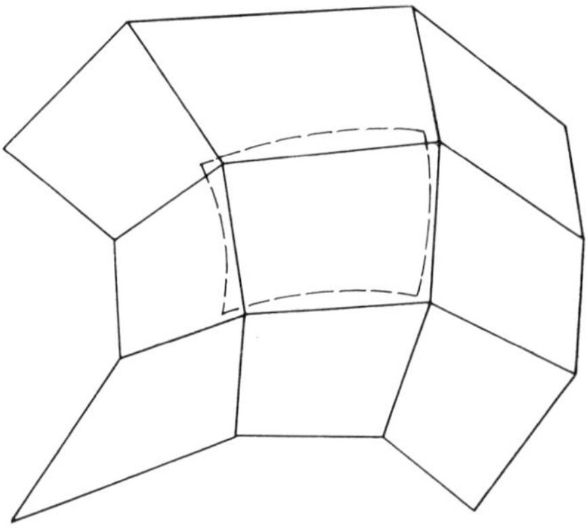

Figure 5-10

(3) For $m = n = 3$, the corresponding bicubic B-spline patch is one of the most important patches commonly used in CAGD (see Fig. 5-10).

The bicubic Coons patch, the Bézier patch and the B-spline patch are different representations of the bicubic surface. These representations are equivalent in the sense that one of them can be transformed into another by a nonsingular transformation. However, this does not mean that they are all the same in applications. Recall that we pointed out in a previous section that the Bézier patch provides a geometric explanation for the twists in the Coons representation. And bicubic B-spline patches provide a simple solution of C^2-continuity between two adjacent patches. This is guaranteed automatically by the C^2-continuity of the cubic B-spline functions $\{F_{i,3}(u)\}$.

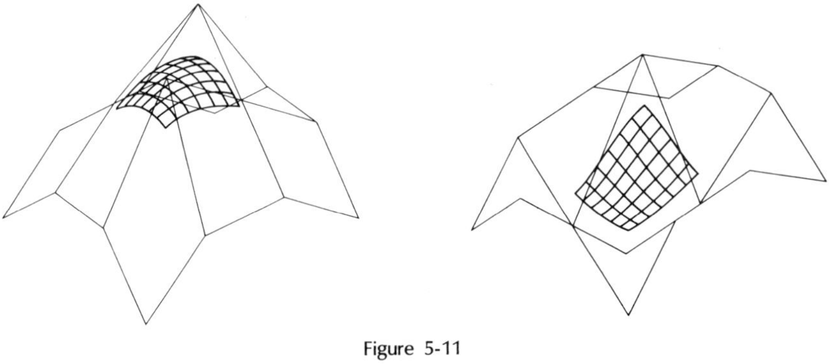

Figure 5-11

Bicubic B-Spline Patches.

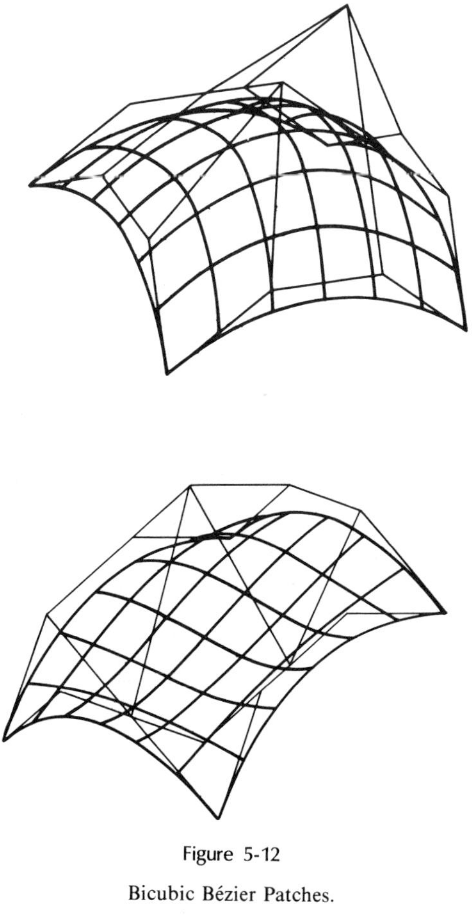

Figure 5-12

Bicubic Bézier Patches.

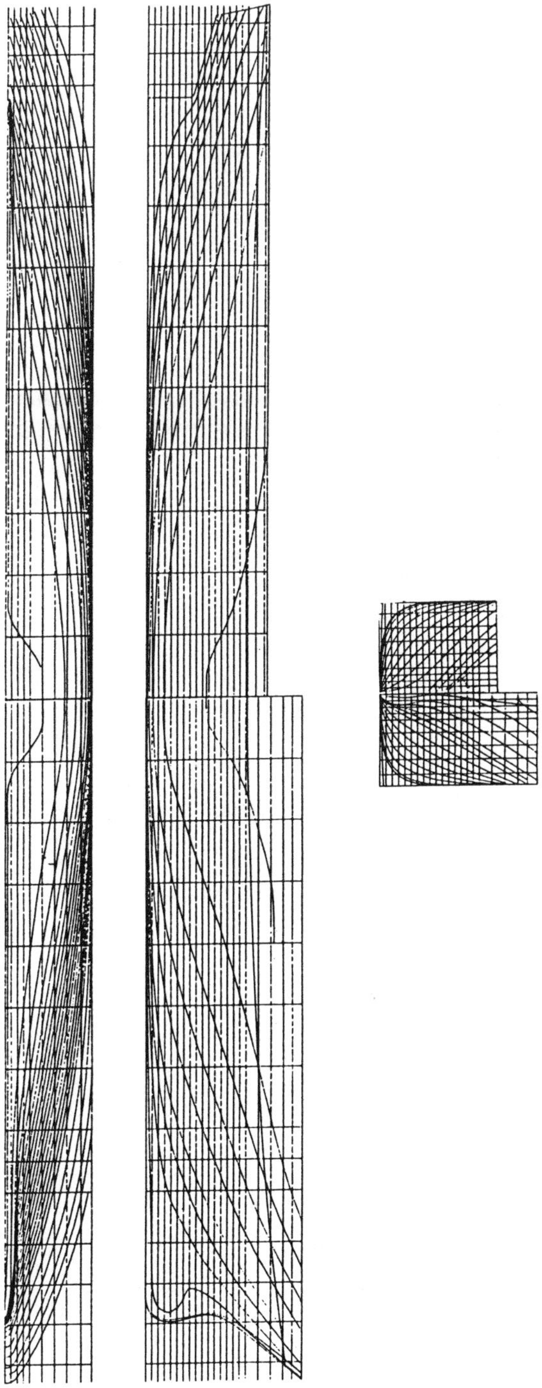

Figure 5-13
Ship Hull Represented by Bézier Surfaces.

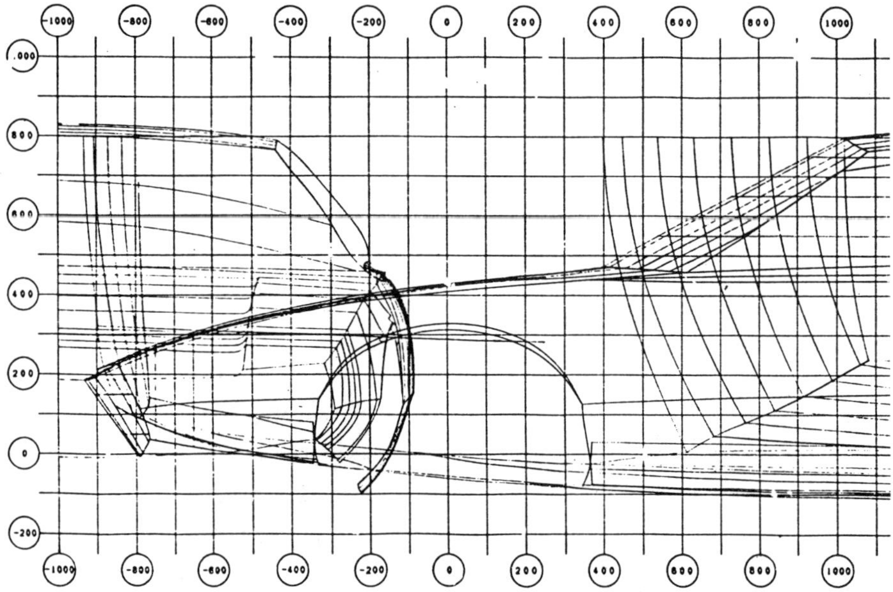

Figure 5-14

Car Body Represented by Bézier Surfaces.

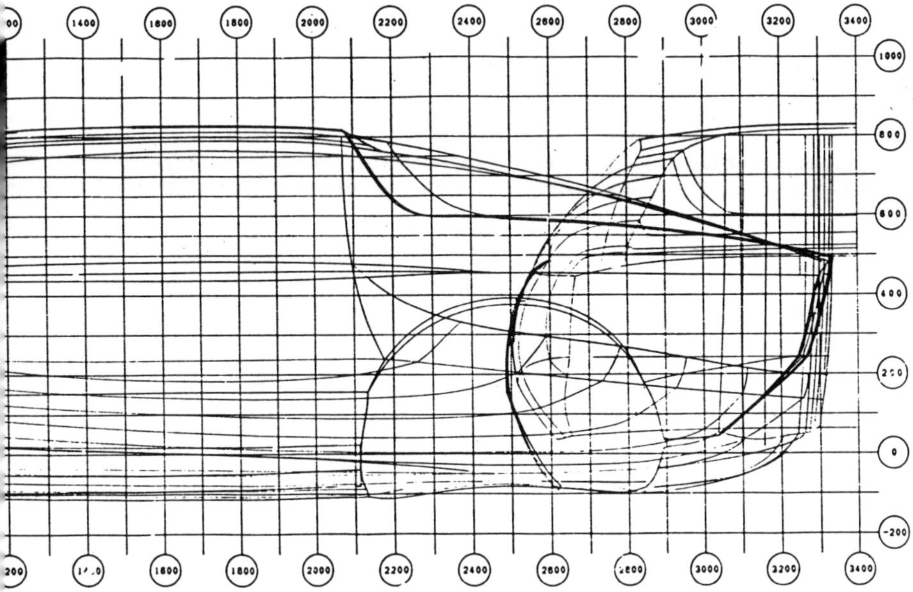

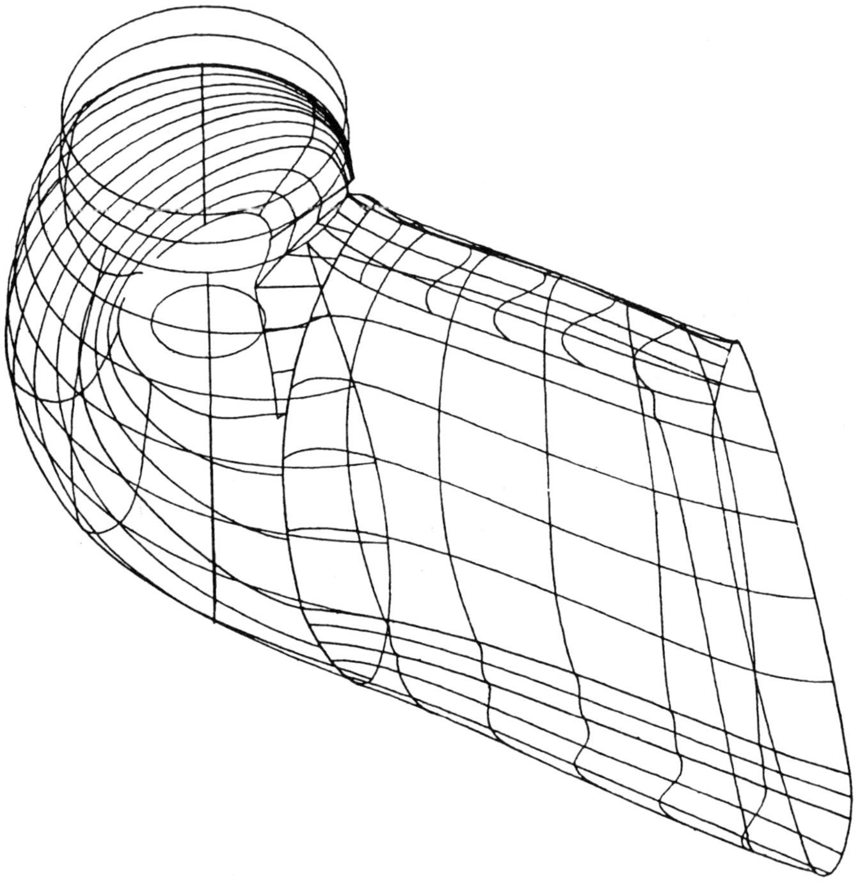

Figure 5-15

Air Tube of a Turbine Represented by Bézier Surfaces.

CHAPTER VI

Nonlinear Splines

We have introduced some spline functions with two common features:

(1) Given a partition of an interval, all spline functions of each kind form a linear space, and the continuity equations of these are systems of linear algebraic equations, which are therefore easy to deal with.
(2) Since the spline functions produce good fitting only in the case of small deflection, they are not geometrically invariant.

Since the parametric cubic splines discussed in Chapter III are geometrically invariant, they are suitable for large deflection. Particularly, the parametric cubic spline curve of cumulative chord length is one kind of large-deflection spline which is used in geometric design and has the advantages of simple computation and shape fairness.

Since the mid 1960s, other kinds of large-deflection spline curves have been studied in greater depth. The most interesting questions, such as how to establish a strict mathematical model of large-deflection wooden splines, how to set the continuity conditions of the spline, and how to solve continuity equations, have only been addressed in recent years. These questions are what we will discuss in the first three sections of this chapter, i.e., geometric splines, local cubic splines, and mechanical splines.

With the wide use of Numerical Control Machines, we hope to find splines that can be used directly in NC processes. As most present NC machines are equipped with arc and straight-line interpolatory installation, if we construct a spline curve formed by arcs then it can be used as input information without processing afterward. Biarc interpolations and circular-arc interpolatory spline curves, introduced in Sections 4 and 6 of this chapter are just GC^1-continuous spline curves which are suited to NC processes. In Section 5 we will discuss the extension of biarc interpolations, i.e., interpolations by pairs of quadratic curves. With the same precision, the number of segments of interpolation by pairs of hyperbolas is half that of biarc interpolation when an NC Machine equipped with quadratic interpolatory devices exists.

The splines discussed in this chapter do not form linear spaces; even their continuity equations are nonlinear. For that reason, they are called *nonlinear spline curves.* The main property of these curves is their non-linearity. Therefore we cannot directly use the effective theory of linear algebra and the standard methods of approximation theory to cope with polynomial functions, as we did for cubic spline functions, but shall use special methods to deal wth individual problems.

The second property of these curves is their clear geometric meaning. From raising questions to solving them, we shall mainly use geometric methods that have nothing to do with the choice of coordinate system, so that they meet the needs of geometric design.

1 Geometric Spline Curves

1.1 Mechanical Background and Definition

In discussing cubic spline functions in Chapter II, we introduced the mathematical model of the wooden spline. The load equilibrium equation between two adjacent knots is

$$\frac{d^2k}{ds^2}=0, \tag{1.1}$$

with s being the arc length of the deflection curve and $k(s)$ its curvature at s. Wooden splines should satisfy (1.1) at every point except the knots. Assuming small deflections, and the approximate relations $s \approx x$ and $k \approx d^2y/dx^2$, we can deduce the cubic spline function from (1.1).

In the case of large deflections, the above linearized method cannot be used. Between adjacent knots, the solution of (1.1) is

$$k = as + b, \tag{1.2}$$

in which a and b are integral constants. The plane curve represented by (1.2) is called the *Cornu spiral* or *Euler spiral.* Figure 6-1 shows a Cornu spiral which looks like two pieces of a clockwork spring. Actually, the intrinsic equation of the clockwork spring is just (1.2).

Definition Let a set of knots $\{P_i\}$ be given on the plane. An interpolatory spline which satisfies the following conditions is defined as a *geometric spline*:

(1) Between any two adjacent knots, it is a Cornu spiral;
(2) The whole spline is GC^2-continuous, i.e., its tangent line and curvature are continuous at the joints.

The reason why we call such splines geometric splines is that their equations consist only of geometric quantities such as curvature and arc length, and thus they differ from the splines represented by functional equations in coordinates system. As both curvature and arc length are intrinsic geometric quantities of curves, some authors also call geometric splines *intrinsic splines* (Adams [3], 1975; Pal and Nutbourne, 1977; Pal [1], [2], 1978; Schechter [1], [2], 1978).

1.2 Continuity Equations

In order to establish continuity equations of the geometric spline, the first thing we should do is to find differential relations of a GC^2-continuous curve among the arc length parameter s, chord parameter L and the angles Θ_1, Θ_2 formed by the chord and tangent lines at the end-points.

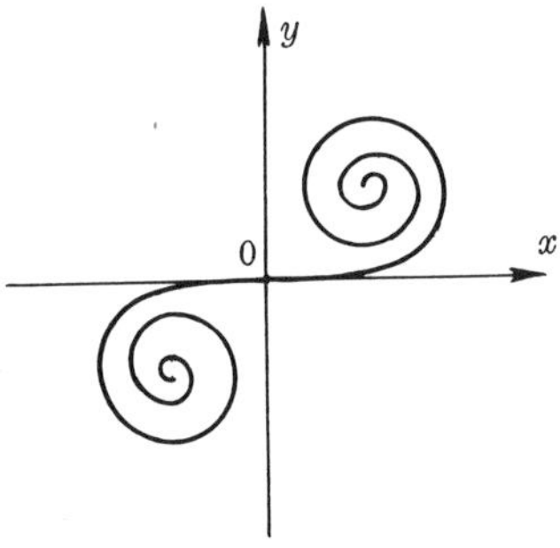

Figure 6-1

As shown in Figure 6-2, on any segment of a GC^2-continuous plane curve, we assume that the fixed point $\boldsymbol{P}_0$ corresponds to $s=0$, and the moving point $\boldsymbol{P}$ to s. We denote the directional chord $\overline{\boldsymbol{P}_0\boldsymbol{P}}$ by $\boldsymbol{L}$, the angles formed by the tangent lines at $\boldsymbol{P}_0$, $\boldsymbol{P}$ and $\boldsymbol{L}$ by Θ_1, Θ_2 respectively, and the angle between the two tangent lines by $\Psi=\Theta_2-\Theta_1$. With $\boldsymbol{P}$ moving ds along the curve, a right-angled differential triangle is formed, as indicated by the shaded part in Fig. 6-2. Its three sides are ds, dL, and $L d\Theta_1$, after neglecting higher-order terms. At the point $\boldsymbol{P}$, $k=d\Psi/ds$, and therefore we obtain the differential equations of the functions L, Θ_1, and Θ_2 with respect to s as follows:

$$\begin{aligned} \frac{dL}{ds} &= \cos\Theta_2, \\ \frac{d\Theta_1}{ds} &= -\frac{\sin\Theta_2}{L}, \\ \frac{d\Theta_2}{ds} &= k-\frac{\sin\Theta_2}{L}. \end{aligned} \tag{1.3}$$

The initial values are

$$L(0)=0, \qquad \Theta_2(0)=\Theta_1(0)=0. \tag{1.4}$$

We can solve the nonlinear system of equations (1.3) by an expansion in power series. According to (1.4), we have

$$L(0)=0, \qquad \left.\frac{dL}{ds}\right|_0=\cos\Theta_2|_0=1, \qquad \left.\frac{d^2L}{ds^2}\right|_0=-\frac{d\Theta_2}{ds}\sin\Theta_2|_0=0,$$

so that we get the following expansion of L in powers of s:

$$L=s+O(s^3). \tag{1.5}$$

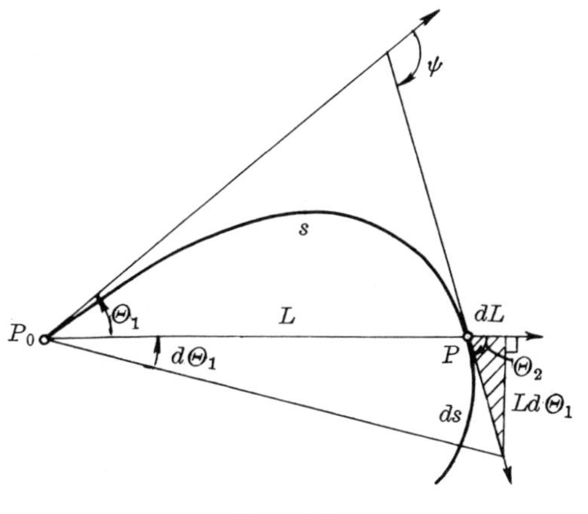

Figure 6-2

When the curve is the Cornu spiral (1.2), we expand Θ_1 and Θ_2 in s:

$$\begin{aligned}\Theta_1 &= A_1 s + \tfrac{1}{2}B_1 s^2 + O(s^3),\\ \Theta_2 &= A_2 s + \tfrac{1}{2}B_2 s^2 + O(s^3).\end{aligned} \tag{1.6}$$

Substituting (1.6) into the second and third equations of (1.3), and using (1.5), we have

$$A_1 = -\frac{b}{2},\ B_1 = -\frac{a}{3}; \qquad A_2 = \frac{b}{2},\ B_2 = \frac{2a}{3}. \tag{1.7}$$

Denoting end-points of the Cornu spiral by $\boldsymbol{P}_1$ and $\boldsymbol{P}_2$, the corresponding arc length parameters by 0 and s_0, chord length by $L_0 = \overline{\boldsymbol{P}_1\boldsymbol{P}_2}$, directional angles between the tangent lines at the end points and the chord line by θ_1 and θ_2, then $\theta_1 = \Theta_1(s_0)$ and $\theta_2 = \Theta_2(s_0)$. Furthermore, denoting the curvatures at the end-points of the segment of the curve by k_1 and k_2, the two integral constants in (1.2) are

$$a = \frac{k_2 - k_1}{s_0}, \qquad b = k_1.$$

In (1.6), assuming $s = s_0$ and by (1.7) and (1.5), the relations between θ_1, θ_2 and k_1, k_2, L_0 are obtained:

$$\begin{aligned}\theta_1 &= -\frac{L_0}{6}(2k_1 + k_2) + O(L_0^3),\\ \theta_2 &= \frac{L_0}{6}(k_1 + 2k_2) + O(L_0^3).\end{aligned} \tag{1.8}$$

Now it is easy to derive the continuity conditions of the geometric spline curve based upon (1.8).

Let $n+1$ knots $\boldsymbol{P}_i$ $(i = 0, 1, \ldots, n)$ on the plane be given. The angle θ_i $(i = 1, 2, \ldots, n-1)$ denotes the angle formed by the adjacent chord vectors $\overrightarrow{\boldsymbol{P}_{i-1}\boldsymbol{P}_i}$ and $\overrightarrow{\boldsymbol{P}_i\boldsymbol{P}_{i+1}}$. Figure 6-4 shows the joining of the ith and $(i+1)^{\text{th}}$ segments of the Cornu spiral at the point $\boldsymbol{P}_i$. As it possesses GC^2-continuity,

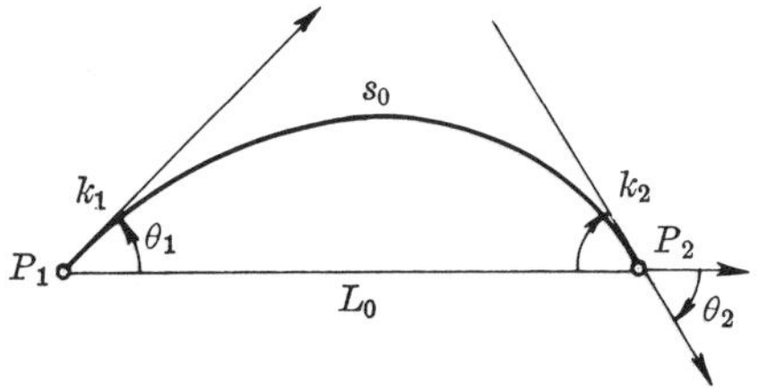

Figure 6-3

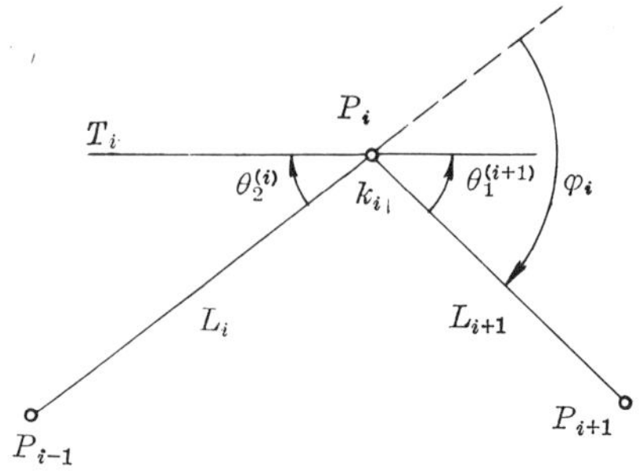

Figure 6-4

we denote the common curvature of the two segments at $\boldsymbol{P}_i$ by k_i, and the directional angles between the common tangent line T_i and the left and right chord lines by $\theta_2^{(i)}$ and $\theta_1^{(i+1)}$. According to (1.8), $\theta_1^{(i+1)}$ and $\theta_2^{(i)}$ are expressed by

$$\begin{aligned} \theta_1^{(i+1)} &= -\frac{L_{i+1}}{6}(2k_i + k_{i+1}) + O(L_{i+1}^3), \\ \theta_2^{(i)} &= \frac{L_i}{6}(k_{i-1} + 2k_i) + O(L_i^3). \end{aligned} \tag{1.9}$$

There exists a continuity relation among $\theta_1^{(i)}$, $\theta_2^{(i+1)}$ and ϕ_i:

$$\theta_2^{(i)} - \theta_1^{(i+1)} = \phi_i. \tag{1.10}$$

Hence

$$\mu_i k_{i-1} + 2k_i + \lambda_i k_{i+1} = 3K_i + O(\phi^2) \qquad (i = 1, 2, \ldots, n-1), \tag{1.11}$$

with $\lambda_i = L_{i+1}/(L_i + L_{i+1})$, $\mu_i = L_i/(L_i + L_{i+1})$; the curvature of the circle determined by the three points P_{i-1}, P_i and P_{i+1} is

$$K_i = \frac{2\sin\phi_i}{\overline{\boldsymbol{P}_{i-1}\boldsymbol{P}_{i+1}}} = \frac{2\phi_i}{L_i + L_{i+1}} + O(\phi_i^2),$$

and $\phi = \max|\phi_i|$. Equations (1.11) are called the k-continuity equations of the geometric spline. The only difference between (1.11) and the k-continuity equations of the parametric cubic spline of cumulative chord appears in the term $O(\phi^2)$ (Liu Dingyuan [1], 1978).

In the case of local small deflection, the terms of high degree in (1.11) and (1.9) can be omitted. Then adding appropriate end conditions k_0 and k_n, we can easily get the curvature k_i and the tangent line T_i at the point $\boldsymbol{P}_i$ by solving a tridiagonal system. How to determine the position of every segment of the Cornu spiral is discussed in the following sections.

1.3 Interpolatory Formulas

Since the position of a curve cannot be determined only by intrinsic equations (1.3), we should express the interpolatory formulas of the geometric spline curve in a coordinate system. Naturally we choose a local orthogonal coordinate system $\{\boldsymbol{P}_1; x, y\}$, i.e., $\boldsymbol{P}_1$ is the origin, $\overrightarrow{\boldsymbol{P}_1\boldsymbol{P}_2}$ is the x-axis, and the y-axis is determined by the right-hand rule. We will leave out the index i again and represent adjacent knots by $\boldsymbol{P}_1$, $\boldsymbol{P}_2$. The tangent angle θ_1 at $\boldsymbol{P}_1$ is given by (1.11) and (1.9). The tangent angle $\theta(s)$ at $\boldsymbol{P}$ corresponding to the arc parameter s is obtained by intergrating the curvature:

$$\theta(s) = \int_0^s k(s)\, ds + \theta_1 = \tfrac{1}{2}as^2 + bs + \theta_1. \tag{1.12}$$

Therefore the segment of the Cornu spiral between $\boldsymbol{P}_1$ and $\boldsymbol{P}_2$ is represented in the local orthogonal coordinate system by parametric equations with respect to s:

$$\begin{aligned} x &= \int_0^s \cos\theta(\tau)\, d\tau, \\ y &= \int_0^s \sin\theta(\tau)\, d\tau. \end{aligned} \tag{1.13}$$

Equations (1.13) are just the interpolatory formulas of the geometric spline, and the right-hand sides of the equations are two Frenet integrals. Though they cannot be expressed as elementary functions, we proceed with numerical integration by using a standard computational program. This is certainly troublesome, but in the case of local small deflection, we can choose the approximation of first order in (1.13), i.e.,

$$\cos\theta = 1 + O(\theta^2), \qquad \sin\theta = \theta + O(\theta^3).$$

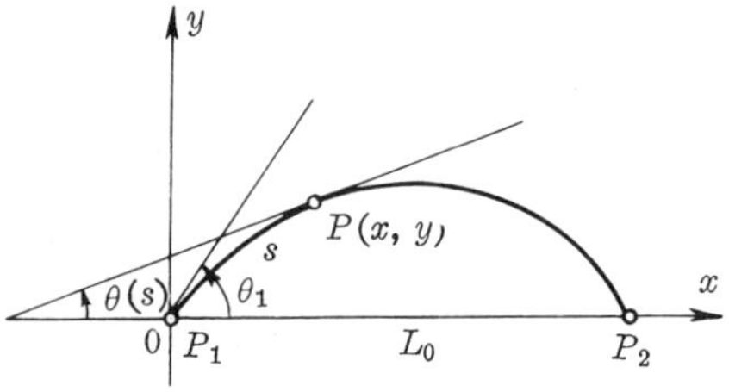

Figure 6-5

Then (1.13) becomes

$$x = s + O(\phi^3),$$

$$y = \tfrac{1}{6}as^3 + \tfrac{1}{2}bs^2 + \theta_1 s + O(\phi^4).$$

Omitting the terms of higher order in the above equations, the approximate expression of the geometric spline in each local orthogonal coordinate system is a cubic polynomial,

$$y = \tfrac{1}{6}ax^3 + \tfrac{1}{2}bx^2 + \theta_1 x.$$

This suggests that if the GC^2-continuous interpolatory spline is formed directly from cubic polynomials in the local orthogonal coordinate system, it may have the advantages of simple calculation and shape fairness, and that is the background of the construction of local cubic spline curves.

2 Local Cubic Spline Curves

2.1 Definition and Continuity Equations

A set of data points $\boldsymbol{P}_i$ $(i = 0, 1, \ldots, n)$ in a plane is given, and a local orthogonal coordinate system is established, by using two adjacent data points $\boldsymbol{P}_{i-1}$ and $\boldsymbol{P}_i$, in which the cubic polynomial taking $\boldsymbol{P}_{i-1}$ and $\boldsymbol{P}_i$ as end-points is called the local cubic curve. Such curves were used earlier by Fowler and Wilson (1963), whose method was based on iteration and approximation. Furthermore, Sun Jiachang (1977) established continuity equations and coped with them by linearization, with a discussion on estimating the order of approximation and the variational properties.

Definition An interpolatory spline is called a *local cubic spline* if it satisfies the following conditions:

(1) In each local orthogonal coordinate system, it is a segment of a local cubic curve.

(2) The whole curve is GC^2-continuous, i.e., its tangent line and curvature are continuous at the joints.

We again omit the index i, and denote adjacent data points by $\boldsymbol{P}_1$ and $\boldsymbol{P}_2$ and assume chord length $L = \overline{\boldsymbol{P}_1\boldsymbol{P}_2}$. In a local orthogonal coordinate system, the equation of a local cubic curve is

$$y = ax^3 + bx^2 + cx. \tag{2.1}$$

Since it starts from $\boldsymbol{P}_1(0,0)$ and ends at $\boldsymbol{P}_2(L,0)$, we have

$$c=-aL^2-bL. \tag{2.2}$$

Denote the first and second derivatives of the curve at $\boldsymbol{P}_1$ and $\boldsymbol{P}_2$ by y_1', y_2' and y_1'', y_2''. From (2.1) and (2.2), we derive the relations

$$\begin{aligned} y_1' &= -\frac{L}{6}(2y_1''+y_2''),\\ y_2' &= \frac{L}{6}(y_1''+2y_2''). \end{aligned} \tag{2.3}$$

Let θ_1 and θ_2 represent the oriented angles formed by the tangent lines at $\boldsymbol{P}_1$ and $\boldsymbol{P}_2$ and the chord $\boldsymbol{P}_1\boldsymbol{P}_2$, and let k_1 and k_2 represent the curvatures (see Fig. 6-6). Then (2.3) becomes

$$\begin{aligned} \operatorname{tg}\theta_1 &= -\frac{L}{6}\left(\frac{2}{\cos^3\theta_1}k_1+\frac{1}{\cos^3\theta_2}k_2\right),\\ \operatorname{tg}\theta_2 &= \frac{L}{6}\left(\frac{1}{\cos^3\theta_1}k_1+\frac{2}{\cos^3\theta_2}k_2\right). \end{aligned} \tag{2.4}$$

Expanding θ_1 and θ_2 of (2.4) in a power series, we have

$$\begin{aligned} \theta_1 &= -\frac{L}{6}(2k_1+k_2)+O(\theta^3),\\ \theta_2 &= \frac{L}{6}(k_1+2k_2)+O(\theta^3), \end{aligned} \tag{2.5}$$

in which $\theta=\max(|\theta_1|,|\theta_2|)$. Adding the index i, we have

$$\begin{aligned} \theta_1^{(i+1)} &= -\frac{L_{i+1}}{6}(2k_i+k_{i+1})+O(\phi^3),\\ \theta_2^{(i)} &= \frac{L_i}{6}(k_{i-1}+2k_i)+O(\phi^3), \end{aligned} \tag{2.6}$$

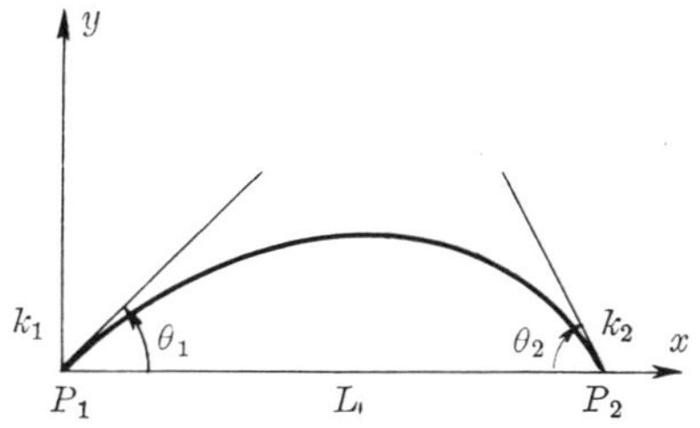

Figure 6-6

where $\theta_1^{(i+1)}$ and $\theta_2^{(i)}$ denote the oriented angles between the common tangent line and each chord line of adjacent segments of the local cubic curve at the point $\boldsymbol{P}_i$ (Fig. 6-7), k_i is the common curvature, and ϕ_i is as shown in Fig. 6-7. When we substitute (2.6) into the tangent continuity relation

$$\theta_2^{(i)} - \theta_1^{(i+1)} = \phi_i, \tag{2.7}$$

the k-continuity equations of the local cubic spline are obtained:

$$\mu_i k_{i-1} + 2k_i + \lambda_i k_{i+1} = 3K_i + O(\phi^2) \qquad (i = 1, 2, \ldots, n-1), \tag{2.8}$$

in which each symbol has the same meaning as in (1.11). Comparing (1.11) with (2.8), it is clear that the k-continuity equations are those of the geometric spline if the higher-order term $O(\phi^2)$ is not considered.

Similarly, the θ-continuity equations of local cubic spline are

$$\lambda_i\theta_{i-1} + 2\theta_i + \mu_i\theta_{i+1} = -2\lambda_i\phi_i - \mu_i\phi_{i+1} + O(\phi^3) \qquad (i = 1, 2, \ldots, n-1), \tag{2.9}$$

with $\theta_i \equiv \theta_1^{(i+1)}$.

As to the problems of convergence of the local cubic spline, there is a theorem concerning the order of approximation. We state it here without proof.

Theorem *Let* Γ *be any* C^4*-continuous curve interpolating the given data points* $\boldsymbol{P}_i$ $(i = 0, 1, \ldots, n)$. *If the local cubic spline curve* S *has the same interpolatory and end conditions as* Γ, *then in each local orthogonal coordinate system, the order of approximation of* S *to* Γ *is*

$$S^{(\alpha)}(x) - \Gamma^{(\alpha)}(x) = O(\phi^{4-\alpha}) \qquad (\alpha = 0, 1, 2).$$

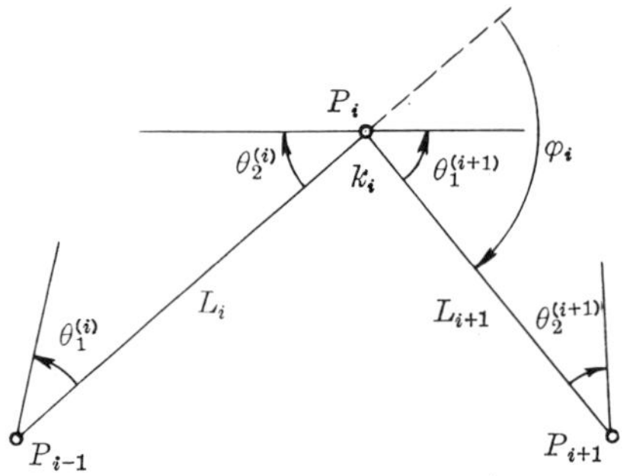

Figure 6-7

2.2 Linearized Local Cubic Splines

In the calculation of geometric design, a set of local small-deflection data points often appears. While using the local cubic spline for interpolation, further simplification can be made. That is, we omit the terms of higher order in each formula and turn nonlinear problems into linear ones, i.e., we divide the whole large-deflection curve into several local small-deflection segments. The following is the detailed scheme.

The first step. Solve for k_i $(i=0,1,\ldots,n)$. Leaving out the $O(\phi^2)$ term in (2.8), we have the linearized continuity equations

$$\mu_i k_{i-1}+2k_i+\lambda_i k_{i+1}=3K_i \qquad (i=1,2,\ldots,n-1). \tag{2.10}$$

Attaching two suitable end conditions, we will get unique solutions k_i $(i=0,1,\ldots,n)$ by the method of solving a tridiagonal system.
The second step. Solve for tangent angles $\theta_1^{(i)}$ and $\theta_2^{(i)}$ $(i=1,2,\ldots,n)$. Substituting the values for k_i $(i=0,1,\ldots,n)$ into the first equation in (2.6) with $O(\phi^3)$ omitted, we have the tangent angle at $\boldsymbol{P}_i$,

$$\theta_1^{(i+1)}=-\frac{L_{i+1}}{6}(2k_i+k_{i+1}), \tag{2.11}$$

and another tangent angle from (2.7),

$$\theta_2^{(i)}=\phi_i+\theta_1^{(i+1)}. \tag{2.12}$$

The third step. Give an interpolatory expression in each local orthogonal coordinate system. We omit the index i for simplicity. Referring to Fig. 6-6 and (2.1), we know that a, b, c satisfy

$$\begin{aligned} \operatorname{tg}\theta_1&=c,\\ \operatorname{tg}\theta_2&=3aL^2+2bL+c,\\ 0&=aL^2+bL+c. \end{aligned}$$

Thus we have

$$a=\frac{\operatorname{tg}\theta_1+\operatorname{tg}\theta_2}{L^2}, \qquad b=-\frac{2\operatorname{tg}\theta_1+\operatorname{tg}\theta_2}{L}, \qquad c=\operatorname{tg}\theta_1, \tag{2.13}$$

in which θ_1 and θ_2 have been determined by (2.11) and (2.12).

The interpolatory spline resulting from (2.10), (2.11), (2.12), (2.13) and (2.1) is called the *linearized local cubic spline curve.* It possesses GC^1-continuity strictly and GC^2-continuity approximately. Actually, GC^1-continuity is guaranteed by (2.12). Furthermore, the difference between the right and left curvatures of the linearized spline at each data point and the accurate value is $O(\phi^2)$; within the precision of engineering requirements, we will not feel the jumping of curvature. It is easy to prove that linearized splines are of the same order of approximation as local cubic splines.

We believe that in the case of the interpolation of local small-deflection data points, the linearized local cubic spline has advantages, i.e., simple calculation and fairness, and thus we can avoid the trouble of using iteration to obtain an accurate solution of (2.8) and can reproduce the wooden spline more precisely. Taking the geometric spline as the standard mathematical model of the wooden spline, a comparision of (1.11) with (2.10) shows that the curvature of the local cubic spline at data points differs from that of the geometric spline, though it is linearized, by order $O(\phi^2)$.

In the numerical control system of ship-hull production, the linearized local cubic spline has been used as an interpolatory curve in the Hudong Ship Building Factory for many years. The above ideas have proved to be of practical meaning (Liu Digyuan and Su Wenrong, [1], 1980).

Comparing the k-continuity equations of the linearized local cubic spline with that of the parametric cubic spline curve of cumulative chord length, we immediately find that their principal parts are the same, the only difference being in the term $O(\phi^2)$, and therefore they have the same order of approximation. In a comparison test for interpolation to the same set of local small-deflection data points, the two kinds of curves coincide almost completely. But near local large-deflection data points, the two curves are different, as expected, and we cannot say which one is better.

Theoretical analysis and practical tests have shown that the parametric cubic spline of cumulative chord length and the linearized local cubic spline are two kinds of practical large-deflection interpolatory splines, and they both have the merits of simple calculation and fairness.

3 Mechanical Spline Curves

3.1 Definition

Another mathematical model of the wooden spline is formed from the minimal principle of energy. If we omit the constant factor $(EI)^2$, the square of rigidity of the wooden spline, then

$$U = \int_0^{s_0} k^2 \, ds \tag{3.1}$$

represents the energy of a segment of the wooden spline which is between two adjacent ducks and is of length s_0. The curve that satisfies $U = \min$ is the equilibrium position of the wooden spline. The curve is called an *M-curve* as long as it makes the first variation zero, i.e.,

$$\delta U = 0, \tag{3.2}$$

and we write the curve as

$$M: \boldsymbol{r} = \boldsymbol{r}(s), \tag{3.3}$$

where s is the arc length parameter of the curve.

Definition Let a set of data points be given. If each segment of a curve between two adjacent data points is an M-curve and the whole curve is GC^2-continuous at the joints, then the curve is said to be a *mechanical spline curve.*

Many authors have studied the properties of mechanical spline curves, particularly M-curves, in different ways and have applied them to engineering (MacLaren, 1958; Birkhoff, Burchard and Thomas, 1965; Glass, 1966; Larkin, 1966; Lee and Forsythe, 1973; Malcolm, 1977). The most well known application may be the AUTOKON geometric design system of the Norway shipbuilding industry, based mathematically on the theory and algorithm of mechanical splines studied by Mehlum ([1] 1969, [2] 1974). A series of algorithmic programs of his is known as KURGLA, an abbreviation of Norwegian *Kurve Glatting* (curve fitting).

Unlike others' studies of M-curves, Mehlum used typical differential geometric methods. As the problems are nonlinear, we cannot discuss them without the methods of numerical calculation by iterative approximation, power series expansion and so on. We will not explore many of those methods but will discuss only the elementary mathematical theory of mechanical splines. Readers who are interested in numerical calculation can refer to related articles cited in the References of this book.

3.2 Space M-Curves

Denote the tangent vector, normal vector, and binormal vector of a space M-curve represented by (3.3) at the point $\boldsymbol{r}(s)$ by $\boldsymbol{T}(s)$, $\boldsymbol{N}(s)$, and $\boldsymbol{B}(s)$, respectively. These form a *Frenet frame* and satisfy the relations

$$\boldsymbol{r}' = \boldsymbol{T}, \qquad \boldsymbol{B} = \boldsymbol{T} \times \boldsymbol{N}, \tag{3.4}$$

and the Frenet formulas

$$\begin{aligned} \boldsymbol{T}' &= k\boldsymbol{N}, \\ \boldsymbol{N}' &= -k\boldsymbol{T} + \tau\boldsymbol{B}, \\ \boldsymbol{B}' &= -\tau\boldsymbol{N}, \end{aligned} \tag{3.5}$$

where k and τ are the curvature and torsion of the M-curve, and the prime symbol represents differentiation with respect to arc length s. Substituting

$$k^2 = (\boldsymbol{T}')^2$$

into the energy integral (3.1) and noting that

$$\boldsymbol{T}^2 = 1 \tag{3.6}$$

and

$$\boldsymbol{r}' = \boldsymbol{T}, \tag{3.7}$$

we can then take (3.2) as a variational problem with two constrained conditions (3.6) and (3.7). By the Lagrangian multiplier method in vector form, we have

$$\delta \int_0^{s_0} F(\boldsymbol{T}, \boldsymbol{T}'; \boldsymbol{r}'; s)\, ds = 0, \tag{3.8}$$

in which

$$F \equiv (\boldsymbol{T}')^2 + \lambda(s)(\boldsymbol{T}^2 - 1) + 2\boldsymbol{\Psi}(s)(\boldsymbol{r}' - \boldsymbol{T}).$$

According to the Euler equation of (3.8) we obtain

$$\begin{aligned} -\boldsymbol{T}'' + \lambda \boldsymbol{T} &= \boldsymbol{\Psi}, \\ \boldsymbol{\Psi}' &= 0. \end{aligned} \tag{3.9}$$

i.e.,

$$(\lambda + k^2)\boldsymbol{T} - k'\boldsymbol{N} - k\tau \boldsymbol{B} = \boldsymbol{\Psi}, \tag{3.10}$$

where $\boldsymbol{\Psi}$ is a constant vector. Differentiating the above equation with respect to s and using (3.5) gives

$$\lambda = D - \tfrac{3}{2}k^2, \tag{3.11}$$

$$k^2\tau = C, \tag{3.12}$$

with C and D being two integral constants. Squaring each side in (3.10), we have

$$k'^2 + (\tfrac{1}{2}k^2 - D)^2 + \frac{C^2}{k^2} = J^2, \tag{3.13}$$

in which $J = |\boldsymbol{\Psi}|$. Equation (3.13) is a nonlinear ordinary differential equation of first order with respect to k. To express the solution in terms of special functions, we make a new function:

$$\eta = \tfrac{1}{3}D - \tfrac{1}{4}k^2. \tag{3.14}$$

Hence we obtain an ordinary differential equation with respect to η which is equivalent to (3.13):

$$\eta'^2 = 4\eta^3 - g_2\eta - g_3, \tag{3.15}$$

with constants

$$g_2 = \tfrac{1}{3}D^2 + J^2, \qquad g_3 = \tfrac{1}{27}D^3 - \tfrac{1}{3}DJ^2 + \tfrac{1}{4}C^2.$$

As we know, the solution of (3.15) is a Weierstrass elliptic $\mathcal{P}$-function

$$\eta = \mathcal{P}(s + A;\, g_2, g_3),$$

with A being an integral constant. Hence the solution of equation (3.13) is

$$k^2 = \tfrac{4}{3}D - 4\mathcal{P}(s + A;\, g_2, g_3). \tag{3.16}$$

The geometric relations (3.12) and (3.16) determine the curvature and torison of the M-curve and hence the shape of the M-curve. C, D, J, A in (3.16) are four integral constants.

3.3 Plane M-Curves

We now restrict the space of M-curves to the plane. In this case $\tau = 0$, so that $C = 0$ in (3.12). Substituting this into (3.13), we have an equation which is satisfied by the curvature k of a plane M-curve:

$$k'^2 + (\tfrac{1}{2}k^2 - D)^2 = J^2. \tag{3.17}$$

Its solution is also given by (3.16), but the C in the constant g_3 vanishes. Considering the complication of elliptic $\mathcal{P}$-functions, we end our theoretical analysis here. The following are some special cases.

Differentiation of (3.17) gives

$$k'' + k(\tfrac{1}{2}k^2 - D) = 0. \tag{3.18}$$

(1) When D is very large, i.e., $\frac{1}{2}k^2 \ll D$, (3.18) becomes

$$k'' - Dk = 0. \tag{3.19}$$

The solution of (3.19) is a hyperbolic function. In the case of small deflection, it corresponds to a spline function in tension and $\sqrt{D}$ denotes the tension parameter. This was discussed in Chapter II. We will return to the spline construction of (3.19) in the large-deflection case in Section 7 of this chapter.

(2) When $D = 0$, (3.18) becomes

$$k'' + \tfrac{1}{2}k^3 = 0. \tag{3.20}$$

Equation (3.20) was first derived by Birkhoff and deBoor and published in 1965, but the mathematical models they used were slightly different. Let

A and B be two adjacent data points with the distance L_0. Then

$$U^* = \int_A^B k^2 \, ds \tag{3.21}$$

is called the *energy* of the wooden spline between A and B, where the arc length s is a variable. All plane curves which satisfy

$$\delta U^* = 0 \tag{3.22}$$

are called M^*-curves.

By (1.3), we rewrite (3.21) as

$$U^* = \int_A^B k^2 \, ds = \int_0^{L_0} \frac{k^2}{\cos \Theta_2} \, dL = \int_0^{L_0} F(\Theta_2', \Theta_2, L) \, dL,$$

in which

$$F \equiv \left(\frac{\operatorname{tg} \Theta_2}{L} + \frac{d\Theta_2}{dL} \right)^2 \cos \Theta_2.$$

The Euler equation of (3.22) is

$$2 \frac{d^2 \Theta_2}{dL^2} - \left(\frac{d\Theta_2}{dL} \right)^2 \operatorname{tg} \Theta_2 - \frac{\operatorname{tg} \Theta_2}{L^2} (3 + \sec^2 \Theta_2) = 0.$$

Again by (1.3), we have

$$\frac{d^2 \Theta_2}{ds^2} + \frac{1}{2} \left(\frac{d\Theta_2}{ds} \right)^2 \operatorname{tg} \Theta_2 - \frac{\sin \Theta_2 \cos \Theta_2}{2L^2} (3 + \sec^2 \Theta_2) = 0, \tag{3.23}$$

and

$$\frac{dk}{ds} = \frac{k}{l \cos \Theta_2} - \frac{1}{2} \operatorname{tg} \Theta_2 k^2. \tag{3.24}$$

Differentiation of (3.24) gives (3.20).

Therefore it can be seen that the mathematical models of wooden splines studied by Birkhoff and deBoor are just special cases of those Mehlum studied, the latter including splines in tension. The tension parameter D is related to the total arc length s_0. We can imagine that while $s_0 \to L_0$, i.e., tightening the curve enough to approach the chord, $D \to +\infty$ must follow.

3.4 Continuity Equations of Plane Mechanical Splines

In this section, we only discuss the continuity conditions of the mechanical spline formed by the M^*-curve (3.20) and leave the spline in tension expressed by (3.19) to Section 7.

The first integration of the nonlinear equation (3.20) is

$$\left(\frac{dk}{ds}\right)^2 = \tfrac{1}{4}(c_1^4 - k^4).$$

Integrating it again would result in the elliptic function, hence we would rather choose the method of expansion in power series and, from (3.20), we have

$$k = k_1 + \frac{k_2 - k_1}{s_0} s - \tfrac{1}{4}k_1^3 s(s - s_0) + O(s_0^3).$$

As in the discussion of geometric splines, the continuity equations of the mechanical spline, resulting from (1.3), are given by (1.11). The only difference is in the term $O(\phi^2)$.

So far we have seen that parametric cubic splines of cumulative chord length, normalized splines, geometric splines, local cubic splines and mechanical splines have the same continuity equations if we neglect the higher order term $O(\phi^2)$ (Liu Dingyuan [1], 1978). It is worthwhile to analyse $O(\phi^2)$ carefully, to study the differences of these kinds of splines in the higher order terms, and then to estimate more accurately the errors among interpolatory splines which have the same interpolatory conditions.

However, Mehlum did not use the above-mentioned method of expansion in power series in his KURGLA algorithm; he used instead the segments of circular arcs which are joined with GC^1-continuity and then, by the iterative approximation scheme, made the circular arc spline approximately satisfy the interpolatory conditions. We now describe it in detail.

We take the vector product of the first equation in (3.9) and $\boldsymbol{T}$, and then integrate the resulting equation. This gives

$$\boldsymbol{T} \times \boldsymbol{T}' = \boldsymbol{\Psi} \times \boldsymbol{r} - \boldsymbol{E}, \tag{3.25}$$

with $\boldsymbol{E}$ as an integral constant vector. The scalar product of (3.25) and $\boldsymbol{B}$ is

$$k = \boldsymbol{\Phi}\boldsymbol{r} + e, \tag{3.26}$$

where $\boldsymbol{\Phi} = \boldsymbol{B} \times \boldsymbol{\Psi}$ and $e = \boldsymbol{BE} = \pm|\boldsymbol{E}|$. Again we see from (3.10) that $\boldsymbol{\Psi}$ of the plane M-curve lies on the plane of the curve, and so does $\boldsymbol{\Phi}$. Moreover, $\boldsymbol{\Phi}$ can be obtained by rotating $\boldsymbol{\Psi}$ by an angle of $\pi/2$. Let an orthogonal coordinate system be chosen on the plane such that the vector $\boldsymbol{\Phi}$ indicates the positive direction of the x-axis. Then the coordinate form of (3.26) is

$$k = Jx + e. \tag{3.27}$$

This shows that the curvature of the plane M-curve changes linearly along a certain direction $\boldsymbol{\Phi}$ on the plane. The direction of $\boldsymbol{\Phi}$ depends on the choice of the total arc length s_0. As there exists one degree of freedom, we

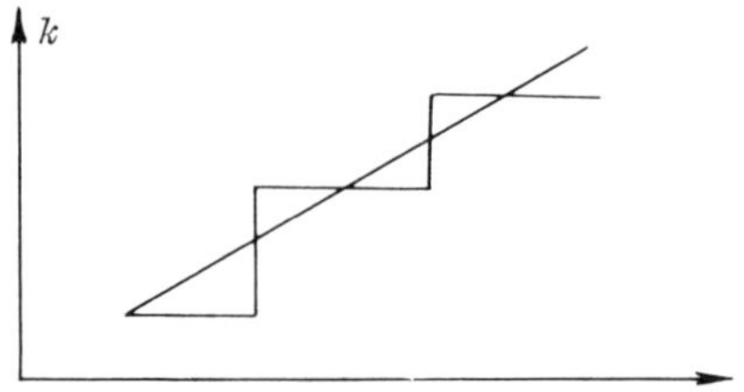

Figure 6-8

may as well let $\mathbf{\Phi}$ be parallel with the chord line $\overrightarrow{\boldsymbol{AB}}$ ($\boldsymbol{A}$ and $\boldsymbol{B}$ are two end-points of the M-curve).

Second, we approximate the linear curvature (3.27) with a staircase curvature function (see Fig. 6-8). The staircase curvature approximation means that we approach the M-curve by a set of circular arcs. An iterative approximation scheme is designed especially for that purpose. Our final goal is to get a GC^1-continuous spline, made of several circular arcs, which passes through given data points approximately. To save space, we will not state the details of the iterative approximation.

If the reader happened to read the circular arcs approximation of the KURGLA algorithm (Mehlum [1], 1969), he or she might get the impression that the iterative approximation of circular arcs seems to have nothing to do with the first half of the statement on M-curves. This is because Mehlum did not study the continuity conditions of M-curves, so the curvature k_i at each data point $\boldsymbol{P}_i$ was unknown. The iterative approximation program designed in the second part actually constructs a GC^1-continuous circular arc spline. Why not construct it directly? That is the problem we will discuss in Sections 4 and 6.

4 Biarc Interpolation

The spline consisting of circular arcs has only GC^1-continuity at its joints, but it can be used directly as input information for a numerical control machine without "postprocessing." It therefore has many applications in a variety of departments.

4.1 Definition of Biarc Interpolation and Trajectory of Joints

While interpolating a set of data points $\{\boldsymbol{P}_i\}$ with a local cubic spline (or other suitable spline), we hope it can be drawn by a numerical control drafting machine. But a general drafting machine cannot draw a cubic curve directly. The fundamental graphs it can draw often are straight lines and circular arcs, and therefore it requires several segments of circular arcs to approximate the cubic curves. The simplest way is to use two segments of circular arc, i.e., so-called *biarcs* (Bolton, 1975). In applications, we retain only the tangent line of the local cubic spline at each data point and replace the cubic curve between two adjacent points by two segments of circular arc.

To make the biarc interpolation have good fairness, we first find all inflection points on the local cubic spline and take them as new data points inserted in with the old ones, still written as $\{\boldsymbol{P}_i\}$. Then in any segment of the local cubic spline there exist no inflection points.

Omitting the index i, we denote two adjacent data points by $\boldsymbol{P}_1$ and $\boldsymbol{P}_2$ and the tangent lines of this segment of the local cubic spline at $\boldsymbol{P}_1$ and $\boldsymbol{P}_2$ by m_1 and m_2 respectively.

Definition Let $\boldsymbol{P}_1$, $\boldsymbol{P}_2$ and m_1, m_2 be given. Introduce two segments of circular arcs D_1 and D_2 which satisfy the following:

(1) D_i passes through $\boldsymbol{P}_i$ and is tangential to m_i at $\boldsymbol{P}_i$ $(i=1,2)$.
(2) D_1 and D_2 are tangential to each other at their joint.

Such a method is called *biarc interpolation.*

The definition shows that biarc interpolation is actually a GC^1-continuous Hermite interpolation in geometric form.

We know that a circular arc on the plane is uniquely determined by three conditions. Therefore biarc interpolation has six degrees of freedom, but the definition uses only five. This shows that the joint is not unique. We will show that the trajectory of joints is a circular arc passing through $\boldsymbol{P}_1$ and $\boldsymbol{P}_2$.

Let m_1 and m_2 intersect at $\boldsymbol{P}^*$, D_1 and D_2 be tangential at $\boldsymbol{P}$, and let the common tangent line m intersect m_1 and m_2 respectively at $\boldsymbol{M}_1$ and $\boldsymbol{M}_2$ (see Fig. 6-9). In the figure we mark some oriented angles $\delta(-\pi/2<\delta\pi/2)$, θ_1, θ_2, ψ_1, ψ_2. Note the signs of those angles in the following computations.

$\triangle \boldsymbol{P}_1\boldsymbol{M}_1\boldsymbol{P}$ is an isosceles triangle. Therefore

$$\psi_1-\delta=\theta_1-\psi_1,$$

i.e.,

$$\psi_1=\frac{\theta_1+\delta}{2}. \tag{4.1}$$

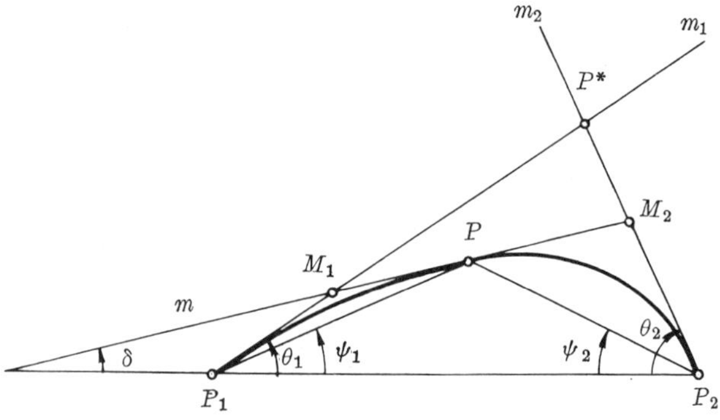

Figure 6-9

Similarly,

$$\psi_2 = \frac{\theta_2 + \delta}{2}. \tag{4.2}$$

In $\triangle \boldsymbol{P}_1\boldsymbol{P}\boldsymbol{P}_2$

$$\angle \boldsymbol{P}_1\boldsymbol{P}\boldsymbol{P}_2 = \pi - (\psi_1 - \psi_2) = \pi - \frac{\theta_1 - \theta_2}{2}, \tag{4.3}$$

hence the trajectory of tangent points (joints) $\boldsymbol{P}$ is a circular arc passing through $\boldsymbol{P}_1$ and $\boldsymbol{P}_2$. We denote it by C.

It is easy to see that the incenter $\boldsymbol{N}$ of $\triangle \boldsymbol{P}_1\boldsymbol{P}^*\boldsymbol{P}_2$ satisfies (4.3) also, i.e., the incenter $\boldsymbol{N}$ is on the circular arc C (see Fig. 6-10).

As mentioned before, if there are no inflection points on the spline curve between $\boldsymbol{P}_1$ and $\boldsymbol{P}_2$, then the two circular arcs cannot be oppositely joined. To ensure this, we can only take the points on C which are inside $\triangle \boldsymbol{P}_1\boldsymbol{P}^*\boldsymbol{P}_2$, the part expressed by the bold line in Fig. 6-10, as the joint of the biarc, i.e.,

$$|\delta| < \min(|\theta_1|, |\theta_2|). \tag{4.4}$$

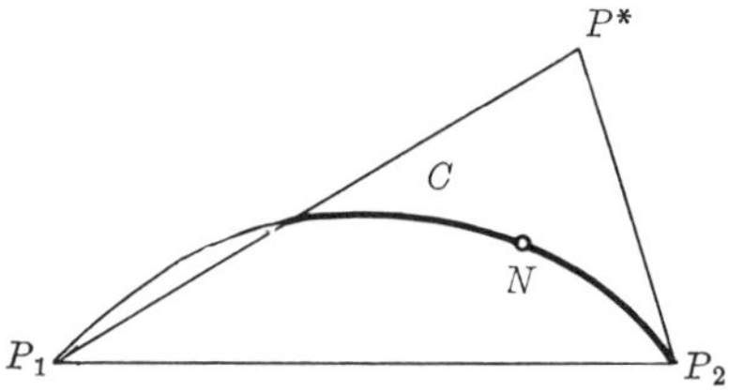

Figure 6-10

4.2 Formula of Radius for the Biarc

In Fig. 6-11, let the chord length be $L=\overline{P_1P_2}$, let P be a joint of the biarc, and let O_1 and O_2 be the two centers of the two circular arcs. Denote the two radii by $R_1=\overline{O_1P_1}$, and $R_2=\overline{O_2P_2}$. Then $O_1P_1 \perp P_1P^*$, and $O_2P_2 \perp P_2P^*$.

In $\triangle P_1PP_2$, by the sine law we have

$$\overline{P_1P}=\frac{\sin\psi_2}{\sin(\psi_1-\psi_2)}L.$$

Draw $O_1D_1 \perp P_1P$. Then in the right-angled triangle $\triangle O_1P_1D_1$, R_1 is obtained as

$$\begin{aligned}R&=\frac{\overline{P_1D_1}}{\sin(\theta_1-\psi_1)}=\frac{\overline{P_1P}}{2\sin(\theta_1-\psi_1)}\\&=\frac{\sin\psi_2}{2\sin(\theta_1-\psi_1)\sin(\psi_1-\psi_2)}L\\&=\frac{\sin\dfrac{\theta_2+\delta}{2}}{2\sin\dfrac{\theta_1-\delta}{2}\sin\dfrac{\theta_1-\theta_2}{2}}L.\end{aligned}$$

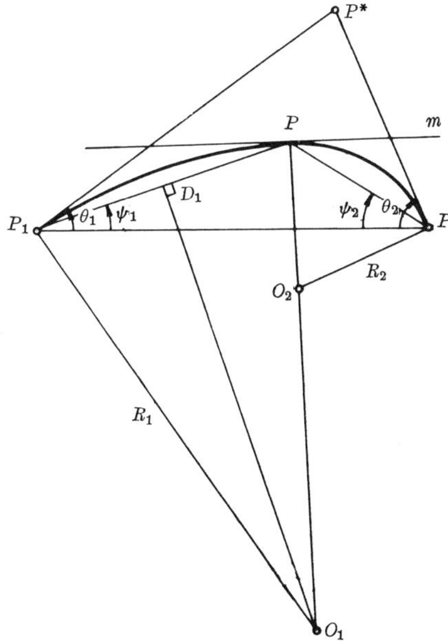

Figure 6-11

R_2 is found the same way. Thus we have

$$R_1 = \frac{\sin \dfrac{\theta_2 + \delta}{2}}{2 \sin \dfrac{\theta_1 - \delta}{2} \sin \dfrac{\theta_1 - \theta_2}{2}} L,$$

$$R_2 = \frac{\sin \dfrac{\theta_1 + \delta}{2}}{2 \sin \dfrac{\theta_2 - \delta}{2} \sin \dfrac{\theta_1 - \theta_2}{2}} L. \tag{4.5}$$

Note that θ_1, θ_2, δ are all oriented angles. As the chord length L is always positive, R_1 and R_2 may be positive or negative. $R_1 < 0$ indicates that the first circular arc is chosen clockwise from $\boldsymbol{P}_1$ to $\boldsymbol{P}$ and vice versa, and similarly for R_2. This makes it easy to judge the orientation of the circular arc, which is important information for drafting. In fact, (4.5) gives the relative curvature radii of the biarc.

4.3 Choosing Joints

We will now explain how to choose a joint of the biarc on the trajectory C. Certainly, any point on C is a joint, but we hope to make efficient use of the remaining degree of freedom, so that the jointed biarc is as fair as possible. If $\theta_1 = -\theta_2$, we know from (4.5) that $R_1 = R_2 = L/2 \sin \theta_2$ no matter how large δ may be, indicating that the biarc is just one circular arc. We will therefore assume $\theta_1 \neq -\theta_2$ to avoid such a special case.

The joint $\boldsymbol{P}$ can be chosen in the following four ways:

(1) $|R_1/R_2 - 1| = \min$, i.e., $\delta = 0$. This is the choice used in the Hudong Ship Building Factory (Liu Dingyuan, Su Wenrong [1], 1980).

(2) $|R_2 - R_1| = \min$, i.e., $\delta = (\theta_1 + \theta_2)/2$. The BRITSHIPS system of the British shipbuilding industry has used this choice since 1971 (Bolton, 1975).

(3) $|1/R_2 - 1/R_1| = \min$, i.e., $\delta = -(\theta_1 + \theta_2)/2$. This is used by the Computing Center of the Chinese Academy of Sciences and some domestic aircraft departments (Sun Jiachang and Zhen Huilin, 1981).

(4) Choosing the intersection of C and the local cubic spline as $\boldsymbol{P}$ (the intersection exists uniquely). Zhejiang University used this in a drafting program (Dong Guangchang, Liang Youdong, He Yuanjun, 1978).

The first three attempt to make the difference of the curvatures or the radii of the biarc as small as possible. The fourth choice is based on the consideration of approximation: As the local cubic spline is thought to be fair, if the joint is on the spline curve, perhaps the biarc approximates a segment of a fair curve more efficiently. Moreover there are five intersections of the biarc and the spline curve (being tangential at an end point is considered as two intersections).

We now give some properties related to biarcs and pay more attention to the first method.

(1) ***The property of extreme value.*** By (4.5), we write

$$H(\delta) \equiv \left|\frac{R_1}{R_2} - 1\right| = \left|\frac{\sin\dfrac{\theta_2+\delta}{2}\sin\dfrac{\theta_2-\delta}{2}}{\sin\dfrac{\theta_1+\delta}{2}\sin\dfrac{\theta_1-\delta}{2}} - 1\right|$$

$$= \left|\frac{\cos\delta - \cos\theta_2}{\cos\delta - \cos\theta_1} - 1\right| = \frac{A}{\cos\delta - \cos\theta_1},$$

in which $A = |\cos\theta_1 - \cos\theta_2| > 0$. The absence of the symbol of absolute value in the denominator in the last step is because of (4.4). Taking the first and second derivatives of H with respect to δ, we see immediately that when $\delta = 0$, $|R_1/R_2 - 1|$ is minimal.

In the same way, it can be proved easily that when $\delta = (\theta_1 + \theta_2)/2$, $|R_2 - R_1| = \min$; and when $\delta = -(\theta_1 + \theta_2)/2$, $|1/R_2 - 1/R_1| = \min$.

(2) ***Geometric meaning.*** When $\delta = 0$, the common tangent m is parallel to $\overrightarrow{\boldsymbol{P}_1\boldsymbol{P}_2}$ and

$$\psi_1 = \frac{\theta_1}{2}, \qquad \psi_2 = \frac{\theta_2}{2},$$

i.e., the joint is the intersection of the two bisectors of the base angles of the triangle $\Delta \boldsymbol{P}_1\boldsymbol{P}^*\boldsymbol{P}_2$, or the incenter $\boldsymbol{N}$.

If $\delta = -(\theta_1 + \theta_2)/2$, we have

$$\psi_1 = -\psi_2 = \frac{\theta_1 - \theta_2}{4}.$$

This shows that the joint coincides with $\boldsymbol{M}$, the intersection of C and the line bisecting and perpendicular to the chord $\boldsymbol{P}_1\boldsymbol{P}_2$.

The geometric significance of the joint in the second method is not obvious.

Denote the joints of the three kinds of methods respectively by $\boldsymbol{N}$, $\boldsymbol{P}$, $\boldsymbol{M}$. When $|\theta_1| < |\theta_2|$, Fig. 6-12 shows a relative position of the three points. The incenter $\boldsymbol{N}$ is between the other two.

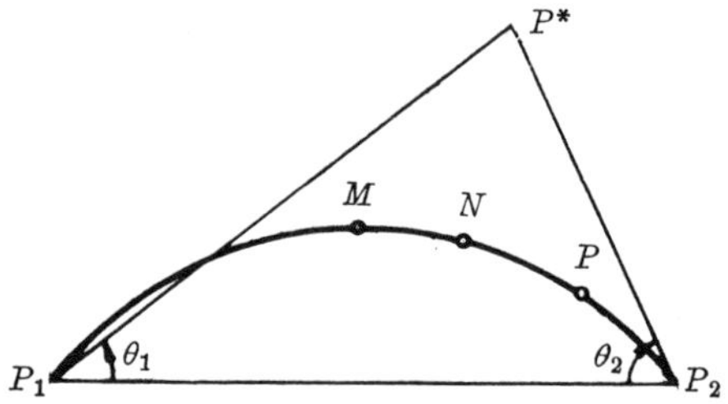

Figure 6-12

(3) ***Property of monotone curvature.*** If $\delta = 0$, the curvatures with the same sign of a local cubic spline curve at $\boldsymbol{P}_1$ and $\boldsymbol{P}_2$ are k_1 and k_2 respectively, and $k_1 < k_2$, then

$$k_1 < \frac{1}{R_1} < \frac{1}{R_2} < k_2. \tag{4.6}$$

(If $k_1 > k_2$, all inequalities in (4.6) should be reversed.)

Proof We will prove the above result under the assumption of local small deflections, i.e., linearizations such as $\sin\theta_1 \approx \theta_1$, $\sin\theta_2 \approx \theta_2$ are allowed. We can set $k_1, k_2 > 0$ without loss of generality. Then by (2.5) and (4.5), omitting higher-order terms, we have

$$\begin{aligned} \frac{1}{R_1} &= \frac{\theta_1(\theta_1-\theta_2)}{\theta_2 L} = \frac{(2k_1+k_2)(k_1+k_2)}{2(k_1+2k_2)} = k_1\frac{(1+t/2)(1+t)}{(1+2t)}, \\ \frac{1}{R_2} &= \frac{\theta_2(\theta_1-\theta_2)}{\theta_1 L} = \frac{(k_1+2k_2)(k_1+k_2)}{2(2k_1+k_2)} = k_2\frac{(1+t^*/2)(1+t^*)}{(1+2t^*)}, \end{aligned} \tag{4.7}$$

in which we write $t \equiv k_2/k_1 > 1$, $t^* = 1/t < 1$. Because of

$$\left(1+\frac{t}{2}\right)(1+t) = 1 + 2t\left(\frac{3+t}{4}\right)\begin{cases} >1+2t, & \text{for } t>1, \\ <1+2t, & \text{for } 1>t>0, \end{cases}$$

we have

$$\frac{1}{R_1} > k_1, \qquad \frac{1}{R_2} < k_2.$$

Again by (2.5), $|\theta_1| < |\theta_2|$ follows from $0 < k_1 < k_2$. Then according to (4.5), in which $\delta = 0$, we have

$$\frac{1/R_2}{1/R_1} = \left(\frac{\sin(\theta_2/2)}{\sin(\theta_1/2)}\right)^2 > 1.$$

Thus (4.6) is proved.

The conclusion tells us that if a sequence of curvatures $\{k_i\}$ of a local cubic spline at data points $\{\boldsymbol{P}_i\}$, under the assumption of local small deflections, is monotonic, then the sequence of curvatures of the circular arcs obtained by biarc interpolation with $\delta = 0$ for each segment is also monotonic. That guarantees the fairness of the biarc interpolatory curves. This fact has been verified by our experiences in the Hudong Ship Building Factory for many years.

(4) Choosing the joint at which $\delta = 0$, there is at least one intersection of the biarc and a local cubic spline between two adjacent data points $\boldsymbol{P}_1$ and $\boldsymbol{P}_2$.

Proof Without loss of generality, we assume that $0 < k_1 < k_2$. According to (4.6), the first circular arc D_1 lies on one side of the spline curve and the second circular arc D_2 on the other side, as shown by Fig. 6-13. Thus at least one intersection exists, indicating that the choice of $\delta = 0$ can also ensure the occurrence of five intersections of the biarc and the local cubic spline.

4.4 Algorithm for Biarc Interpolation

In this section, we introduce the algorithm of biarc interpolation used in the plotting program for an NC plotter which has been adopted in the NC system of ship-body production at the Hudong Ship Building Factory since 1977.

(1) Let a set of data points $\{\boldsymbol{P}_i\}$ and end conditions on the plane be given. Then by the method mentioned in Section 2, we construct an interpolatory linearized local cubic spline curve and find all inflection-points of it, which are used as new data points inserted in with the old ones, and solve for the tangent line at each data point. Thus, between any two adjacent data points $\boldsymbol{P}_1$ and $\boldsymbol{P}_2$, we have obtained oriented angles θ_1, θ_2 formed by the tangent lines at the end points and the chord line, and furthermore a triangle $\triangle \boldsymbol{P}_1 \boldsymbol{P}^* \boldsymbol{P}_2$ is obtained.

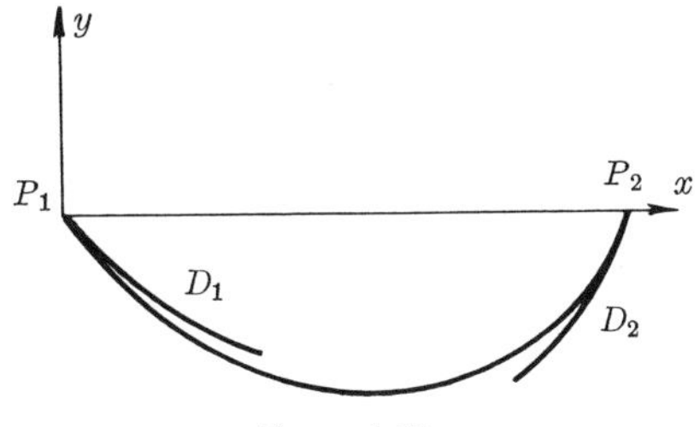

Figure 6-13

(2) In the orthogonal coordinate system $\{\boldsymbol{P}_1; x, y\}$ shown by Fig. 6-14, we see that

(i) The oriented radii of the biarc are

$$R_1 = \frac{\sin\dfrac{\theta_2}{2}}{2\sin\dfrac{\theta_1}{2}\sin\dfrac{\theta_1-\theta_2}{2}}L,$$
$$R_2 = \frac{\sin\dfrac{\theta_1}{2}}{2\sin\dfrac{\theta_2}{2}\sin\dfrac{\theta_1-\theta_2}{2}}L. \tag{4.8}$$

(ii) The coordinates of the joint $\boldsymbol{N}$ (the incenter of the triangle $\boldsymbol{P}_1\boldsymbol{P}^*\boldsymbol{P}_2$) of the biarc are

$$x_0 = -R_1 \sin\theta_1,$$
$$y_0 = -R_1(1-\cos\theta_1). \tag{4.9}$$

(iii) The coordinates of the two centers $\boldsymbol{O}_1(x_1, y_1)$ and $\boldsymbol{O}_2(x_2, y_2)$ of the biarc are

$$x_1 = x_0, \qquad x_2 = x_0,$$
$$y_1 = R_1\cos\theta_1; \qquad y_2 = R_2\cos\theta_2. \tag{4.10}$$

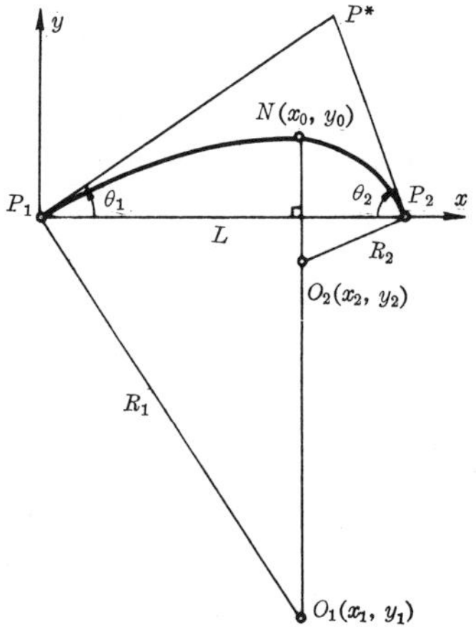

Figure 6-14

Expressions (4.8), (4.9), (4.10) already contain all the information needed for drawing biarcs by an NC plotter. The sign of the oriented radii R_1 and R_2 indicates the direction in which the circular arc runs, more precisely, a positive sign indicates a counter-clockwise direction and a negative sign indicates a clockwise one.

Generally, algorithms (4.9) and (4.10) require a well known extra coordinate transformation from a local orthogonal coordinate system to a fixed orthogonal coordinate system, but we will not state the details here.

5 Interpolation by Pairs of Quadratic Curves

In Section 4.3 we introduced four choices for joints of the biarc. The last choice, in which the joint is on the local cubic spline, is based on approximation.

We continue to investigate problems with emphasis on approximations, but we replace the two circular arcs (i.e., biarc) by two quadratic segments and use the latter as interpolating segments in order to get better approximation results. Here we only describe the theoretical conclusions without detailed derivations (Su Buchin, Hua Xuanji, 1979).

Let a set of data points and end conditions on the plane be given. We first work out a cubic spline function interpolating them. (In the case of a large deflection, we use a local cubic spline instead. Except that a transformation should be applied to the local orthogonal coordinate system, the following discussion is still valid.) We then find all inflection points of the spline, which are used as new data points inserted in with the old ones, and we solve for the first derivative $\{m_i\}$ at each data point.

Let the interpolatory cubic spline function between each two adjacent data points $\boldsymbol{P}_1(x_1, y_1)$ and $\boldsymbol{P}_2(x_2, y_2)$ be

$$S\colon y = y_1 + \frac{y_2 - y_1}{x_2 - x_1}(x - x_1) + \tfrac{1}{6}(x - x_1)(x - x_2) \times \left[2M_1 + M_2 + \frac{M_2 - M_1}{x_2 - x_1}(x - x_1)\right], \tag{5.1}$$

in which M_1 and M_2 are the second derivatives of the spline S at $\boldsymbol{P}_1$ and $\boldsymbol{P}_2$ respectively. Because we have inserted inflection points for the old cubic spline S, $M_1 M_2 \geqslant 0$ always exists.

We arbitrarily take the point $\boldsymbol{P}_0(x_0, y_0)$ as the joint of the pair of quadratic curves (L_1, L_2) such that (L_1, L_2) is tangential to S at $\boldsymbol{P}_1, \boldsymbol{P}_0$ and $\boldsymbol{P}_0, \boldsymbol{P}_2$ respectively. Then the equations are

$$L_i\colon [(y - y_0)(x_i - x_0) - (x - x_0)(y_i - y_0)]^2 = C_i[(y - y_i) - m_i(x - x_i)][(y - y_0) - m_0(x - x_0)] \qquad (i = 1, 2), \tag{5.2}$$

in which m_0, m_1, m_2 denote the first derivatives of S at P_0, P_1, P_2 respectively (see Fig. 6-15).

Lemma *A quadratic curve L which takes P_1, P_0 as two end-points and m_1, m_0 as tangent lines at P_1, P_0 and intersects S at a point $P_1^*(x_1^*, y_1^*)$ between P_1 and P_0 must be a hyperbola.*

The Lemma indicates that, for Hermite interpolation with given end-points P_1, P_0 and tangent lines m_1, m_0, a hyperbola may intersect the cubic spline S approximated by the hyperbola at five points (the point at which two curves are tangential to each other should be regarded as two intersections), whereas if the hyperbola is replaced by an ellipse (including a circular arc) or parabola, there are at most four intersections. Hence the hyperbola may be the best for the approximation. In order to have five intersections we need only arbitrarily choose a point $P_1^*(x_1^*, y_1^*)$ on S between P_1 and P_0 and solve for the coefficient C_1 from (5.2):

$$C_1 = \frac{[(y_1^* - y_0)(x_1 - x_0) - (x_1^* - x_0)(y_1 - y_0)]^2}{[(y_1^* - y_1) - m_1(x_1^* - x_1)][(y_1^* - y_0) - m_0(x_1^* - x_0)]}. \tag{5.3}$$

Then the hyperbola L_1 represented by (5.2) is uniquely defined.

Applying the Lemma to the segment of the spline S between P_0 and P_2, we have

Theorem *A pair of C^1-continuous quadratic curves (L_1, L_2) intersects a cubic spline S between P_1 and P_2 in at most eight points. Conversely, those pairs of quadratic curves which have eight intersections must be pairs of hyperbolas.*

Naturally, we raise the question of how to determine the joint P_0 of the pair of hyperbolas.

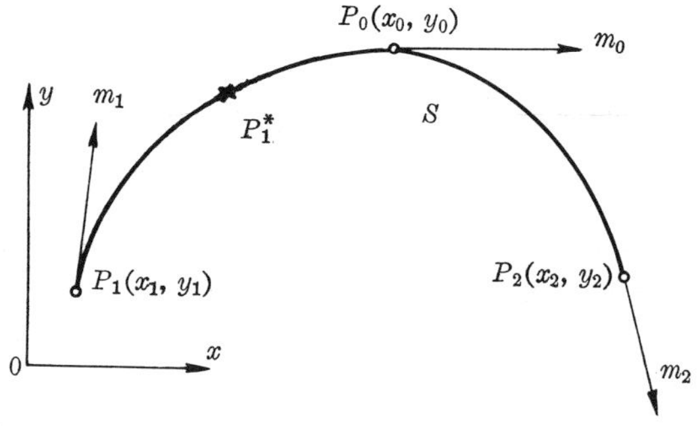

Figure 6-15

(1) For $M_1M_2 \neq 0$, let $\boldsymbol{P}_1^*$ and $\boldsymbol{P}_1$, and $\boldsymbol{P}_2^*$ and $\boldsymbol{P}_2$ be coincident. Then the pair of hyperbolas (L_1, L_2) and the cubic spline S have equal second derivatives at each end-point. In this case, two ways can be given to determine the joint $\boldsymbol{P}_0$ uniquely:

(*i*) Setting

$$\int_{g \cap L \neq \varnothing} n\dot{g} = \int_{g \cap (L_1, L_2) \neq \varnothing} m\dot{g},$$

in which g is an arbitrary straight line, $\dot{g}$ represents the linear density, m is the number of intersections of g and (L_1, L_2), and n is the number of intersections of g and L (Su Buchin [8], 1980).

(*ii*) Setting

$$|y''_{01} - y''_{02}| = \min,$$

where y_{01} and y_{02} are the second derivatives of L_1 and L_2 at $\boldsymbol{P}_0$ respectively.

(2) For $M_1M_2 = 0$, say $M_1 = 0$ for example, then the choice

$$x_0 = x_1 + \frac{3\sqrt{2} - 2}{4}(x_2 - x_1)$$

makes (L_1, L_2) have C^2-continuity at the joint $\boldsymbol{P}_0$ and

$$|(y''_{11} - M_1) - (y''_{22} - M_2)| = \min,$$

where y''_{11} and y''_{22} represent the second derivatives of L_1 at $\boldsymbol{P}_1$ and L_2 at $\boldsymbol{P}_2$.

A pair of hyperbolas (L_1, L_2) approximates a cubic spline S better than the biarc does, as the former has eight intersections with S but the latter has only five. If such a method is applied to the numerical control plotter with a hyperbola interpolatory function under the same approximation precision, almost half of the drawing information will be saved that is important to improve the drawing speed and to decrease data storage.

6 Arc Splines

As mentioned in Section 4, to meet the needs of drawing information we have to use circular arcs to approximate the spline which interpolates the data points. This procedure is said to be postprocessing. Could we interpolate the data points directly by a GC^1-continuous arc spline? (Sun Jiachang [1], 1977.)

Let a set of data points $\boldsymbol{P}_i$ $(i=0, 1, \ldots, n)$ be given on a plane, let C_i be a circular arc passing through $\boldsymbol{P}_i$, and denote the tangent line at $\boldsymbol{P}_i$ by m_i. Then the problem of joining C_i and C_{i+1} with GC^1-continuity turns out to be the problem of joining the biarc under the conditions of given end-points and tangent lines m_i, m_{i+1}. The related formulas of biarcs can be used directly in this case, if the index i is added. To make the arc spline symmetric, the joint is chosen to be the point M_i, the intersection of the midperpendicular of $\boldsymbol{P}_i\boldsymbol{P}_{i+1}$ and the trajectory arc (see Fig. 6-16). According to the discussion in Section 4, we know that this is equivalent to $\delta = -(\theta_1^{(i+1)} + \theta_2^{(i+1)})/2$. Thus by (4.5) we derive the radius of C_i between $\boldsymbol{P}_i$ and $\boldsymbol{P}_{i+1}$ as

$$R_1^{(i+1)} = \frac{-L_{i+1}}{4 \sin \dfrac{3\theta_1^{(i+1)} + \theta_2^{(i+1)}}{4} \cos \dfrac{\theta_1^{(i+1)} - \theta_2^{(i+1)}}{4}}, \tag{6.1}$$

and the radius of C_i between $\boldsymbol{P}_{i-1}$ and $\boldsymbol{P}_i$ as

$$R_2^{(i)} = \frac{L_i}{4 \sin \dfrac{\theta_1^{(i)} + 3\theta_2^{(i)}}{4} \cos \dfrac{\theta_1^{(i)} - \theta_2^{(i)}}{4}}. \tag{6.2}$$

Actually the two arcs are two parts of a circle C_i, and they should have the

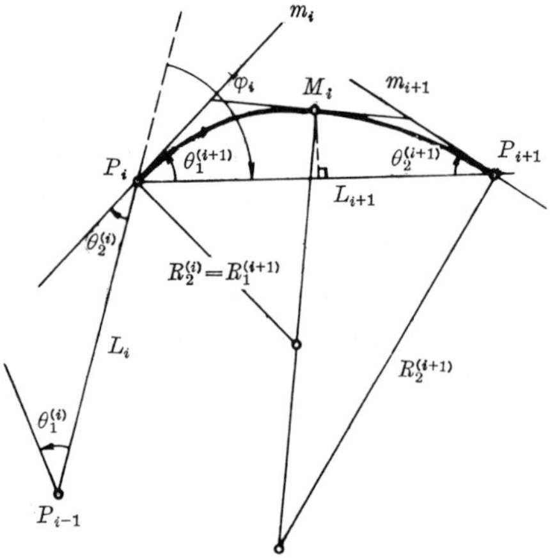

Figure 6-16

same tangent line and radius at $\boldsymbol{P}_i$. Therefore

$$\begin{aligned} \theta_2^{(i)} - \theta_1^{(i+1)} &= \phi_i; \\ R_2^{(i)} &= R_1^{(i+1)}. \end{aligned} \tag{6.3}$$

From (6.1), (6.2), (6.3), we have

$$-\lambda_i \sin\frac{\theta_{i-1}+3\theta_i+3\phi_i}{4}\cos\frac{\theta_{i-1}-\theta_i-\phi_i}{4}$$

$$= \mu_i \sin\frac{3\theta_i+\theta_{i+1}+\phi_{i+1}}{4}\cos\frac{\theta_i-\theta_{i+1}-\phi_{i+1}}{4} \qquad (i=1,2,\ldots,n-1), \tag{6.4}$$

in which $\theta_i \equiv \theta_1^{(i+1)}$, $\lambda_i = L_{i+1}/(L_i+L_{i+1})$, and $\mu_i = L_i/(L_i+L_{i+1})$.

It is difficult to solve the system of nonlinear equations (6.4) directly; linearization is needed. Expanding the trigonometric functions in (6.4) and separating from it the main part, through arrangement, we will obtain the θ-continuity equations of the arc spline

$$\lambda_i\theta_{i-1}+3\theta_i+\mu_i\theta_{i+1} = -3\lambda_i\phi_i - \mu_i\phi_{i+1} + H_i \qquad (i=1,2,\ldots,n), \tag{6.5}$$

in which

$$\begin{aligned} H_i \equiv{}& \mu_i\left[\theta_{i+1}+\phi_{i+1}-4\sin\frac{3\theta_i+\theta_{i+1}+\phi_{i+1}}{4}\cos\frac{\theta_i-\theta_{i+1}-\phi_{i+1}}{4}\right] \\ &+\lambda_i\left[\theta_{i-1}+3\phi_i-4\sin\frac{\theta_{i-1}+3\theta_i+3\phi_i}{4}\cos\frac{\theta_{i-1}-\theta_i-\phi_i}{4}\right]+3\theta_i. \end{aligned}$$

It is easily seen that $H_i = O(\phi^3)$ in which $\phi = \max_i|\phi_i|$ is an infinitesimal two orders higher than the main part $-3\lambda_i\phi_i - \mu_i\phi_{i+1}$. While adding two suitable end conditions, $\{\theta_i\}$ can be obtained from (6.5) by a simple iterative method. Substituting $\{\theta_i\}$ into (6.2), we obtain not only the radius of C_i at $\boldsymbol{P}_i$ but also the coordinates of the center of the circle C_i. Therefore GC^1-continuous interpolatory arc splines are established.

The θ-continuous equations (6.5) of the arc spline are very similar to those of the parametric cubic spline of cumulative chord length described in Chapter III. The only differences are the coefficients of the middle terms in the left-hand side of the equations and the higher-order terms. In the case of local small deflections, the convexity preserving ability of arc splines is slightly stronger than that of parametric cubic splines of cumulative chord length, but the fairness of the former is slightly worse. It can be shown that the order of approximation of arc splines is $O(\phi^3)$, one order less than that of the latter. Generally, arc splines are applicable to cases in which fairness is not much claimed.

The corresponding k-continuity equations of the arc spline are

$$\mu_i k_{i-1} + 3k_i + \lambda_i k_{i+1} = 4K_i + O(\phi^2) \qquad (i = 1, 2, \ldots, n-1), \tag{6.6}$$

in which k_i represents the curvature of C_i at $\boldsymbol{P}_i$, i.e., $1/R_2^{(i)}$, and K_i is the discrete curvature at $\boldsymbol{P}_i$.

Comparing arc splines with interpolatory quadratic splines discussed in Chapter II, we see that the θ-continuity equations and k-continuity equations of the arc splines correspond to the m-continuity equations and M-continuity equations of the quadratic splines. Similar statements can be made about local cubic splines and interpolatory cubic splines. The continuity equations of arc splines and local cubic splines involve only geometric quantities which are independent of coordinate systems, so that difficulties caused by large deflections are overcome by these splines. For convexity preserving there are similar conclusions.

Now we have seen that the splines in geometric form are much better than those in functional form in the requirement of geometric design. Certainly, the splines in geometric form also have their weakness, e.g., the difficulty of mathematical treatment brought by nonlinearity.

7 Local Spline Curves in Tension

In Chapter II, we derived a differential equation for the curvature k:

$$\frac{d^2k}{ds^2} - \rho^2 k = 0, \tag{7.1}$$

in which the tension parameter is $\rho > 0$, and s is the arc length parameter of the curve. Differing from Chapter II, we give up here the assumption of small deflections (Liu Dingyuan [2], 1979).

Take a segment of spline in tension between two adjacent data points $\boldsymbol{P}_1$ and $\boldsymbol{P}_2$. Assume that the curvatures at the end-points are k_1 and k_2, the total length of the segment is s_0 and the chord length is $L = \overline{\boldsymbol{P}_1\boldsymbol{P}_2}$. Then the solution of (7.1) is a hyperbolic function

$$k = k_1 \frac{\operatorname{sh} \rho(s_0 - s)}{\operatorname{sh} \rho s_0} + k_2 \frac{\operatorname{sh} \rho s}{\operatorname{sh} \rho s_0}. \tag{7.2}$$

Choosing a local orthogonal coordinate system $\{\boldsymbol{P}_1; x, y\}$, let the oriented angle between the tangent line of the segment at s and the x-axis be θ. Then

$$\theta = \int k\, ds = -k_1 \frac{\operatorname{ch} \rho(s_0 - s)}{\rho \operatorname{sh} \rho s_0} + k_2 \frac{\operatorname{ch} \rho s}{\rho \operatorname{sh} \rho s_0} + c, \tag{7.3}$$

where c is an integral constant. The equations of the segment in the coordinate system are

$$x=\int_0^s \cos\theta\, ds=\int_0^s [1+O(\theta^2)]\, ds=s+O(\theta^3),$$

$$y=\int_0^s \sin\theta\, ds=\int_0^s [\theta+O(\theta^3)]\, ds \tag{7.4}$$

$$=k_1\frac{\operatorname{sh}\rho(s_0-s)}{\rho^2\operatorname{sh}\rho s_0}+k_2\frac{\operatorname{sh}\rho s}{\rho^2\operatorname{sh}\rho s_0}+cs-\frac{k_1}{\rho^2}+O(\theta^4).$$

In (7.4), let $s=s_0$. Then the corresponding point on the segment is $\boldsymbol{P}_2(L, 0)$ and

$$c=\frac{k_1-k_2}{\rho^2 s_0}+O(\theta^3).$$

In (7.3), let $s=0$, s_0 respectively. We then obtain the tangent angles at the end-points $\boldsymbol{P}_1$ and $\boldsymbol{P}_2$:

$$\theta_1=-\frac{k_1}{\rho^2}\left(-\frac{1}{s_0}+\frac{\rho\operatorname{ch}\rho s_0}{\operatorname{sh}\rho s_0}\right)-\frac{k_2}{\rho^2}\left(\frac{1}{s_0}-\frac{\rho}{\operatorname{sh}\rho s_0}\right)+O(\theta^3),$$

$$\theta_2=\frac{k_1}{\rho^2}\left(\frac{1}{s_0}-\frac{\rho}{\operatorname{sh}\rho s_0}\right)+\frac{k_2}{\rho^2}\left(-\frac{1}{s_0}+\frac{\rho\operatorname{ch}\rho s_0}{\operatorname{sh}\rho s_0}\right)+O(\theta^3). \qquad (7.5$$

As

$$L=s_0+O(\theta^3),$$

s_0 in (7.5) can be replaced by L and the equality still holds, since the difference caused by the substitution is $O(\theta^3)$. Then we have

$$\theta_1=-dk_1-ek_2+O(\theta^3),$$

$$\theta_2=ek_1+dk_2+O(\theta^3), \tag{7.6}$$

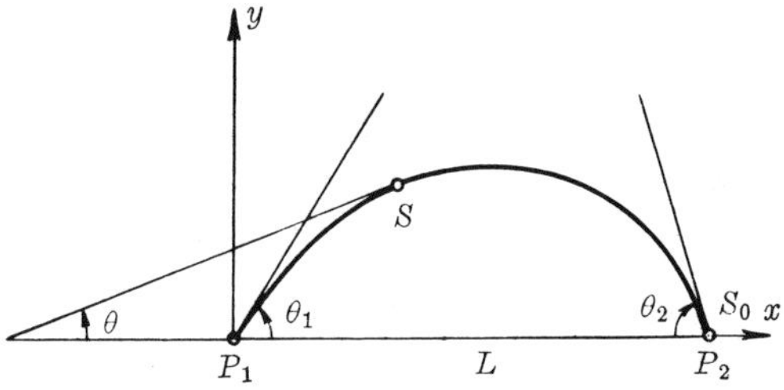

Figure 6-17

in which

$$e = \frac{1}{\rho^2}\left(\frac{1}{L} - \frac{\rho}{\text{sh } \rho L}\right), \qquad d = \frac{1}{\rho^2}\left(\frac{\rho \text{ ch } \rho L}{\text{sh } \rho L} - \frac{1}{L}\right).$$

Suppose a set of data points $\boldsymbol{P}_i$ $(i = 0, 1, \ldots, n)$ is given on the plane. To derive the continuity equations of the interpolatory spline in tension, we again adopt the method which we applied to deal with geometric splines. First adding an index i to (7.6), then using Fig. 6-4 and the relations (1.10), we get the k-continuity equations of the spline curve in tension:

$$e_i k_{i-1} + (d_i + d_{i+1})k_i + e_{i+1}k_{i+1} = \phi_i + O(\phi^3) \qquad (i = 1, 2, \ldots, n-1), \quad (7.7)$$

in which

$$e_i = \frac{1}{\rho_i^2}\left(\frac{1}{L_i} - \frac{\rho_i}{\text{sh } \rho_i L_i}\right),$$

$$d_i = \frac{1}{\rho_i^2}\left(\frac{\rho_i \text{ ch } \rho_i L_i}{\text{sh } \rho_i L_i} - \frac{1}{L_i}\right),$$

where ρ_i is the tension parameter between the data points $\boldsymbol{P}_{i-1}$ and $\boldsymbol{P}_i$ (the ith segment) and $\phi = \max_i |\phi_i|$. After adding two suitable end conditions, a complete system of continuity equations is obtained.

In application, we can omit the higher-order term $O(\phi^3)$ in (7.7) and write the resulting system of linear algebraic equations as (7.7)*. Similarly, we omit the higher-order terms $O(\phi^3)$ and $O(\theta^4)$ in (7.4) and change (7.4) into

$$y = k_{i-1}\frac{\text{sh } \rho_i(L_i - x)}{\rho_i^2 \text{ sh } \rho_i L_i} + k_i \frac{\text{sh } \rho_i x}{\rho_i^2 \text{ sh } \rho_i L_i} + \frac{k_{i-1} - k_i}{\rho_i^2 L_i} x - \frac{k_{i-1}}{\rho_i^2}. \quad (7.8)$$

The curvature of the spline curve, expressed by (7.8), in which the coefficients k_i are solved from (7.7)*, has a small jump of order $O(\theta^3)$ at the data point $\boldsymbol{P}_i$. Such small jumps are entirely negligible under the assumption of local small deflections. Such splines obtained by linearization are called *local spline curves in tension.* Relations between them and the spline functions in tension discussed in Chapter II is the same as between linearized local cubic spline curves and interpolatory cubic spline functions.

Similarly, the problem of choosing convexity preserving parameters $\{\rho_i\}$ is to solve the system of nonlinear inequalities

$$\phi_i > \frac{e_i}{d_{i-1} + d_i}\phi_{i-1} + \frac{e_{i+1}}{d_{i+1} + d_{i+2}}\phi_{i+1} \qquad (i = 0, 1, \ldots, n). \quad (7.9)$$

We can derive a sufficient condition for convexity preserving of the linearized local cubic spline:

$$K_i > \tfrac{1}{2}(\mu_i K_{i-1} + \lambda_i K_{i+1}) \qquad (i = 0, 1, \ldots, n), \tag{7.10}$$

where K_i represents the discrete curvature at the data point $\boldsymbol{P}_i$ (assuming that all the discrete curvatures are positive), and

$$\lambda_i = \frac{L_{i+1}}{L_i + L_{i+1}}, \qquad \mu_i = \frac{L_i}{L_i + L_{i+1}}.$$

8 Determination of the Tangent Line at a Data Point

For interpolation by biarcs or pairs of quadratic curves, it is necessary to assign the tangent line at each data point in advance. The problem can be solved, for example, by the solution of the continuity equations of linearized local cubic spline curves. To find the tangent line at a data point, all data points are involved.

Two local and explicit expressions for the tangent line at a data point will be presented in this section. The computation is rather simple, since by using three or five data points we can determine the tangent line at the middle data point. But the methods are experimental and lack theoretical background.

8.1 The Bessel Method

An orthogonal coordinate system on a plane is given. Let the given data points be $\boldsymbol{P}_i(x_i, y_i)$ $(i = 0, 1, \ldots, n)$. The first divided difference of two adjacent data points $\boldsymbol{P}_{i-1}$ and $\boldsymbol{P}_i$ is

$$D_i = \frac{y_i - y_{i-1}}{x_i - x_{i-1}}. \tag{8.1}$$

A quadratic polynomial interpolating to three points $\boldsymbol{P}_{i-1}$, $\boldsymbol{P}_i$ and $\boldsymbol{P}_{i+1}$ provides the slope of the tangent line at $\boldsymbol{P}_i$:

$$m_i = \lambda_i D_i + \mu_i D_{i+1} \qquad (i = 1, 2, \ldots, n-1), \tag{8.2}$$

in which

$$\lambda_i = \frac{h_{i+1}}{h_i + h_{i+1}}, \qquad \mu_i = \frac{h_i}{h_i + h_{i+1}}, \qquad h_i = x_i - x_{i-1}.$$

This is called the Bessel method.

8.2 The Akima Method

This method was first published in 1970. The slope of the tangent line at the data point $\boldsymbol{P}_i$ is given by

$$m_i = \alpha_i D_i + \beta_i D_{i+1} \qquad (i = 1, 2, \ldots, n-1), \tag{8.3}$$

in which

$$\alpha_i = \frac{W_{i+1}}{W_{i-1} + W_{i+1}}, \qquad \beta_i = \frac{W_{i-1}}{W_{i-1} + W_{i+1}}, \qquad W_i = |D_{i+1} - D_i|.$$

In both the Bessel and the Akima methods, the slope of the tangent line at $\boldsymbol{P}_i$ is taken to be the weighted mean of the slopes of two adjacent chords $\boldsymbol{P}_{i-1}\boldsymbol{P}_i$ and $\boldsymbol{P}_i\boldsymbol{P}_{i+1}$. The weight factors in the former involve only three points, $\boldsymbol{P}_{i-1}$, $\boldsymbol{P}_i$, and $\boldsymbol{P}_{i+1}$, while five points, $\boldsymbol{P}_{i-2}$, $\boldsymbol{P}_{i-1}$, $\boldsymbol{P}_i$, $\boldsymbol{P}_{i+1}$, and $\boldsymbol{P}_{i+2}$, are involved in the latter. Tangent lines determined by these methods lie in the oriented angle formed by rotating the vector $\overrightarrow{\boldsymbol{P}_{i-1}\boldsymbol{P}_i}$ to $\overrightarrow{\boldsymbol{P}_i\boldsymbol{P}_{i+1}}$.

The Akima method came from the following geometric consideration. Five data points, namely $\boldsymbol{P}_{i-2}$, $\boldsymbol{P}_{i-1}$, $\boldsymbol{P}_i$, $\boldsymbol{P}_{i+1}$, and $\boldsymbol{P}_{i+2}$, are shown in Fig. 6-18. Each two adjacent data points are joined by a line segment. Denote the intersection of the straight lines $\boldsymbol{P}_{i-1}\boldsymbol{P}_{i-2}$ and $\boldsymbol{P}_i\boldsymbol{P}_{i+1}$ by $\boldsymbol{B}_{-1}$, and the intersection of $\boldsymbol{P}_{i-1}\boldsymbol{P}_i$ and $\boldsymbol{P}_{i+1}\boldsymbol{P}_{i+2}$ by $\boldsymbol{B}_1$. The tangent line l_i at the middle data point $\boldsymbol{P}_i$ intersects the straight lines $\boldsymbol{P}_{i-1}\boldsymbol{P}_{i-2}$ and $\boldsymbol{P}_{i+1}\boldsymbol{P}_{i+2}$ at $\boldsymbol{A}_{-1}$ and $\boldsymbol{A}_1$ respectively. Originally the tangent l_i was determined by

$$\overline{\boldsymbol{P}_{i-1}\boldsymbol{A}_{-1}}/\overline{\boldsymbol{A}_{-1}\boldsymbol{B}_{-1}} = \overline{\boldsymbol{P}_{i+1}\boldsymbol{A}_1}/\overline{\boldsymbol{A}_1\boldsymbol{B}_1}. \tag{8.4}$$

In a suitable Cartesian coordinate system, (8.4) can be expressed in terms of coordinates. From the coordinate expression, it can be easily shown that the slope m_i of the tangent line l_i satisfies (8.3), but the coefficients α_i and

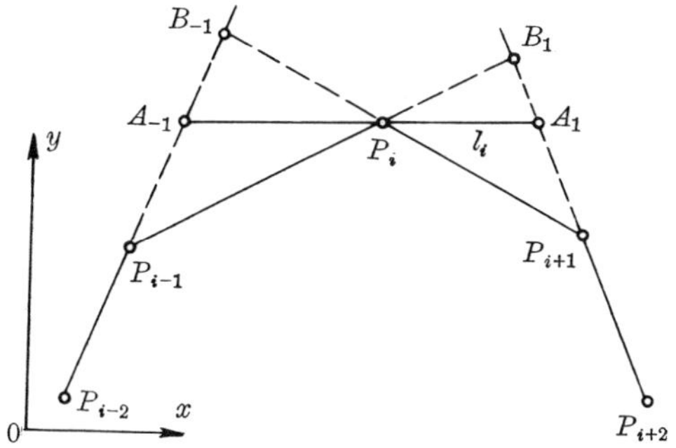

Figure 6-18

β_i should be replaced by

$$\alpha_i^* = \frac{U_i V_{i+1}}{U_i V_{i+1} + U_{i+1} V_{i-1}}, \qquad \beta_i^* = 1 - \alpha_i^*$$

where

$$U_i = \sqrt{|D_{i+1} - D_{i-1}|}, \qquad V_i = \sqrt{|D_{i+1} - D_i|}.$$

The weight factors α_i and β_i in the formulas below (8.3) are improved forms of α_i^* and β_i^* respectively.

The determinations of the slope m_i of the tangent line l_i by the above two methods certainly depend on coordinate systems. By "choosing a suitable Cartesian coordinate system" we mean to change the problem into the most suitable small deflection possible. In large-deflection cases, subtraction of two large numbers will be involved in the calculation of W_i, and thus the calculation is not stable. We have seen that when a method is too much dependent on the coordinate system, large-deflection problems often occur, whereas an effective method which can overcome the difficulty of large deflections is to geometrize the problem.

The geometrized procedure for the Bessel method is the following. Write the slope and the first divided difference in terms of the corresponding angle, and replace the difference h_i of the x-coordinates by the distance $L_i = \overline{\boldsymbol{P}_{i-1}\boldsymbol{P}_i}$ in Fig. 6-19 by setting

$$\theta_i = \lambda_i \phi_i, \tag{8.5}$$

in which $\lambda_i = L_{i+1}/(L_i + L_{i+1})$. Thus we determine the tangent line l_i at the point P_i.

Note that θ_i and ϕ_i in (8.5) are angles without orientations. The tangent line l_i obtained in such a way coincides with that at $\boldsymbol{P}_i$ of the circle passing through the three points $\boldsymbol{P}_{i-1}$, $\boldsymbol{P}_i$ and $\boldsymbol{P}_{i+1}$, in the sense that $O(\phi_i^3)$ is neglected.

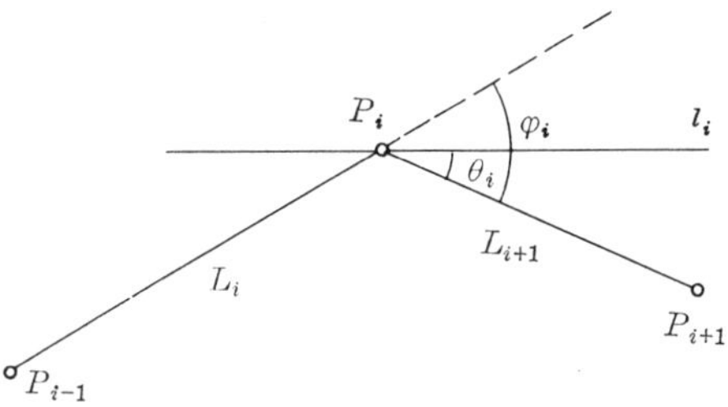

Figure 6-19

For the Akima method, we can determine the tangent line l_i at the point $\boldsymbol{P}_i$ also by (8.5), but the weight factor should be replaced by the geometric quantity in area form,

$$\lambda_i = \frac{W_{i+1}}{W_{i-1} + W_{i+1}}, \qquad W_i = |\overrightarrow{\boldsymbol{P}_{i-1}\boldsymbol{P}_i} \times \overrightarrow{\boldsymbol{P}_i\boldsymbol{P}_{i+1}}|.$$

Based on the Bessel and Akima algorithms, we can establish two C^1 interpolants of piecewise cubics by using Hermite interpolation between each two adjacent data points. It has been shown that the orders of approximation are $O(h^3)$ and $O(h^2)$ for the Bessel and Akima methods respectively, where $h = \max_i h_i$. Recall that the order of approximation for the interpolatory cubic spline function is $O(h^4)$ and that the cubic splines approximate quite well to the wooden spline with satisfactory fairness.

Consideration of the approximation orders suggests that the spline curves constructed by the Bessel and Akima methods may not be desirable for their fairness.

CHAPTER VII

Curves and Net Fairing

1 Conditions for Fairing

We discussed interpolatory spline functions and curves in Chapters II, III and VI. The concept of "fairness" of a curve was touched on in brief. The fact that an interpolatory curve that mimics a wooden spline is the "fairest" curve has been justified. But to get a fair curve, it is only the first step to set up a mathematical model of a wooden spline. To determine whether a set of data points is fair or not remains a problem. Suppose we are given a group of data points with a zigzag distribution. Then whichever kind of spline curve is used to interpolate the given data points, the resulting curve must be undulant and cannot be called a fair one. So it is natural to raise the question, What is a fair set of data points and how do we get it?

In mathematical lofting the information of a geometric shape is given by a set of data points, while in geometric design other ways of representations are available. For instance, a Bézier surface or a B-spline surface can be characterized by its characteristic net. In car, aircraft, and shipbuilding industries, a fair geometric shape is expected through the shape computation process. And this leads to the question, What is the definition of a fair shape? How do we generate a fair shape? In this chapter, we will give answers to these questions. The first question is to be discussed in this section.

Definition 1 A plane curve is called *fair* if the following three conditions are satisfied:

(1) The curve is of GC^2-continuity;
(2) There are no unwanted inflection-points on the curve;
(3) The curvature of the curve varies in an even manner.

Condition (1) is the concept of smoothness. Since it only concerns a small neighborhood of a point on the curve, it reflects the local property of the curve. Conditions (2) and (3) are global concepts which concern the whole curve, so they are more difficult and complicated to deal with. In practice, the overall fairness property is more important than local smoothness. In Chapter VI, we gave up the strict GC^2-continuity in the interpolation of biarcs. Even though a small jump in curvature occurs at the joint of the curve, it could not be recognized. Conversely, if two unwanted inflection points occur on a flat segment, however little undulant they are, the curve will be inelegant.

Condition (2) can be used to control the change of convexity and concavity of a curve to minimize the number of inflection points on the curve. For example, the sine curve is smooth, but it cannot be called a fair curve, because there are many inflection points on it.

Condition (3) takes charge of controlling the local fullness of a curve, places that are full or, conversely, are just the positions of the local extreme points of the curvature of the curve. More specifically, this condition has the following implications:

(*i*) The number of extreme points of the curvature should be as small as possible.
(*ii*) The curvature of the curve between two adjacent extreme points should vary almost linearly.

The geometric spline and its approximate linearization of the first order, i.e., the local cubic spline (including the parametric cubic spline of cumulative chord length) discussed in the last chapter, are suitable mathematical analogues of the wooden spline. If we choose them to be the interpolatory spline, (*ii*) is satisfied. As for (*i*), we will discuss it in the next section along with curve fairing.

Let us compare curve I with curve II in Fig. 7-1. Obviously, there is only one curvature extreme point on curve I, which is marked by a cross. For curve II, there are three crosses. Although there are no inflection points on either curve, curve II fails to be fair.

In the case of space curves, another definition for a fair curve is unnecessary. We need only project a space curve to three planes which are orthogonal each other and regard the fair conditions for the three projected curves as the ones for the space curve.

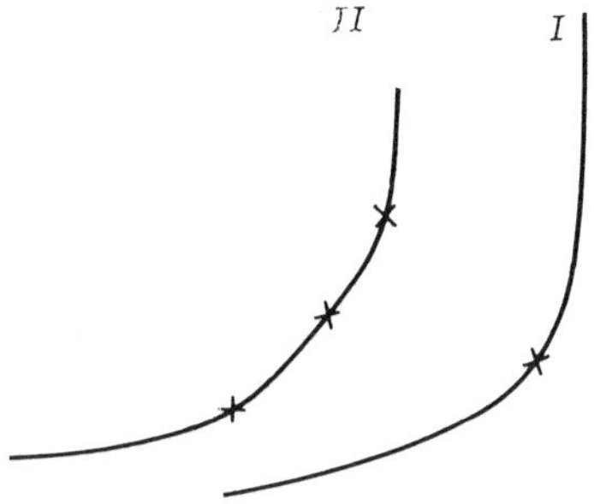

Figure 7-1

There are few articles on surface fair conditions. One suggestion is made as follows. If the curve, which is the cross-section of an arbitrary plane and the surface, is fair, then the surface is said to be fair. But this condition is not applicable. In practical applications, to justify whether a surface is fair or not, only two or three families of network curves on the surface are concerned.

In geometric design, to make use of fair conditions, we may settle in advance on the number of inflection points and the range in which they exist. Therefore for condition (2) we will have some quantitative information. Although many methods are available, we recommend the cubic B-spline curves and surfaces, because the fairness property for B-spline curves can be easily governed by their characteristic polygons (for details, see section 3.3 in Chapter IV).

Unlike geometric design, in the mathematical lofting of geometric shapes such as ship hull lofting, we deal with data points given by the ship design department. It is necessary to give a standard for fair data points.

Definition 2 A set of data points $\{\boldsymbol{P}_i\}$ given on a plane is said to be fair if there exists at least one fair curve which interpolates to the data points.

In the mathematical lofting of a geometric shape, we not only make the original data points fair but also minimize the difference between the modified data points and the original ones so as to guarantee that the main standards (such as the displacement of the ship) are unaffected.

Let a group of data points $\{\boldsymbol{P}_i\}$ be given. Interpolation means to generate a curve which passes through every point of $\{\boldsymbol{P}_i\}$. If the resulting curve does not pass through the points exactly but only lies close to them, it is called a *fitting curve.* We need some other conditions to establish the rules for the way that a curve approximates the data points. The content of this chapter is, in fact, the method of curve fitting associated with fairness conditions. Surely, interpolation can be regarded as a special case of fitting.

2 Curve Fairing

The methods of curve fairing introduced in this section are mainly for use in the mathematical lofting of geometric shapes. The process involves the modification of original data points given by the design department, which may not be sufficiently fair, and constructing a fair curve which fits the data points.

The discrete curvature method and the energy method deal with data points and fit curves in such a way that they are independent of the choice of coordinate system, i.e., they are perfectly geometrical. Therefore, they are applied to large-deflection curves or closed curves. Other methods are only suitable for small-deflection curves. The energy method uses the parametric cubic spline of cumulative chord length as the fitting curve, so it has the advantage of fairing space curves directly.

Another characteristic of the discrete curvature method is that the interpolatory curve is not needed in the entire process of fairing. It implies that by searching the geometric positions of the data points directly, the "bad" points can be found quickly and the modification can be calculated. Thus it has a reputation for its simplicity and swiftness.

The least-squares method, energy method, and bounce method all have an overall modification nature, whose fairing processes involve all the data points. The cardinal spline and discrete curvature methods are point-choosing methods, i.e., good points are left unchanged, and only the bad ones are modified. Moreover, modifications are made as small as possible. These two methods have been used by the Jiangnan and Hudong Shipbuilding Factories for many years.

In this section, several influential curve fairing methods are discussed. Essentially, there are some intrinsic relationships among these methods.

2.1 The Least-Squares Method

In the early 1960s, when mathematical ship-hull lofting was in its infancy, the method of least squares was an influential one. Here we summarize its main points.

Suppose a set of data points $\boldsymbol{P}_i(x_i, y_i)$ $(i = 0, \ldots, n)$ is given on the plane. We then get a partition of the interval $[a, b]$ on the x-axis:

$$\Delta: a = x_0 < x_1 < \cdots < x_n = b.$$

A cubic spline defined on the partition Δ takes the form of a truncated power series, as

$$S(x)=\sum_{i=0}^{3} c \quad a_i x^i+\sum_{i=1}^{n-1} b_i(x-x_i)_+^3 \qquad x\in[a, b], \tag{2.1}$$

where we set

$$x_+=x, \qquad x>0,$$

$$x_+=0, \qquad x\leqslant 0.$$

The $n+3$ coefficients $\{a_i\}$ and $\{b_i\}$ are uniquely determined in such a way that the object function I takes its minimum. Now we get a cubic spline $S(x)$ which passes through the original data points approximately. It is called the *least-square fairing curve.* The points $\boldsymbol{P}_i^*(x_i, S(x_i))$ $(i=0, \ldots, n)$ are called *faired* data points.

Generally, the object function is

$$I\equiv\sum_{i=0}^{n} \alpha_i[S(x_i)-y_i]^2+\sum_{i=1}^{n-1} \beta_i b_i^2, \tag{2.2}$$

in which $2n$ positive weight factors α_i $(i=0, \ldots, n)$ and β_i $(i=1, \ldots, n-1)$ are assigned in advance by the designer. From the analysis of the following two extreme cases, we can recognize the concrete significance of these factors.

(1) When all $\beta_i=0$ and $\alpha_i\neq 0$, since $I=\min$, we have

$$S(x_i)=y_i \qquad (i=0, \ldots, n).$$

Thus (2.1) turns into a cubic interpolatory spline. This means that the cubic spline passes through the data points $\{\boldsymbol{P}_i\}$ $(i=0, \ldots, n)$ exactly. Therefore it implies that there are no modifications made to the data points $\{\boldsymbol{P}_i\}$ after the fairing process.

(2) When all the $\alpha_i=0$ and $\beta_i\neq 0$, from $I=\min$, we immediately get that

$$b_i=0 \qquad (i=1, \ldots, n-1),$$

so (2.1) becomes a cubic polynomial on the whole interval $[a, b]$:

$$S(x)=\sum_{i=0}^{3} a_i x^i.$$

The coefficients b_i $(i=0, \ldots, n)$, the concentrated load of $S(x)$, are all zero. Thus in this case the spline $S(x)$ is the fairest one.

For the cases in between, we can see from the contrast of $\{a_i\}$ and $\{\beta_i\}$, the larger the coefficients $\{\alpha_i\}$ are, the less the difference between the faired data points and the original ones will be, but the fairness of the curve may be poor since b_i is large. On the other hand, when $\{\beta_i\}$ are set to be large numbers, b_i becomes small and the curve is fair at the cost of much difference between $S(x_i)$ and y_i, which brings about a poor approximation. We will call $\{\alpha_i\}$ and $\{\beta_i\}$ the *weight of difference* and the *weight of fairness* respectively. In applications, it is the designer who compromises these two aspects. Conventionally, experience plays an important part in the process.

Substituting (2.1) into (2.2), the object function becomes a function of $n+3$ coefficients in the spline $S(x)$:

$$I = I(a_0, \ldots, a_3; b_1, \ldots, b_{n-1}).$$

Thus the problem of minimizing the object function I is transformed into a problem of solving a system of linear equations for $n+3$ unknowns $a_0, \ldots, a_3$, and $b_1, \ldots, b_{n-1}$, i.e.,

$$\begin{aligned} \frac{\partial I}{\partial a_i} &= 0 \qquad (i=0, \ldots, 3), \\ \frac{\partial I}{\partial b_j} &= 0 \qquad (j=1, \ldots, n-1). \end{aligned} \tag{2.3}$$

It can be proved that the solution to (2.3) uniquely exists. Moreover, if we use cubic B-splines as the basis functions instead of a truncated power series, the stability in calculating (2.3) will be improved.

2.2 The Energy Method

In 1969, a curve fairing method was proposed by Hosaka based on the energy extremum principle, which is applicable to space curves and large-deflection cases. Its main idea is similar to the least-squares method, i.e., compromising fairness with difference. But it has variations, i.e.,

(1) The parametric cubic spline of cumulative chord length is used as a fitting curve.
(2) The energy integration of the spline takes the place of the concentrated load in the object function.

The mechanical model of the energy method is rather intuitive. A set of data points $\boldsymbol{Q}_i$ $(i=0, \ldots, n)$ is given, which is to be faired, an elastic string which interpolates to the faired data points $\boldsymbol{P}_i$ $(i=0, \ldots, n)$ can be obtained, and a small spring with elastic coefficient α_i is suspended between $\boldsymbol{P}_i$ and $\boldsymbol{Q}_i$ (see Fig. 7-2). Thus we have a system which consists of the string and small springs. Its potential energy is expressed by

$$U=\tfrac{1}{2}\sum_{i=0}^{n}\alpha_i(\boldsymbol{P}_i-\boldsymbol{Q}_i)^2+\tfrac{1}{2}(EI)^2\int k^2\,ds, \tag{2.4}$$

where the constant EI represents the rigidity of the elastic string.

The elastic string which passes through $\{\boldsymbol{P}_i\}$ is taken to be a parametric cubic spline of cumulative chord length. We make an assumption that the fitting curve always has a local small deflection in the discussion of the energy method. So, as we have studied before, linearization is to be made in calculating the arc length and curvature of a curve.

According to Chapter III, the parametric cubic spline curve of cumulative chord length which passes through $\{\boldsymbol{P}_i\}$ has its representation as follows: the segment between $\boldsymbol{P}_{i-1}$ and $\boldsymbol{P}_i$ is

$$\boldsymbol{P}(t)=[1,(t-t_{i-1}),(t-t_{i-1})^2,(t-t_{i-1})^3]$$

$$\cdot\begin{bmatrix}1 & 0 & 0 & 0\\ 0 & 0 & 1 & 0\\ -\dfrac{3}{l_i^2} & \dfrac{3}{l_i^2} & -\dfrac{2}{l_i} & -\dfrac{1}{l_i}\\ \dfrac{2}{l_i^3} & -\dfrac{2}{l_i^3} & \dfrac{1}{l_i^2} & \dfrac{1}{l_i^2}\end{bmatrix}\begin{bmatrix}\boldsymbol{P}_{i-1}\\ \boldsymbol{P}_i\\ \boldsymbol{m}_{i-1}\\ \boldsymbol{m}_i\end{bmatrix},\qquad t_{i-1}\leqslant t\leqslant t_i, \tag{2.5}$$

in which

$$t_i=\sum_{j=1}^{i} l_j,\qquad l_j=|\boldsymbol{P}_j-\boldsymbol{P}_{j-1}|,\qquad \boldsymbol{m}_i=\left.\frac{d\boldsymbol{P}}{dt}\right|_{t=t_i},$$

$$\boldsymbol{M}_i=\left.\frac{d^2\boldsymbol{P}}{dt^2}\right|_{t=t_i}\qquad (i,j=1,\ldots,n).$$

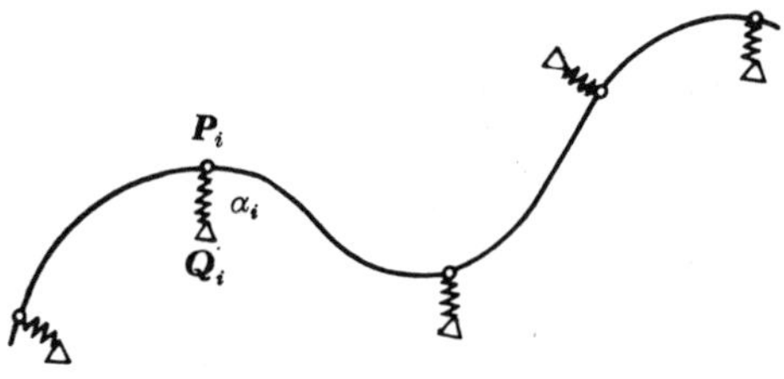

Figure 7-2

The relation between the first derivative vector and the second derivative vector can be described by

$$\begin{aligned} \boldsymbol{M}_i &= -\frac{2}{l_i}(3\boldsymbol{e}_i - \boldsymbol{m}_{i-1} - 2\boldsymbol{m}_i) \\ &= \frac{2}{l_{i+1}}(3\boldsymbol{e}_{i+1} - 2\boldsymbol{m}_i - \boldsymbol{m}_{i+1}), \end{aligned} \tag{2.6}$$

in which the unit vector $\boldsymbol{e}_i = (\boldsymbol{P}_i - \boldsymbol{P}_{i-1})/l_i$ is on the chord.

Now we take the linearizations to the arc length s and the curvature k of the curve to be

$$ds \approx dt, \qquad k^2 = \left(\frac{d^2\boldsymbol{P}}{ds^2}\right)^2 \approx \left(\frac{d^2\boldsymbol{P}}{dt^2}\right)^2.$$

Thus the energy function (2.4) is approximately expressed as

$$U = \tfrac{1}{2}\sum_{i=0}^{n} \alpha_i(\boldsymbol{P}_i - \boldsymbol{Q}_i)^2 + \tfrac{1}{2}(EI)^2 \sum_{i=1}^{n} \int_{t_{i-1}}^{t_i} \left(\frac{d^2\boldsymbol{P}}{dt^2}\right)^2 dt. \tag{2.7}$$

By substituting (2.5) into (2.7), we turn the energy U into a function of $\{\boldsymbol{P}_i\}$ and $\{\boldsymbol{m}_i\}$. If we choose $\{\boldsymbol{P}_i\}$ and $\{\boldsymbol{m}_i\}$ to make $U = \min$ then we can conclude that

$$\left.\begin{aligned} \frac{\partial U}{\partial \boldsymbol{P}_i} &= 0, \\ \frac{\partial U}{\partial \boldsymbol{m}_i} &= 0, \end{aligned}\right\} \quad (i = 0, \ldots, n). \tag{2.8}$$

Introducing (2.5) and (2.6) and using integration by parts, we have

$$\frac{\partial}{\partial \boldsymbol{P}_{i-1}}\left[\frac{1}{2}\int_{t_{i-1}}^{t_i}\left(\frac{d^2\boldsymbol{P}}{dt^2}\right)^2 dt\right] = \frac{1}{l_i}(\boldsymbol{M}_i - \boldsymbol{M}_{i-1}),$$

$$\frac{\partial}{\partial \boldsymbol{P}_{i}}\left[\frac{1}{2}\int_{t_{i-1}}^{t_i}\left(\frac{d^2\boldsymbol{P}}{dt^2}\right)^2 dt\right] = -\frac{1}{l_i}(\boldsymbol{M}_i - \boldsymbol{M}_{i-1}),$$

$$\frac{\partial}{\partial \boldsymbol{m}_{i-1}}\left[\frac{1}{2}\int_{t_{i-1}}^{t_i}\left(\frac{d^2\boldsymbol{P}}{dt^2}\right)^2 dt\right] = -\boldsymbol{M}_{i-1},$$

$$\frac{\partial}{\partial \boldsymbol{m}_{i}}\left[\frac{1}{2}\int_{t_{i-1}}^{t_i}\left(\frac{d^2\boldsymbol{P}}{dt^2}\right)^2 dt\right] = \boldsymbol{M}_i.$$

Hence (2.8) becomes

$$\begin{aligned} \boldsymbol{P}_i &= \boldsymbol{Q}_i - \beta_i \Delta^2 \boldsymbol{M}_i, \\ \boldsymbol{M}_i(-) &= \boldsymbol{M}_i(+), \end{aligned} \qquad (i = 1, \ldots, n-1), \tag{2.9}$$

in which

$$\beta_i = \frac{1}{\alpha_i}(EI)^2, \qquad \Delta^2 f_i = \frac{f_{i+1} - f_i}{l_{i+1}} - \frac{f_i - f_{i-1}}{l_i}.$$

The second equation in (2.9) actually indicates the continuity of the second derivative vector of a spline at the inner knot. Since a parametric cubic spline of cumulative chord length is C^2-continuous, this requirement is satisfied automatically. Conversely, it is a consequence of the hypothesis, $U = \min$, that the curve has C^2-continuity for a parametric cubic spline of cumulative chord length. This shows that, for a spline, the C^2-continuity relates closely to the fairness. In other words, the global fairness of a curve depends on the local C^2-continuity.

We may rewrite the second equation in (2.9) in the form of the M-continuity equations (6.5) which appeared in Chapter III.

$$\mu_i \boldsymbol{M}_{i-1} + 2\boldsymbol{M}_i + \lambda_i \boldsymbol{M}_{i+1} = \frac{6}{l_i + l_{i+1}} \Delta^2 \boldsymbol{P}_i \qquad (i = 1, \ldots, n-1).$$

Eliminating $\boldsymbol{P}_i$ in the first equation in (2.9), we obtain

$$\mu_i \boldsymbol{M}_{i-1} + 2\boldsymbol{M}_i + \lambda_i \boldsymbol{M}_{i+1} + \frac{6}{l_i + l_{i+1}} \Delta^2(\beta_i \Delta^2 \boldsymbol{M}_i) = \frac{6}{l_i + l_{i+1}} \Delta^2 \boldsymbol{Q}_i \qquad (i = 1, \ldots, n-1). \tag{2.10}$$

(2.10) is a system of algebraic equations with respect to $\{\boldsymbol{M}_i\}$ associated with suitable end conditions, in which $\lambda_i = l_{i+1}/(l_i + l_{i+1})$, $\mu_i = l_i/(l_i + l_{i+1})$. In the course of curve fairing, the modification of data points $|\boldsymbol{P}_i - \boldsymbol{Q}_i|$ is relatively small compared with the length of the chord, so the length of a chord can be taken as approximately $l_i = |\boldsymbol{Q}_i - \boldsymbol{Q}_{i-1}|$.

The computation proceeds as follows. First we solve for $\{\boldsymbol{M}_i\}$ from (2.10) according to the first equation in (2.9). The faired data points $\{\boldsymbol{P}_i\}$ are obtained. We then solve for $\{\boldsymbol{m}_i\}$ from (2.6). At last we get (2.5), which represents the resulting fair fitting curve.

The energy method can easily be generalized to two-dimensional net fairing, but we shall leave this discussion for the next section.

The energy method and the least-squares method differ in the choice of object function. The former chooses the energy of a wooden spline, but the latter takes the sum of the squares of the concentrated load. But in nature, these two methods are consistent. We rewrite the first equation in (2.9) as

$$|\boldsymbol{P}_i - \boldsymbol{Q}_i| = \beta_i |\Delta^2 \boldsymbol{M}_i|. \tag{2.11}$$

The right-hand side of the equality, $|\Delta^2 \boldsymbol{M}_i|$, is the concentrated load at $\boldsymbol{P}_i$, while the left-hand side represents the amount of modification of the data points. They differ by a proportional factor β_i. This implies that when the concentrated load of a spline curve is small, either the least-squares method or the energy method can be used to fair the curve, and the difference in the data points will be small.

2.3 The Bounce Method

In ship-hull mathematical lofting, Zhejiang University proposed a new curve fairing method, the *bounce method.* That is, by fixing the bouncing of two groups of data points in turns, we decrease the energy of the spline so as to make it fair (Dong Guangchang *et al.*, 1978).

Let a group of data points $P_i(x_i, y_i)$ $(i = 0, 1, \ldots, n)$ on a plane and appropriate end conditions be given. The bounce method proceeds in five steps.

(1) For a given partition

$$\Delta: a = x_0 < x_1 < \cdots < x_n = b$$

and data points $\{\boldsymbol{P}_i(x_i, y_i)\}$, we construct a cubic interpolatory spline $S(x)$.

(2) Calculating the mid-point of every two adjacent knots,

$$\xi_i = \tfrac{1}{2}(x_i + x_{i+1}) \qquad (i = 0, \ldots, n-1),$$

set $\xi_{-1} = a$, $\xi_n = b$ and evaluate $S(\xi_i)$.

(3) For another partition,

$$\Delta^*: a = \xi_{-1} < \xi_0 < \cdots < \xi_{n-1} < \xi_n = b$$

and data points $\{\boldsymbol{Q}_i(\xi_i, S(\xi_i))\}$ $(i = -1, 0, \ldots, n)$, we construct an interpolatory cubic spline $S^*(x)$.

(4) The points $\boldsymbol{P}_i^*(x_i, S^*(x_i))$ $(i = 0, \ldots, n)$ are called new data points.

(5) Repeat the above four steps until the following conditions are satisfied:

$$|S^*(x_i) - S(x_i)| < \varepsilon \qquad (i = 0, \ldots, n),$$

where the constant ε has been given. The data points and cubic spline obtained in the last step are taken as the fair data points and curve respectively. Generally $\varepsilon = 3$ mm is used in mathematical ship-hull lofting.

Note that while constructing the cubic splines $S(x)$ and $S^*(x)$, the end conditions remain unchanged throughout the whole process.

The method described above is called the mid-point bounce method, which is the foundation of the bounce method. The knots in step (2) can be taken as weighted means, which gives a reformulation of the mid-point bounce method:

$$\xi_i = \alpha_i x_i + (1-\alpha_i)x_{i+1} \qquad (i=0,\ldots,n-1),$$

where the weight factor $\alpha_i \in (0, 1)$, which is set in such a way that $\alpha_i/(1-\alpha_i)$ equals the proportion of the concentrated load at x_i and x_{i+1}.

Intuitively, through the bounce process, the energy of a spline decreases gradually and the curve tends to be fair. So the bounce method can be regarded as an energy method of an iterative approximation.

The bounce method is easily applicable with a satisfactory fairing effect and has explicit mechanical significance. But the number of iterations should not be large, lest the differences between the original data points and the faired ones be too large. Moreover, small undulations on the segment are difficult to remove.

2.4 The Cardinal Spline Method

When we use curve fairing conditions in the mathematical lofting of a ship-hull, a prerequisite should be made clear, i.e., the data points provided by the design department are mostly "good" points, and only a few data points need to be modified to generate a fair geometric shape.

The cardinal spline method and the discrete curvature method are both point-choosing modification methods. The basic hypothesis of a point-choosing modification method is that most data points are good points. The method selects a few "bad" points and then modifies them. The method has the following advantages:

(1) Only bad data points are modified.
(2) The curve fairing conditions are strictly satisfied without small undulations on the flat segment.
(3) The method has a rather powerful modification ability.

These methods are applicable to geometric shape fairing since most data points of such problems are good points. But in data fitting, we use a global fairing method, since it is difficult to distinguish good points from bad ones because of the influence of random error and systematic error.

We now introduce the cardinal spline method in detail.

First we quantify the three curve fairing conditions given in the previous section.

(1) Given data points $P_i(x_i, y_i)$ $(i=0,\dots,n)$ and end conditions y'_0, y'_n we get a cubic interpolatory spline $S(x)$ in terms of cardinal splines. It satisfies the C^2-continuity requirements. From Section 1.3 in Chapter II, we have

$$S(x)=\sum_{i=0}^{n} y_i\phi_i(x)+y'_0\phi_{n+1}(x)+y'_n\phi_{n+2}(x), \tag{2.12}$$

where $\{\phi_i(x)\}$ represents the cubic cardinal spline set.

(2) Calculating the second derivative at every knot x_i $(i=0,1,\dots,n)$, $M_i=S''(x_i)$, we get a set of signs $\{\text{sign}(M_i)\}$. A point which makes this set change signs successively is called a bad one. The aim of data-point fairing is to eliminate the bad points. This step is called *rough fairing*, and has the effect of removing the unwanted inflection points.

(3) Calculating the first-order difference of M_i, $\Delta M_i=M_i-M_{i-1}$, we then make a set of signs of $\{\Delta M_i\}$, i.e., $\{\text{sign}(\Delta M_i)\}$. A point is termed to be *bad* if, as in (2), it makes the set change signs successively. This step is called *fine fairing*, and has the effect of smoothing the variation of curvature of a curve.

For example, in the set $+++-++++$, the fourth point is a bad one. We have to change the fourth point (or maybe the third or the fifth one) to make the sign of the set be positive. The set $+++----++$, on the other hand, is regarded as a fair one.

Generally, suppose $P_k(x_k, y_k)$ is a bad point, and it is modified to be $P^*_k(x_k, y_k+\rho_k)$ with other data points unchanged. The resulting cubic spline $S^*(x)$ relates to $S(x)$ in the following way:

$$S^*(x)=S(x)+\rho_k\phi_k(x). \tag{2.13}$$

We wish to solve the following equation:

$$B^*\equiv\sum_{i=1}^{n-1} b_i^{*2}=\min, \tag{2.14}$$

where b_i^* is the concentrated load of $S^*(x)$ at $\boldsymbol{P}_i$. In other words, we minimize the sum of the bounce force at every duck to fair a curve.

According to the definition,

$$b_i^* = S^{*'''}(x_i+0) - S^{*'''}(x_i-0).$$

Denote the concentrated load of $S(x)$ and the cardinal spline $\phi_k(x)$ at the knot x_i by b_i and $\bar{b}_i$ respectively. Then from (2.13),

$$b_i^* = b_i + \rho_k \bar{b}_i. \tag{2.15}$$

Equation (2.14) can be rewritten as

$$\frac{dB^*}{d\rho_k} = 0,$$

i.e.,

$$\sum_{i=1}^{n-1} (b_i + \rho_k \bar{b}_i)\bar{b}_i = 0.$$

Thus,

$$\rho_k = -\frac{\sum_{i=1}^{n-1} b_i \bar{b}_i}{\sum_{i=1}^{n-1} \bar{b}_i^2}, \tag{2.16}$$

where $\sum_{i=1}^{n-1} \bar{b}_i^2$ is a non-zero constant related to the partition, according to the property of cardinal splines $\{\phi_k(x)\}$ in Section 4 of this chapter.

In most cases, the fairing process of the kth point modification reaches the fairness requirement, but there is another possibility, that modification of the $(k-1)^{\text{th}}$ point or the $(k+1)^{\text{th}}$ point would give a better result. Thus, we may figure out modified values ρ_{k-1}, ρ_k, ρ_{k+1}, respectively, then compare the three corresponding B^*s and choose the point which minimizes the B^* of the three as the new data point.

In the fairing process, all the bad points are selected to be modified. First, rough fairing proceeds until condition (2) is satisfied. Then fine fairing is carried out to fulfill condition (3).

The cardinal spline method uses the sum of the squares of the concentrated load of the spline as the object function, while the energy method chooses the energy. Though these two object functions are not the same in form, they are consistent in effect. We give an analysis of this fact in sketch.

Since the point $\boldsymbol{P}_k$ to be modified is a bad one, its concentrated load, b_k, is larger than other points. On the other hand, from the property of cubic cardinal splines introduced in Chapter II, we know that if the distribution of knots is even, the absolute value of the concentrated load $\bar{b}_k$ of the cardinal spline $\phi_k(x)$ takes its maximum at $\boldsymbol{P}_k$, then $\bar{b}_i$ at $\boldsymbol{P}_i$ decreases at the rate of $\lambda^{|i-k|}$, where $\lambda \approx -0.268$. Therefore according to (2.16), the modification made by the cardinal spline method is approximately

$$\rho_k \approx -\frac{1}{\bar{b}_k} b_k.$$

Comparing this to the energy method, from (2.11), we see that the proportional factor β_k of the energy has its counterpart $-1/\bar{b}_k$ in the cardinal spline method. The main difference in the two methods is that one method is a global fairing, the other is a point-choosing modification.

Since 1974, when Su Buchin *et al.* put forward the cardinal spline method, the Jiangnan Shipbuilding Factory has used this method for mathematical lofting, and it has proved to have a satisfactory fairing effect. Now that we have discussed the fairing method for curves, we will introduce surface fairing in three directions in the next section, where the cardinal spline method is generalized.

2.5 The Discrete Curvature Method

The discrete curvature method is also a point-choosing modification method. The interpolatory curve is not needed in the course of fairing. Like the energy method, a coordinate system is not necessarily introduced in the fairing process, so there is no problem of a large deflection.

Given data points $\boldsymbol{P}_i$ $(i=0, \ldots, n)$ and two boundary tangent vectors $\boldsymbol{m}_0$ and $\boldsymbol{m}_n$, the discrete curvature at $\boldsymbol{P}_i$, K_i, is defined to be the relative curvature of the circle which passes through three adjacent points $\boldsymbol{P}_{i-1}$, $\boldsymbol{P}_i$, $\boldsymbol{P}_{i+1}$. When the arc $\boldsymbol{P}_{i-1}\boldsymbol{P}_i\boldsymbol{P}_{i+1}$ runs clockwise, K_i is negative, and vice versa. At the end-point $\boldsymbol{P}_0$, the discrete curvature K_0 is determined by the circle which passes through $\boldsymbol{P}_0$, $\boldsymbol{P}_1$ and having tangent vector $\boldsymbol{m}_0$ at $\boldsymbol{P}_0$. K_n is defined in a similar way. Thus we get a set of discrete curvatures $\{K_i\}$ corresponding to data points $\{\boldsymbol{P}_i\}$.

The discrete curvature method, like the cardinal spline method, can be divided into two parts, namely rough fairing and fine fairing, except that it uses the discrete curvature K_i instead of the second-order derivative M_i.

(1) ***Rough fairing.*** A point is said to be a bad one if it makes the set of signs $\{\mathrm{sign}(K_i)\}$ change its sign successively. The object of rough fairing is to eliminate the bad points to make sure that the set does not change sign successively.

(2) ***Fine fairing.*** Calculate the first order difference $\Delta K_i = K_i - K_{i-1}$. A point is termed to be a bad one if it makes the set of signs $\{\mathrm{sign}(\Delta K_i)\}$

change sign successively. The object of fine fairing is to eliminate such bad points.

The discrete curvature method uses the second-order difference of the discrete curvature as the object function, and curve fairing is the process to minimize this function.

Definition The second-order difference of the discrete curvature at $\boldsymbol{P}_i$ is

$$D_i = \lambda_i K_{i-1} + \mu_i K_{i+1} - K_i \qquad (i = 1, \ldots, n-1), \tag{2.17}$$

where

$$\lambda_i = \frac{l_{i+1}}{l_i + l_{i+1}}, \qquad \mu_i = \frac{l_i}{l_i + l_{i+1}}, \qquad l_i = \overline{\boldsymbol{P}_{i-1}\boldsymbol{P}_i}.$$

If $\boldsymbol{P}_i$ is a bad point in rough fairing, then K_{i-1} and K_{i+1} are of the same sign, but K_i is of opposite sign, thus $|D_i|$ is relatively large. In this way, $|D_i|$ reflects the fairness of a neighbourhood of $\boldsymbol{P}_i$.

The modification which turns a bad point $\boldsymbol{P}_i$ into $\boldsymbol{P}_i^*$ is as follows. Suppose $\boldsymbol{P}_i^*$ replaces $\boldsymbol{P}_i$, and other points are left unchanged. Denote by $\{K_i^*\}$ the set of discrete curvatures of the new data points. The standard by which we choose $\boldsymbol{P}_i^*$ is that the second difference of the discrete curvature at $\boldsymbol{P}_i^*$ is

$$D_i^* = 0. \tag{2.18}$$

In this way, the new set $\{K_i^*\}$ will be distributed more evenly, as we expected. In fact, (2.17) can be rewritten as

$$D_i = \frac{l_i l_{i+1}}{l_i + l_{i+1}} \left(\frac{K_{i+1} - K_i}{l_{i+1}} - \frac{L_i - K_{i-1}}{l_i} \right),$$

so that $D_i = 0$ implies that the first differences of the discrete curvature at $\boldsymbol{P}_{i-1}$, $\boldsymbol{P}_i$, $\boldsymbol{P}_{i+1}$, which are $K_i - K_{i-1}$ and $K_{i+1} - K_i$, are proportional to the corresponding lengths of the chords l_i, l_{i+1}.

In ship-hull mathematical lofting, the data points and modifications should be described in a Cartesian coordinate system for the use of this method. Suppose $\boldsymbol{P}_i(x_i, y_i)$, which is a bad point, is changed to $\boldsymbol{P}_i^*(x_i, y_i + \rho_i)$. After linearization, by (2.18), we have

$$\rho_i = -\frac{l_i l_{i+1}}{g_i} D_i, \tag{2.19}$$

where D_i is the second difference of the discrete curvature at $\boldsymbol{P}_i$. The coefficient

$$g_i = 2\left(\sin\psi_i + \frac{l_{i+1}}{l_{i-1}+l_i}\lambda_i \sin\psi_{i-1} + \frac{l_i}{l_{i+1}+l_{i+2}}\mu_i \sin\psi_{i+1}\right) \tag{2.20}$$

is independent of the u-coordinate of the point $\boldsymbol{P}_i(x_i, y_i)$. Moreover, $g_i > 0$ (see Fig. 7-3). Under the assumptions of small deflection and even distribution of data points, we have

$$g_i \approx 3.$$

The proof is omitted here.

If we want to apply the discrete curvature method to geometric design, such as for fairing the cubic B-spline curve discussed in Section 3.3 of Chapter IV, we need only regard the vertices of the characteristic polygon as the data points and proceed in the above way.

In fact, the discrete curvature method is consistent in nature with those methods discussed before. We will now make clear this consistency, under the assumption of an even distribution of data points.

We choose the local cubic spline to interpolate to the data points. According to (2.10) of Chapter VI, the continuity equations with equidistant partitions are

$$K_i = \tfrac{1}{3}(\tfrac{1}{2}k_{i-1} + 2k_i + \tfrac{1}{2}k_{i+1}) \qquad (i = 1, \ldots, n-1), \tag{2.21}$$

where k_i is the curvature of the spline at $\boldsymbol{P}_i$. If the curve is of small deflection, the concentrated load of the spline at $\boldsymbol{P}_i$ is

$$b_i = \frac{k_{i+1} - k_i}{l_{i+1}} - \frac{k_i - k_{i-1}}{l_i}.$$

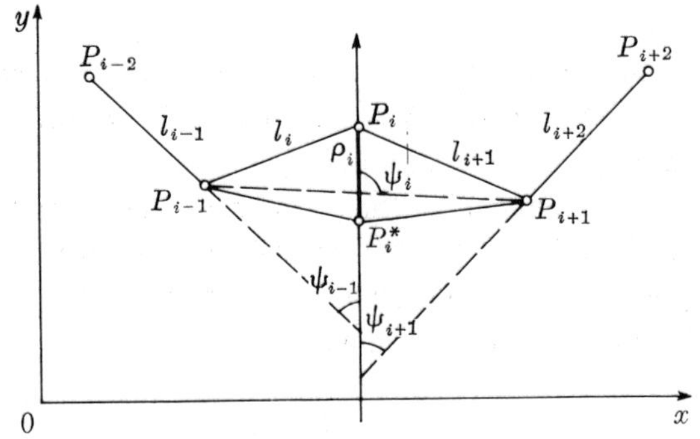

Figure 7-3

For an equidistant partition, all chord lengths are equal, $l_i = l$, so we have

$$\begin{aligned} b_i &= \frac{1}{l}(k_{i-1} + k_{i+1} - 2k_i), \\ D_i &= \tfrac{1}{2}(K_{i-1} + K_{i+1} - 2K_i), \end{aligned} \qquad (i = 1, \ldots, n-1), \qquad (2.22)$$

where D_i is the second difference of the discrete curvature. Comparing (2.21) with (2.22), we get

$$D_i = \frac{l}{6}\left(\tfrac{1}{2}b_{i-1} + 2b_i + \tfrac{1}{2}b_{i+1}\right) \qquad (i = 1, \ldots, n-1). \qquad (2.23)$$

Denote by b and D, $\max_i |b_i|$ and $\max_i |D_i|$ respectively. Then from (2.23), it can be easily derived that

$$|D_i| \leq \frac{l}{2}\, b, \qquad |b_i| \leq \frac{6}{l}\, D,$$

i.e.,

$$\frac{2}{l}\, D \leq b \leq \frac{6}{l}\, D.$$

Through the above analysis, we see that the essence of the discrete curvature method is that by decreasing the second difference D of the discrete curvature, we make b small, and in this way the fairness of a curve is achieved.

The discrete curvature method begins with rough fairing and ends at fine fairing, in which only bad points are changed.

It must be pointed out that at the stage of rough fairing, even though the three adjacent discrete curvatures K_{i-1}, K_i, K_{i+1} are of the same sign, which shows that the segment joining $\boldsymbol{P}_{i-1}$, $\boldsymbol{P}_i$, $\boldsymbol{P}_{i+1}$ is convex, it is not sure that the curvatures of the local cubic spline at $\boldsymbol{P}_{i-j}$, $\boldsymbol{P}_i$, $\boldsymbol{P}_{i+1}$, namely k_{i-1}, k_i, k_{i+1}, are of the same sign. This fact can be seen from the discussion of convexity in Section 7 of Chapter VI. Thus if a piece of curve has no inflection points, i.e., if the discrete curvatures are of the same sign, then the convexity preserving condition (7.10) in Chapter VI must be imposed to select out the bad points, so as to make sure that through rough fairing the interpolatory spline has no unwanted inflection points.

We give an example to show that the discrete curvature method has a rather powerful ability for curve fairing. We came across this problem in the process of mathematical lofting at the Hudong Shipbuilding Factory, where a 25,000-ton cargo ship was being built. Because of an error in preparing the work, the y-value 2.65, which should be in the eighth row,

x	y	discrete curvature	faired discrete curvature
43.00	11.60	−2.16	−2.16
51.60	11.52	−7.54	−7.54
60.20	10.88	−16.16	−16.16
68.80	9.00	−15.86	−15.86
73.10	7.57	−8.15	−8.15
77.40	5.96	−1.76	−1.76
81.70	4.31	1.93	−0.43
86.00	974.13	−1.92	1.04
88.15	1.83	1.92	1.79
90.30	1.02	1.92	1.92

was mistaken for 974.13 in thc box. The error was almost 1000 meters. The table of coordinates of the data points and discrete curvature is as follows, in which the units are meters and inverse kilometers respectively.

After the first fairing process by the discrete curvature method, only one point was changed, i.e., the value 974.13 in the bracket was modified to 2.649997, which differs little from the original data 2.65. The changes of the discrete curvature are marked by boxes in the last column of the table. Obviously, the variation of the set of faired discrete curvature is even and smooth.

Figures 7-4 and 7-5 are the cross sections of a ship hull surface. The local cubic spline was used for interpolation to get a large-deflection curve and the discrete curvature method was used for fairing the curve (Liu Dingyuan, Su Wenrong [2], 1979).

2.6 The Smoothing Method

The geometric design group at Jilin University developed a method of data fitting, with emphasis on convexity preserving, which is called the *smoothing method* (Qi Dongxu, 1975; Li Yuesheng and Qi Dongxu, 1979).

The smoothing method consists of two parts, namely, smoothing and adjustment. We only consider the equidistant partition here.

Suppose an equidistant partition on the interval $[a, b]$ with step h,

$$\Delta\colon a = x_0 < x_1 < \cdots < x_n = b,$$

along with $n+1$ data points $\boldsymbol{P}_i(x_i, y_i)$ $(i = 0, 1, \ldots, n)$, is given. Joining each pair of adjacent data points by a line segment, we get L, a piecewise linear function. The spline

$$S_k(x) = \sum_{i=0}^{n} y_i M_k\left(\frac{x - x_i}{h}\right) \tag{2.24}$$

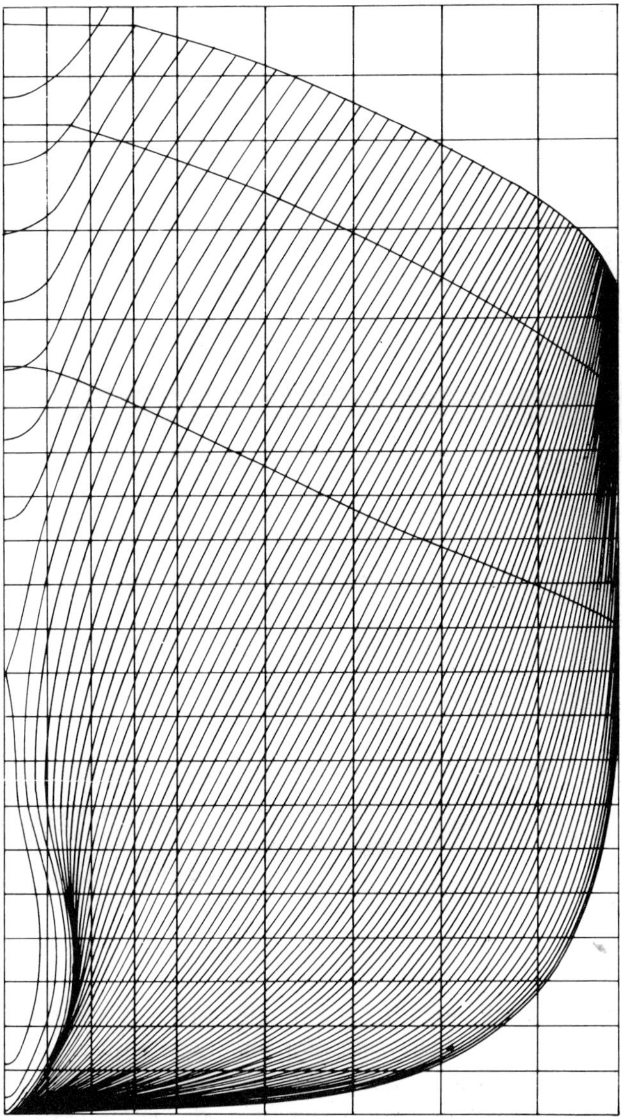

Figure 7-4

is called the $(k-1)^{\text{th}}$ *smoothing function* for L, where $M_k(x)$ is the B-spline of degree k introduced in Chapter II (here end conditions are omitted for simplicity). When $k=1$, (2.24) represents L itself. In practice, k is taken to be 2 or 3. Conventionally, (2.24) is called the variational-diminishing-spline approximation of order $k+1$, which means that the spline $S_k(x)$ of degree k has no more inflection points than the number of turning points on L

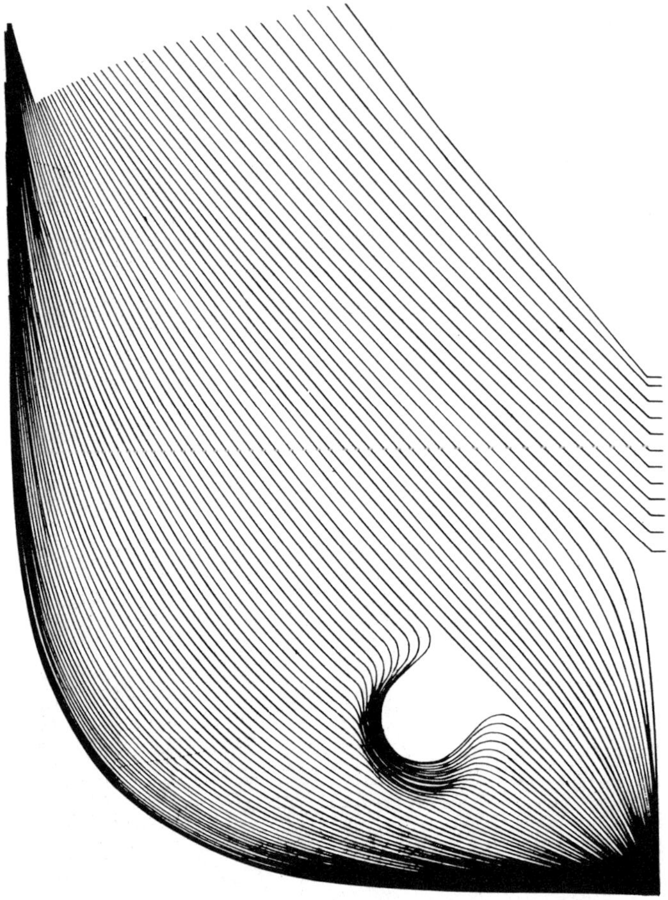

Figure 7-5

where the convexity changes. If $k = 2$ or 3, the two numbers are exactly the same. Thus $S_2(x)$ and $S_3(x)$ have the property of convexity preserving which is necessary in geometric design. Note that the first smoothing ($k = 2$) is the variational diminishing approximation of the B-spline of degree two and the second smoothing ($k = 3$) is the variational diminishing approximation of the B-spline of degree three. The first and second smoothing functions can easily be generalized to parametric form, which are the B-splines of degree two and three respectively. L, the piecewise linear function, is the corresponding B-characteristic polygon.

Generally, a spline in the form of (2.24) has an order of approximation $O(h^2)$, while for a cubic interpolatory spline, the order is $O(h^4)$. The former has the convexity preserving property, which the latter sometimes fails to have. This indicates that the variational diminishing spline approximation expressed by (2.24) achieves convexity preserving at the cost of lowering the order of approximation.

Since variational diminishing approximation does not interpolate to the given data points, the difference at an internal knot x_i is

$$\rho_i = S(x_i) - y_i = \begin{cases} \frac{1}{8}\Delta^2 y_i & k=2, \\ \frac{1}{6}\Delta^2 y_i & k=3, \end{cases}$$

in which

$$\Delta^2 y_i = y_{i-1} - 2y_i + y_{i+1}.$$

The difference ρ_i is too large for the mathematical lofting of a geometric shape. So to decrease the difference at the data points, adjustments should be made, i.e., adding to the original data y_i a compensation $-\rho_i$ at every knot x_i in advance. Then from the new data,

$$y_i^* = y_i - \rho_i,$$

we build up a smoothing function $S_k^*(x)$ according to (2.24). This process is called *adjustment.* It is easy to calculate the difference of data after the adjustment:

$$\rho_i^* = S_k^*(x_i) - y_i = \begin{cases} -\frac{1}{64}\Delta^4 y_i & k=2, \\ -\frac{1}{36}\Delta^4 y_i & k=3, \end{cases}$$

where $\Delta^4 y_i$ denotes the fourth difference of the data $\{y_i\}$. It can be seen from the above formula that, generally, the smoothing function approximates the original data points better through the adjustment.

We could repeat the above process to make adjustments several times if necessary. It has been proved that when the number of adjustments n tends to infinity, the corresponding smoothing function

$$S_k^{(n)}(x) \to f_k(x) \qquad (k=2,3),$$

in which $f_k(x)$ satisfies the interpolatory conditions

$$f_k(x_i) = y_i \qquad (i=0,\ldots,n),$$

and

$$f_k(x) = \sum_{i=0}^{n} \alpha_i M_k\left(\frac{x-x_i}{h}\right),$$

which is a spline of degree k.

It is not the case that the bigger the n the better the result. From the discussion in Section 3 of Chapter II, we know that if the set of data points is convex and the sufficient and necessary condition for convexity preserving

(3.15) or (3.16) is not satisfied, the interpolatory spline may not be convexity-preserving. In practice the adjustment is made as follows. After an adjustment, we check at every knot whether or not the second derivative $S''(x_i)$ and the second difference of data $\Delta^2 y_i$ are of the same sign. If it is true we can proceed with the adjustment, otherwise we stop the computation and return to the last stage. This is the way to approximate the data points with convexity preserved.

It should be pointed out that if the original data does not satsfy the fair conditions, for instance, if the signs of the second difference of three adjacent data, $\Delta^2 y_{i-1}, \Delta^2 y_i, \Delta^2 y_{i+1}$ are $+$, $-$, $+$, then no matter how many adjustments are taken, the smoothing function has two unwanted inflection points in the neighborhood of $\boldsymbol{P}_i$. This shows that the smoothing method is not advantageous for rough fairing, as it stresses convexity preserving (shape preserving).

In brief, the $(k-1)^{\text{th}}$ smoothing function without adjustment is the B-spline of degree k, and the parametric $(k-1)^{\text{th}}$ smoothing function curve is the B-spline curve of degree k. Through adjustment, the difference from the original data for the smoothing function can be decreased, and the convexity of the data will still be preserved. Therefore, the smoothing method is suitable for data fitting which requires convexity preserving.

3 Net Fairing

We have discussed several kinds of curve fairing methods. These methods are the bases for net fairing.

In mathematical ship-hull lofting, the object is to get a fair net. A net is said to be fair if every curve on the net is fair. When we use the least-squares method, the bounce method or the discrete curvature method for net fairing, three families of curves are faired separately with the compatible requirement of the net, i.e., two curves which belong to different families intersect. This process is called *net fairing in three directions.* In order to fulfill the compatible requirement, an iterative process is needed to fair the three families of curves.

While the energy method and the cardinal spline method can be extended to the two-dimensional cases, the methods for net fairing differ from the net fairing in three directions mentioned above.

3.1 The Net Energy Method

This method is a generalization of Hosaka's energy method in the two-dimensional case (Hosaka [3], 1969).

Form a net spanned by two families of elastic strings C_i $(i=0, 1, \ldots, n)$ and D_j $(j=0, 1, \ldots, m)$ whose rigidities are all EI. There are no constraints except for the same displacement at all intersections of two curves belonging to the two families of curves described by the parameters u and v respectively. We refer the reader to Section 2.2 for the following notations:

$\boldsymbol{Q}_{ij}$: a data point of the net
$\boldsymbol{P}_{ij}$: a faired data point of the net
α_{ij}: the elastic coefficient of the spring at a data point
$\boldsymbol{M}^u_{ij}$: the second derivative at $\boldsymbol{P}_{ij}$ in the u-direction of the net
$\boldsymbol{M}^v_{ij}$: the second derivative at $\boldsymbol{P}_{ij}$ in the v-direction

$$\boldsymbol{M}_{ij} = \boldsymbol{M}^u_{ij} + \boldsymbol{M}^v_{ij},$$

$$\beta_{ij} = \frac{(EI)^2}{\alpha_{ij}},$$

$$l^u_{ij} = |\boldsymbol{P}_{ij} - \boldsymbol{P}_{i-1,j}|,$$

$$l^v_{ij} = |\boldsymbol{P}_{ij} - \boldsymbol{P}_{i,j-1}|.$$

The operators Δ^2_u and Δ^2_v are defined by

$$\Delta^2_u f_{ij} = \frac{f_{i+1,j} - f_{ij}}{l^u_{i+1,j}} - \frac{f_{ij} - f_{i-1,j}}{l^u_{ij}},$$

$$\Delta^2_v f_{ij} = \frac{f_{i,j-1} - f_{ij}}{l^v_{i,j+1}} - \frac{f_{ij} - f_{i,j-1}}{l^v_{ij}}.$$

The energy of the system composed of elastic string and small springs is

$$U = \tfrac{1}{2}\sum_{i,j} \alpha_{ij}(\boldsymbol{P}_{ij} - \boldsymbol{Q}_{ij})^2 + \tfrac{1}{2}(EI)^2\left(\sum_i \int_{C_i} k^2\, ds + \sum_j \int_{D_j} k^2\, ds\right).$$

Similar to the discussion in Section 2.2, through linearization and according to

$$U = \min,$$

we can obtain the following equations about $\boldsymbol{P}_{ij}$, $\boldsymbol{M}^u_{ij}$, $\boldsymbol{M}^v_{ij}$:

$$\boldsymbol{P}_{ij} = \boldsymbol{Q}_{ij} - \beta_{ij}(\Delta^2_u \boldsymbol{M}^u_{ij} + \Delta^2_v \boldsymbol{M}^v_{ij}),$$

$$\begin{aligned} l^u_{ij}\boldsymbol{M}^u_{i-1,j} + 2(l^u_{ij} + l^u_{i+1,j})\boldsymbol{M}^u_{ij} + l^u_{i+1,j}\boldsymbol{M}^u_{i+1,j} + 6\Delta^2_u(\beta_{ij}\Delta^2_u \boldsymbol{M}^u_{ij}) &= 6\Delta^2_u \boldsymbol{Q}_{ij}, \\ l^v_{ij}\boldsymbol{M}^v_{i,j-1} + 2(l^v_{ij} + l^v_{i,j+1})\boldsymbol{M}^v_{ij} + l^v_{i,j+1}\boldsymbol{M}^v_{i,j+1} + 6\Delta^2_v(\beta_{ij}\Delta^2_v \boldsymbol{M}^v_{ij}) &= 6\Delta^2_v \boldsymbol{Q}_{ij}. \end{aligned} \tag{3.1}$$

Solving the second and third equations for $\boldsymbol{M}^u_{ij}$ and $\boldsymbol{M}^v_{ij}$, we get the faired data points $\boldsymbol{P}_{ij}$ from the first equation.

3.2 The Cardinal Spline Method for Net Fairing

If we define a vector for the concentrated load of the univariate spline in the cardinal method,

$$\boldsymbol{B} = (b_1, b_2, \ldots, b_{n-1}),$$

fairing the object function minimizes the sum of the squares of the components of the vector, namely,

$$B \equiv \boldsymbol{B}^2 = \sum_{i=1}^{n-1} b_i^2 = \min.$$

These concepts can be extended to the cardinal spline method for net fairing.

Suppose a rectangular partition $\Delta = \Delta_x \otimes \Delta_y$ is given on a plane rectangle $[a, b] \otimes [c, d]$, in which

$$\Delta_x: \qquad a = x_0 < x_1 < \cdots < x_n = b,$$

$$\Delta_y: \qquad c = y_0 < y_1 < \cdots < y_n = d.$$

The bicubic splines defined on Δ, say $f(x, y)$, form a $(m+3)(n+3)$-dimensional linear space $S(x, y; \Delta)$ with a basis

$$\{\phi_s(x)\psi_t(y)\} \qquad (s = 0, \ldots, n+2;\ t = 0, \ldots, m+2).$$

These basis functions are called *bivariate cardinal splines* and can be constructed from the tensor product of two univariate cardinal splines $\{\phi_s(x)\}$ and $\{\psi_t(y)\}$. Only $\phi_{n+1}(x)$, $\phi_{n+2}(x)$ and $\psi_{m+1}(y)$, $\psi_{m+2}(y)$ are associated with boundary conditions. This fact was introduced in Section 1.2 of Chapter V.

The two-dimensional extensions of the concentrated load of the univariate spline at the internal knots are

$$\Delta_{x_i}^{(\alpha)} f \equiv \left.\frac{\partial^{(3+\alpha)} f}{\partial y^\alpha\, \partial x^3}\right|_{x_i+0} - \left.\frac{\partial^{(3+\alpha)} f}{\partial y^\alpha\, \partial x^3}\right|_{x_i-0}$$

$$(i = 1, \ldots, n-1), \qquad (\alpha = 0, \ldots, 3). \tag{3.2}$$

$$\Delta_{y_j}^{(\alpha)} f \equiv \left.\frac{\partial^{(3+\alpha)} f}{\partial x^\alpha\, \partial y^3}\right|_{y_j+0} - \left.\frac{\partial^{(3+\alpha)} f}{\partial x^\alpha\, \partial y^3}\right|_{y_j-0}$$

$$(j = 1, \ldots, m-1),$$

The univariate vector B is extended to an $8(mn-1)$-dimensional vector

$$\boldsymbol{G}(f) = (\boldsymbol{G}_x^{(0)}(f),\ \boldsymbol{G}_x^{(1)}(f),\ \boldsymbol{G}_x^{(2)}(f),\ \boldsymbol{G}_x^{(3)}(f),$$
$$\boldsymbol{G}_y^{(0)}(f),\ \boldsymbol{G}_y^{(1)}(f),\ \boldsymbol{g}_y^{(2)}(f),\ \boldsymbol{G}_y^{(3)}(f)),$$

in which

$$G_x^{(\alpha)}(f)=(\Delta_{x_1}^{(\alpha)}f|_{y_0},\ldots,\Delta_{x_{n-1}}^{(\alpha)}f|_{y_0},\ldots,\Delta_{x_1}^{(\alpha)}f|_{y_m},\ldots,\Delta_{x_{n-1}}^{(\alpha)}|_{y_m}),$$
$$(\alpha=0,\ldots,3).$$
$$G_y^{(\alpha)}(f)=(\Delta_{y_1}^{(\alpha)}f|_{x_0},\ldots,\Delta_{y_{m-1}}^{(\alpha)}f|_{x_0},\ldots,\Delta_{y_1}^{(\alpha)}f|_{x_n},\ldots,\Delta_{y_{m-1}}^{(\alpha)}|_{x_n}),$$

In the course of fairing, we begin by selecting out the bad points through checking every net curve according to the conditions discussed in Section 2.4. These points form a set E. The selection of the point $\boldsymbol{P}_0 \in E$ to be modified can be carried out in the following manner.

Given a suitable boundary condition and data $\{z_{ij}\}$ which are defined on the partition Δ, we construct an interpolatory bicubic spline $f(x, y)$. Denote by $C_{\boldsymbol{P}}(x, y)$ a bivariate cardinal spline which concerns an arbitrary bad point $\boldsymbol{P} \in E$. If $\rho_{\boldsymbol{P}}$ represents the change of data at point $\boldsymbol{P}$ with other data unchanged and the boundary condition remaining the same, then the new bicubic spline $f^*(x, y)$ satisfies

$$f^*(x,y)=f(x,y)+\rho_{\boldsymbol{P}}C_{\boldsymbol{P}}(x,y).$$

The value of $\rho_{\boldsymbol{P}}$ is determined by minimizing the object function

$$G_{\boldsymbol{P}}\equiv \boldsymbol{G}^2(f^*)=\min. \tag{3.3}$$

Note that $\{\Delta_{x_i}^{(\alpha)}\}$ and $\{\Delta_{y_j}^{(\alpha)}\}$ are all linear operators. Thus the operator

$$\boldsymbol{G}: f\to \boldsymbol{G}(f)$$

is also linear, i.e.,

$$\boldsymbol{G}(f^*)=\boldsymbol{G}(f)+\rho_{\boldsymbol{P}}\boldsymbol{G}(C_{\boldsymbol{P}}). \tag{3.4}$$

Combining (3.3) and (3.4) we obtain the modification at $\boldsymbol{P}$

$$\rho_{\boldsymbol{P}}=-\frac{\boldsymbol{G}(f)\cdot \boldsymbol{G}(C_{\boldsymbol{P}})}{\boldsymbol{G}^2(C_{\boldsymbol{P}})}.$$

From the property 3 of bivariate cardinal splines discussed in the next section, we see that $\boldsymbol{G}^2(C_{\boldsymbol{P}})>0$. Thus the expression for $\rho_{\boldsymbol{P}}$ always makes sense.

Finally, we calculate the point $\boldsymbol{P}_0$ such that

$$G_{\boldsymbol{P}_0}=\min_{\boldsymbol{P}\in E} G_{\boldsymbol{P}},$$

then we choose $\boldsymbol{P}_0$ as the point which is to be modified with the modification $\rho_{\boldsymbol{P}_0}$ (Xin Yuanlong [2], 1977).

4 Boundary Conditions for Fairing

Given a group of data points $\{\boldsymbol{P}_i(x_i, y_i)\}$, two end conditions are required to generate uniquely a cubic interpolatory spline. But in some problems of geometric design, these conditions need to be assigned in the algorithm instead of being given in advance. By "suitable" end conditions we mean that data points and end conditions are consistent to make the spline curve a fair one. There are several ways to assign the end derivatives which are worth mentioning. For example, making a parabola which passes through $\boldsymbol{P}_0$, $\boldsymbol{P}_1$, $\boldsymbol{P}_2$ and taking the first derivative y_0' at $\boldsymbol{P}_0$ as an end condition is called the parabolic end condition, which is equivalent to that in the Bessel method introduced in Section 8.1 of Chapter VI.

Xin Yuanlong ([2], 1977) gave an algorithm to determine the boundary conditions and established the existence and uniqueness theorem for the solution which we will discuss in this section. Just as we have used in the cardinal spline fairing method, cubic splines are our tools. Some properties of cubic cardinal splines will be proved in Section 4.3.

We will introduce the univariate and bivariate cases separately. These algorithms, combined with the cardinal spline method, have played an important role in the mathematical lofting in the Jiangnan Shipbuilding Factory for many years.

4.1 The Univariate Spline Case

Given a set of data points $\boldsymbol{P}_i(x_i, y_i)$ $(i=0, 1, \ldots, n)$ let the end conditions be determined as y_0' and y_n'. The cubic interpolatory spline function is represented in cardinal spline form:

$$S(x)=\Phi(x)+y_0'\phi_{n+1}(x)+y_n'\phi_{n+2}(x). \tag{4.1}$$

The part which is independent of the end conditions can be written as

$$\Phi(x)=\sum_{i=0}^{n} y_i\phi_i(x),$$

where $\phi_s(x)$ $(s=0, 1, \ldots, n+2)$ are cubic cardinal splines.

We now set y_0' and y_n' in such a way that b_i, the concentrated load of $S(x)$ at x_i, satisfies

$$B\equiv\sum_{i=1}^{n-1} b_i^2=\min, \tag{4.2}$$

in which $b_i=S'''(x_i+0)-S'''(x_i-0)$ $(i=1, \ldots, n-1)$.

Denote by c_i, d_i, d_i^* $(i=1,\ldots,n-1)$ the concentrated loads at the knot x_i of $\Phi(x)$, $\delta_{n+1}(x)$, $\phi_{n+2}(x)$ respectively.

From (4.1) we have

$$b_i = c_i + y'_0 d_i + y'_n d_i^* \qquad (i=1,\ldots,n-1).$$

Hence

$$\frac{\partial B}{\partial y'_0} = 2\sum_{i=1}^{n-1} (c_i + y'_0 d_i + y'_n d_i^*) d_i,$$

$$\frac{\partial B}{\partial y'_n} = 2\sum_{i=1}^{n-1} (c_i + y'_0 d_i + y'_n d_i^*) d_i^*.$$

In order to make $B=\min$, we must have

$$\frac{\partial B}{\partial y'_0} = 0,$$

$$\frac{\partial B}{\partial y'_n} = 0,$$

or

$$\begin{aligned} y'_0 d + y'_n e &= -c, \\ y'_0 e + y'_n d^* &= -c^*, \end{aligned} \tag{4.3}$$

in which

$$d = \sum_{i=1}^{n-1} d_i^2, \qquad e = \sum_{i=1}^{n-1} d_i d_i^*, \qquad d^* = \sum_{i=1}^{n-1} d_i^{*2},$$

$$c = \sum_{i=1}^{n-1} c_i d_i, \qquad c^* = \sum_{i=1}^{n-1} c_i d_i^*.$$

And then we can solve (4.3) for the end conditions

$$\begin{aligned} y'_0 &= \frac{c^* e - c d^*}{d d^* - e^2}, \\ y'_n &= \frac{c e - c^* d}{d d^* - e^2}. \end{aligned} \tag{4.4}$$

In some cases, only y'_n is unknown. According to (4.3) we have

$$y'_n = -\frac{y'_0 e + c^*}{d^*}. \tag{4.5}$$

If y'_n is known and y'_0 is to be assigned, we have a similar result

$$y'_0 = -\frac{y'_n e + c}{d}. \tag{4.6}$$

From properties 1 and 2 in Section 4.3 below, we see that $d^*, d \neq 0$. Moreover, when $n \geqslant 3$, $\{d_i\}$ and $\{d_i^*\}$ are linearly independent. Therefore by the Cauchy inequality we get

$$e^2 = \left(\sum_{i=1}^{n-1} d_i d_i^*\right)^2 < \left(\sum_{i=1}^{n-1} d_i^2\right)\left(\sum_{i=1}^{n-1} d_i^{*2}\right) = dd^*.$$

So the denominators of (4.4), (4.5), and (4.6) are not zero.

4.2 The Bivariate Spline Case

Suppose $f(x, y) \in S(x, y, \Delta)$ can be represented in terms of cardinal splines as

$$f(x, y) = f_0(x, y) + \sum_{\alpha=1}^{p} a_\alpha c_\alpha(x, y), \tag{4.7}$$

in which $f_0(x, y) \in S(x, y, \Delta)$ is determined by the data points. Each $c_\alpha(x, y)$, which is a cardinal spline composed of $\{\phi_3(x)\}$ and $\{\psi_t(y)\}$, concerns the boundary conditions, and $\{a_\alpha\}$ are coefficients to be determined. Generally, $p \leqslant 2(m+n)+8$.

The constraint on $\{a_\alpha\}$ is

$$\boldsymbol{G}^2(f) = \min. \tag{4.8}$$

We now prove that if $n, m \geqslant 3$, and if (4.8) holds, then $\{a_\alpha\}$ exist uniquely.

In fact, from (4.7), we get

$$\boldsymbol{G}(f) = \boldsymbol{G}(f_0) + \sum_{\alpha=1}^{p} a_\alpha \boldsymbol{G}(c_\alpha).$$

According to

$$\frac{\partial \boldsymbol{G}(f)}{\partial \boldsymbol{a}_\alpha} = 0 \qquad (\alpha = 1, \ldots, p),$$

we have

$$\sum_{\beta=1}^{p} \boldsymbol{G}(c_\alpha)\boldsymbol{G}(c_\beta) a_\beta = -\boldsymbol{G}(c_\alpha)\boldsymbol{G}(f_0) \qquad (\alpha = 1, \ldots, p),$$

or in matrix form,

$$[C]^T[C][X] = -[C]^T[F], \tag{4.9}$$

in which $[C]=[\boldsymbol{G}(C_\alpha)]^T$ is an $8(mn-1)\times p$ matrix, $[F]=[\boldsymbol{G}(f_0)]^T$ is an $8(mn-1)\times 1$ matrix, and $[X]=[a_1,\ldots,a_p]^T$ is a $p\times 1$ matrix.

From property four in Section 4.3 below, we know that if $n, m\geqslant 3$, then $\boldsymbol{G}(C_1),\ldots,\boldsymbol{G}(C_p)$ are linearly independent, and therefore

$$\operatorname{rank}([C]^T[C])=\operatorname{rank}([C])=p.$$

Hence the coefficient matrix of (4.9) is nonsingular, and this indicates that the system of linear equations has a unique solution.

4.3 Some Properties of Cardinal Splines

We denote by $\Delta_{x_i}\phi_s$ the concentrated load of the univariate cardinal spline $\phi_s(x)$ $(s=0,\ldots,n+2)$ at the knot x_i, expressed by the first formula in (3.2), with $\alpha=0$.

Property 1. When $n\geqslant 2$,

$$\Delta_{x_i}\phi_s\neq 0 \qquad (i=1,\ldots,n-1;\ s=0,\ldots,n+2).$$

Actually, we have seen that for arbitrary $\phi_s(x)$, we have

$$\phi_s''(x_i)\phi_s''(x_{i+1})<0 \qquad (i=0,\ldots,n-1).$$

Since $\phi_s''(x)$ is piecewise linear, we know that $\phi_s'''(x)$ is piecewise constant and changes its sign through every knot, and hence $\Delta_{x_i}\phi_s\neq 0$.

Property 2. When $n\geqslant 3$, $\{\Delta_{x_i}\phi_{n+1}\}$ and $\{\Delta_{x_i}\phi_{n+2}\}$ are linearly independent.

Suppose there exist constants λ and μ, with $\lambda^2+\mu^2\neq 0$, such that

$$\lambda\,\Delta_{x_i}\phi_{n+1}+\mu\,\Delta_{x_i}\phi_{n+2}=0 \qquad (i=1,\ldots,n-1),$$

i.e.,

$$\Delta_{x_i}(\lambda\phi_{n+1}+\mu\phi_{n+2})=0 \qquad (i=1,\ldots,n-1).$$

Then the spline $\lambda\phi_{n+1}+\mu\phi_{n+2}$ is a cubic polynomial in x on $[x_0, x_n]$. But according to the definitions of ϕ_{n+1} and ϕ_{n+2} they have $n+1$ zeros in $[x_0, x_n]$, a contradiction for $n\geqslant 3$.

Property 3. The vector $\boldsymbol{G}(\phi_s\psi_t)$ is not the zero vector $(s=0,\ldots,n+2;$ $t=0,\ldots,m+2)$, where $\phi_s(x)\psi_t(y)$ are bivariate cardinal splines.

Suppose that $\boldsymbol{G}(\phi_s\psi_t)=0$, i.e.,

$$\Delta_{x_i}\phi_s\psi_t^{(\alpha)}(y_j)=0 \qquad \begin{pmatrix} i=1,\ldots,n-1;\ j=0,\ldots,m;\\ s=0,\ldots,n+2;\ t=0,\ldots,m+2;\\ \alpha=0,\ldots,3\end{pmatrix}.$$

There exist α and j such that $\psi_t^{(\alpha)}(y_j)\neq 0$, hence

$$\Delta_{x_i}\phi_s=0 \qquad (i=1,\ldots,n-1;\ s=0,\ldots,n+2),$$

which contradicts Property 1.

Property 4. The vectors

$$G(\phi_{n+1}\psi_t),\ G(\phi_{n+2}\psi_t),\ G(\phi_s\psi_{m+1}),\ G(\phi_s\psi_{m+2})$$
$$(s=0,\ldots,n+2;\ t=0,\ldots,m+2)$$

are linearly independent, where $\phi_{n+1}\psi_t$, $\phi_{n+2}\psi_t$, $\phi_s\psi_{m+1}$, $\phi_s\psi_{m+2}$ $(s=0,\ldots,n+2;\ t=0,\ldots,m+2)$ are $2(m+n)+8$ cardinal splines which concern boundary conditions and are elements of $S(x, y, \Delta)$.

Otherwise suppose that

$$\sum_{j=0}^{m} C_j G(\phi_{n+1}\psi_j)+\sum_{j=0}^{m} C_j^* G(\phi_{n+2}\psi_j)+\sum_{i=0}^{n} d_i G(\phi_i\psi_{m+1})$$
$$+\sum_{i=0}^{n} d_i^* G(\phi_i\psi_{m+2})+pG(\phi_{n+1}\psi_{m+1})+p^* G(\phi_{n+2}\psi_{m+1})$$
$$+qG(\phi_{n+1}\psi_{m+2})+q^* G(\phi_{n+2}\psi_{n+2})=0.$$

Write it in the form of its components

$$\sum_{j=0}^{m} C_j\Delta_{x_k}\phi_{n+1}\psi_j^{(\alpha)}(y_l)+\sum_{j=0}^{m} C_j^*\Delta_{x_k}\phi_{n+2}\psi_j^{(\alpha)}(y_l)$$
$$+\sum_{i=0}^{n} d_i\Delta_{x_k}\phi_i\psi_{m+1}^{(\alpha)}(y_l)+\sum_{i=0}^{n} d_i^*\Delta_{x_k}\phi_i\psi_{m+2}^{(\alpha)}(y_l)$$
$$+p\Delta_{x_k}\phi_{n+1}\psi_{m+1}^{(\alpha)}(y_l)+p^*\Delta x_k\phi_{n+2}\psi_{m+1}^{(\alpha)}(y_l)$$
$$+q\Delta_{x_k}\phi_{n+1}\psi_{m+2}^{(\alpha)}(y_l)+q^*\Delta_{x_k}\phi_{n+2}\psi_{m+2}^{(\alpha)}(y_l)=0 \tag{4.10}$$

and

$$\sum_{j=0}^{m} C_j\Delta_{y_g}\psi_j\phi_{n+1}^{(\alpha)}(x_h)+\sum_{j=0}^{m} C_j^*\Delta_{y_g}\psi_j\phi_{n+2}^{(\alpha)}(x_h)$$
$$+\sum_{i=0}^{n} d_i\Delta_{y_g}\psi_{m+1}\phi_i^{(\alpha)}(x_h)+\sum_{i=0}^{n} d_i^*\Delta_{y_g}\psi_{m+2}\phi_i^{(\alpha)}(x_h)$$
$$+p\Delta_{y_g}\psi_{m+1}\phi_{n+1}^{(\alpha)}(x_h)+p^*\Delta_{y_g}\psi_{m+1}\phi_{n+2}^{(\alpha)}(x_h)$$
$$+q\Delta_{y_g}\psi_{m+2}\phi_{n+1}^{(\alpha)}(x_h)+q^*\Delta_{y_g}\psi_{m+2}\phi_{n+2}^{(\alpha)}(x_h)=0$$
$$(k=1,\ldots,n-1;\ l=0,\ldots,m;\ g=1,\ldots,m-1;$$
$$h=0,\ldots,n;\ \alpha=0,\ldots,3). \tag{4.11}$$

Particularly, if $\alpha=0$ in (4.10), by the definitions of $\{\phi_s\}$ and $\{\psi_t\}$, we obtain

$$C_l\Delta_{x_k}\phi_{n+1}+C_l^*\Delta_{x_k}\phi_{n+2}=0.$$

According to Property 2, we have

$$C_l=0 \quad \text{and} \quad C_l^*=0 \qquad (l=0,\ldots,m).$$

Similarly, if $\alpha = 0$ in (4.11), then

$$d_h = 0 \quad \text{and} \quad d_h^* = 0 \qquad (h = 0, \ldots, n).$$

Taking $\alpha = 1$ and $l = 0$, then

$$p = 0 \quad \text{and} \quad p^* = 0.$$

At last, setting $\alpha = 1$ and $l = m$ in (4.10) we get

$$q = 0 \quad \text{and} \quad q^* = 0.$$

CHAPTER VIII

The Intrinsic Affine Invariants of Parametric Curves in Affine Hyperspace

While studying cubic parametric curve segments in Chapter III, by an affine invariant theory of parametric curves, we obtained an important affine invariant:

$$I = \left(\frac{q}{p}\right)^2 - 2\frac{r}{p}.$$

According to the sign of I, we made an affine classification by the number of real singularities and inflection points, and then some practical schemes to judge and control the shape of a cubic parametric curve segment were derived. By a suitable affine transformation, the schemes could be used in the cases of cubic Bézier curves and cubic B-splines analogously.

We will now apply the affine invariant theory to quintic curves and curves of higher degree on the plane. Finally, we will discuss the problems of intrinsic affine invariants of parametric curves of degree n in m-dimensional space. If we know the affine invariants and the distribution of real singularities and inflection-points of parametric curves, then we can realize the shape control for Bézier curves and B-splines of degree n, a question which is not solved completely in the area of computational geometry. Referring to affine invariants of parametric curves, we can consider the corresponding problems for parametric surfaces. The problems, being the theoretical foundation to study Coons, Bézier and B-spline surfaces, will pose considerable difficulties but also be of great significance.

1 Concepts and Conclusions in the Theory of Algebraic Curves

In the plane affine coordinate system, the curve expressed by an algebraic equation

$$F(x, y) \equiv \sum_{\substack{i,j=0 \\ i+j \leq n}}^{n} a_{ij} x^i y^j = 0 \tag{1.1}$$

is called a plane algebraic curve of degree n and is denoted by C_n. Generally, C_n intersects any straight line at n points. Conversely, an algebraic curve that has n intersections with any straight line must be of degree n.

We know that, by a birational transformation, the singularities of C_n are classified into loops and cusps. Let C_n have d loops and s cusps. Then $d+s$ cannot exceed $\frac{1}{2}(n-1)(n-2)$. The number

$$p = \tfrac{1}{2}(n-1)(n-2) - d - s \tag{1.2}$$

is called the *genus* of C_n.

If the homogeneous coordinates (x, y, z) of the moving point on C_n are all polynomials of degree n with respect to the parameter t, C_n is then called a *rational curve of degree n* (Burau, 1962). Any rational curve of degree n must be of the form C_n. This is deduced from the curve having n intersections with any straight line $\lambda x + \mu y + \nu z = 0$. Moreover, the genus P of the curve equals zero. Conversely, a curve C_n with genus $p = 0$ is sure to be a rational curve with respect to a parameter t. Thus the number of all singularities (including loops and cusps) is $\frac{1}{2}(n-1)(n-2)$. Furthermore, $3n-6$ inflection points occur on C_n.

The rational integral curve of degree n is the curve whose non-homogeneous coordinates (x, y) are expressed by parametric equations

$$\begin{aligned} x &= \sum_{i=0}^{n} \frac{1}{i!} a_i t^i, \\ y &= \sum_{i=0}^{n} \frac{1}{i!} b_i t^i. \end{aligned} \tag{1.3}$$

Without loss of generality, we can assume $b_n \neq 0$. Just like the rational curve of the same degree, it also has $\frac{1}{2}(n-1)(n-2)$ singularities, but only $2n-4$ inflection-points. This is why rational integral curves are more useful in most cases of geometric design.

Coons ([2], 1967) and A. A. Ball ([1], 1974, the CONSURF system of British Aircraft Company) once used cubic rational curves to construct parametric nets for surface design in the aircraft industry. They intended to put quadratic algebraic curves (involving ellipses, hyperbolas and parabolas) and cubic rational integral curves entirely into cubic rational curves. It is well known that quadratic algebraic curves have tremendous applications in the conventional design techniques of the aircraft industry, but they cannot be involved in cubic rational integral curves.

In m-dimensional affine space, a general affine transformation is $A_m: \boldsymbol{x} \to \bar{\boldsymbol{x}}, \boldsymbol{x} = (x_1, x_2, \ldots, x_m), \bar{\boldsymbol{x}} = (\bar{x}_1, \bar{x}_2, \ldots, \bar{x}_m)$,

$$\begin{pmatrix} \bar{x}_1 \\ \bar{x}_2 \\ \vdots \\ \bar{x}_m \end{pmatrix} = \begin{pmatrix} a_{11} & a_{12} & \cdots & a_{1m} \\ a_{21} & a_{22} & \cdots & a_{2m} \\ \cdots & \cdots & \cdots & \cdots \\ a_{m1} & a_{m2} & \cdots & a_{mm} \end{pmatrix} \begin{pmatrix} x_1 \\ x_2 \\ \vdots \\ x_m \end{pmatrix} + \begin{pmatrix} a_{10} \\ a_{20} \\ \vdots \\ a_{m0} \end{pmatrix}, \qquad J \equiv \det|a_{ij}| \neq 0. \tag{1.4}$$

If $m = 2$, the inflection points and singularities of the plane curve C_n, not at infinity, are invariant not only under the affine transformation A_2, but also the linear transformation T of the parameter,

$$T: t \to \bar{t}, \qquad t = C\bar{t} + f \qquad (C \neq 0).$$

By T, the coefficients of curve (1.3) are changed as follows:

$$a_i \to \bar{a}_i, b_i \to \bar{b}_i \qquad (i = 0, 1, \ldots, n).$$

If a function Φ $(a_0, \ldots, a_n; b_0, \ldots, b_n)$ satisfies the relation

$$\Phi(\bar{a}_0, \ldots, \bar{a}_n; \bar{b}_0, \ldots, \bar{b}_n) = C^r \Phi(a_0, \ldots, a_n; b_0, \ldots, b_n),$$

where r is an integer, then Φ is said to be a *relative affine invariant* (with respect to T) of weight r. If $r = 0$, Φ is said to be an *intrinsic* affine invariant. For the weight r of the relative invariant of the affine transformation A_2, a similar definition can be obtained so long as we substitute A_2 for T, and J for C, respectively.

2 Certain Quintic Rational Integral Curves

In the theory of spline interpolation, as well as the parametric spline curves of degree three, we often meet those of degree five. Every segment of such a spline is a quintic rational integral curve segment. The principal results of this section are described below (Su Buchin [4], 1977).

In Section 2.1, we will prove that, by appropriate adjustment of the parameters of the quintic rational integral curve of the parametric spline at the end points, the curve of six inflection points is turned into a new one of four inflection points, and we call the latter the "quintic rational curve".

Note that in this section, "quintic rational curve" denotes a special kind of quintic rational curve which is different from that defined in the last section. Two kinds of adjustment are proposed, both of which make the new curve have continuous derivative at the knots.

In Section 2.2, a relative affine invariant I will be derived.

In Section 2.3, we will discuss three relative affine invariants, g, b and a, which are deduced from the equations of inflection points. By the sign of g and b, the distribution of real singularities of the quintic rational curve is determined.

2.1 Quintic Parametric Spline Curves

Generally, a quintic rational integral curve represented by

$$x=\sum_{i=0}^{5}\frac{1}{i!}a_i t^i,$$
$$y=\sum_{i=0}^{5}\frac{1}{i!}b_i t^i \tag{2.1}$$

has six inflection points. To decrease the number of inflection points in the case, the following conditions in (2.2) must be ensured. After the adjustment, the curve has only four inflection points unless the original curve is turned into a simple quintic curve. The curve discussed in this section would be simply called a quintic rational curve.

Assume that in (2.1) $a_5 \neq 0$. Let

$$p_{ij}=a_ib_j-a_jb_i \qquad (i\neq j;\ i,j=1,2,\ldots,5).$$

Throughout the discussion, we imagine

$$p_{35}=0, \qquad p_{45}=0, \qquad p_{25}\neq 0. \tag{2.2}$$

Note that if $p_{25}=0$, then the curve becomes a simple quintic curve with the equation

$$y=ax^5+bx^4+cx^3+dx^2+ex+f.$$

We will not study this special case in our book.

We will now show that each segment of a quintic parametric spline curve can be transformed into a quintic rational curve through a suitable adjustment of the slope parameters (x_0', y_0'), (x_1', y_1') and second derivatives (x_0'', y_0''), (x_1'', y_1'') at the points (x_0, y_0) and (x_1, y_1).

For simplicity, let the parameter t be 0 and 1, respectively, at the end points. We choose a rectangular coordinate system $\{\boldsymbol{O}, x, y\}$ such that the end points coincide with the origin and the point $(l, 0)$, respectively, where l represents the length of the chord between the end-points. Then, the quintic parametric spline curve has equations

$$\begin{aligned} x(t) &= x_0 p_0(t) + x_0' p_1(t) + x_0'' p_2(t) + x_1 q_0(t) + x_1' q_1(t) + x_1'' q_2(t), \\ y(t) &= y_0 p_0(t) + y_0' p_1(t) + y_0'' p_2(t) + y_1 q_0(t) + y_1' q_1(t) + y_1'' q_2(t), \end{aligned} \tag{2.3}$$

where

$$0 \leqslant t \leqslant 1, \qquad x_0' = \left.\frac{dx(t)}{dt}\right|_{t=0}, \qquad x_1' = \left.\frac{dx(t)}{dt}\right|_{t=1}, \qquad x_0'' = \left.\frac{d^2x(t)}{dt^2}\right|_{t=0},$$

$$x_0 = y_0 = 0, \qquad x_1 = l, \qquad y_1 = 0.$$

Furthermore,

$$\begin{aligned} p_0(t) &= 1 - q_0(t), \\ q_0(t) &= t^3(6t^2 - 15t + 10), \\ p_1(t) &= -t(t-1)^3(3t+1), \\ q_1(t) &= -t^3(t-1)(3t-4), \\ p_2(t) &= -\tfrac{1}{2}t^2(t-1)^3, \\ q_2(t) &= \tfrac{1}{2}t^3(t-1)^2. \end{aligned} \tag{2.4}$$

By arrangement, (2.3) can be written in the form (2.1), in which $a_0 = b_0 = 0$ and

$$\begin{aligned} & a_1 = x_0', \qquad a_2 = x_0'', \\ & a_3 = 60l - 36x_0' - 9x_0'' - 24x_1' + 3x_1'', \\ & a_4 = -360l + 192x_0' + 36x_0'' + 168x_1' - 24x_1'', \\ & a_5 = 720l - 360x_0' - 60x_0'' - 360x_1' + 60x_1'', \\ & b_1 = y_0', \qquad b_2 = y_0'', \\ & b_3 = -36y_0' - 9y_0'' - 24y_1' + 3y_1'', \\ & b_4 = 192y_0' + 36y_0'' + 168y_1' - 24y_1'', \\ & b_5 = -360y_0' - 60y_0'' - 360y_1' + 60y_1''. \end{aligned} \tag{2.5}$$

When $x_0', y_0'; x_1', y_1'; x_0'', x_1''$ are given first, a_3, a_4, a_5 and a_1, a_2, b_1 then are known. To make b_2, b_3, b_4 and b_5 satisfy the conditions in (2.2), we have

$$b_3 - \lambda b_5 = 0, \qquad b_4 - \mu b_5 = 0, \tag{2.6}$$

in which

$$\lambda = \frac{a_3}{a_5}, \qquad \mu = \frac{a_4}{a_5}. \tag{2.7}$$

Substituting the related quantities of (2.5) into (2.6), a linear system of equations in terms of y_0'', y_1'' is derived. Under the condition

$$D \equiv \frac{60}{a_5}(x_0' + x_1' - 2l) \neq 0, \tag{2.8}$$

solving for y_0'' and y_1'', we have

$$\begin{aligned} y_0'' &= \frac{1}{D}\{-(4y_0' + y_1') - 20(2y_0' + y_1')\lambda - 5(3y_0' + y_1')\mu\}, \\ y_1'' &= \frac{1}{D}\{3(2y_0' + 3y_1') + 20(y_0' + 2y_1')\lambda + 5(3y_0' + 5y_1')\mu\}. \end{aligned} \tag{2.9}$$

As for the third condition in (2.2), it may be written as

$$(6x_0' + 6x_1' - x_1'' - 12l)y_0'' - (6y_0' + 6y_1' - y_1'')x_0'' \neq 0. \tag{2.10}$$

This is not the only way to fulfill the above adjustment which satisfies (2.2). For instance, we can replace x_0', y_0' and x_1', y_1', respectively, by $\rho x_0', \rho y_0'$ and $\sigma x_1', \sigma y'$ $(\rho\sigma \neq 0)$, keeping the slopes of the curve at the end points unchanged. In general, we can determine ρ and σ (having generally two sets of solutions) such that conditions (2.2) are satisfied.

To sum up what we have discussed, the following theorem is obtained.

Theorem *By a suitable choice of the second derivatives with respect to the parameter t at the end points, or adjustment of the first derivatives with respect to the parameter t while keeping slopes unchanged at the end points, a quintic parametric spline curve can be turned into a quintic rational curve.*

2.2 A Relative Affine Invariant

To a quintic rational curve defined by (2.1) and (2.2), we apply an affine transformation:

$$\begin{aligned} \bar{x} &= \alpha x + \beta y + \xi, \\ \bar{y} &= \gamma x + \delta y + \eta, \end{aligned} \tag{2.11}$$

in which $J \equiv \alpha\delta - \beta\gamma \neq 0$, and a linear transformation of the parameter t:

$$t = e\bar{t} + f, \qquad (e \neq 0). \tag{2.12}$$

Thus, the original curve becomes a new one represented by

$$\bar{x}=\sum_{j=0}^{5}\frac{1}{j!}\bar{a}_j\bar{t}^j,\qquad \bar{y}=\sum_{j=0}^{5}\frac{1}{j!}\bar{b}_j\bar{t}^j,\tag{2.13}$$

in which

$$\begin{aligned}\bar{a}_j&=e^j\sum_{k=0}^{5-j}\frac{1}{k!}(\alpha a_{k+j}+\beta b_{k+j})f^k,\\ \bar{b}_j&=e^j\sum_{k=0}^{5-j}\frac{1}{k!}(\gamma a_{k+j}+\delta b_{k+j})f^k\end{aligned}\qquad (j=1,2,\ldots,5).\tag{2.14}$$

As in dealing with the original curve defined by (2.1), we work out corresponding expressions from (2.13):

$$\bar{p}_{ij}=\bar{a}_i\bar{b}_j-\bar{a}_j\bar{b}_i\qquad (i\neq j;\ i,j=1,2,\ldots,5).$$

Using (2.14) we have

$$\bar{p}_{45}=e^9Jp_{45},$$

$$\bar{p}_{35}=e^8J(p_{35}+fp_{45}),$$

$$\bar{p}_{25}=e^7J(p_{25}+fp_{35}+\tfrac{1}{2}f^2p_{45}).$$

From (2.2), it is easily seen that there are similar relations

$$\bar{p}_{35}=0,\qquad \bar{p}_{45}=0,\qquad \bar{p}_{25}\neq 0.\tag{2.15}$$

This shows that the property of being a quintic rational curve is unchanged under any nonsingular affine transformation and linear transformation of parameter.

It has been proved in Chapter III that a general cubic parametric spline curve is certainly a cubic rational curve, and it has a relative affine invariant in terms of transformations (2.11) and (2.12). We now look for the analogous quantity for quintic rational curves.

To do so, we write the first two relations of (2.2) as

$$\begin{aligned}a_3&=\lambda a_5, & b_3&=\lambda b_5,\\ a_4&=\mu a_5, & b_4&=\mu b_5.\end{aligned}\tag{2.16}$$

Similarly, we write the first two equalities of (2.15) as

$$\begin{aligned}\bar{a}_3&=\bar{\lambda}\bar{a}_5, & \bar{b}_3&=\bar{\lambda}\bar{b}_5,\\ \bar{a}_4&=\bar{\mu}\bar{a}_5, & \bar{b}_4&=\bar{\mu}\bar{b}_5.\end{aligned}\tag{2.17}$$

Actually, it is proved easily from (2.14) and (2.16) that

$$\bar{\lambda}=\frac{1}{e^2}(\lambda+\mu f+\tfrac{1}{2}f^2),$$
$$\bar{\mu}=\frac{1}{e}(\mu+f). \tag{2.18}$$

From (2.16) we have

$$\begin{aligned} p_{13}&=\lambda p_{15}, & p_{14}&=\mu p_{15},\\ p_{23}&=\lambda p_{25}, & p_{24}&=\mu p_{25},\\ p_{34}&=0, & p_{25}&\neq 0. \end{aligned} \tag{2.19}$$

The relations similar to (2.19) also can be derived from (2.17).

Then, from (2.14), we express each $\bar{p}_{ij}$ as a linear combination of p_{rs}. In particular, we get

$$\begin{aligned} \bar{p}_{12}&=e^3J\{p_{12}+\lambda p_{15}f+\tfrac{1}{2}(\lambda p_{25}+\mu p_{15})f^2+\tfrac{1}{6}(2\mu p_{25}+p_{15})f^3+\tfrac{1}{8}p_{25}f^4\},\\ \bar{p}_{25}&=e^7Jp_{25},\\ \bar{p}_{23}&=e^5J\{p_{23}+(\mu+\tfrac{1}{2}f)fp_{25}\},\\ \bar{p}_{13}&=e^4J\{p_{13}+(\mu+\tfrac{1}{2}f)fp_{15}+\tfrac{1}{2}(\lambda+\mu f+\tfrac{1}{2}f^2)fp_{25}\},\\ \bar{p}_{15}&=e^6J(p_{15}+p_{25}f),\\ \bar{p}_{14}&=e^5J\{p_{14}+p_{15}f+(\mu+f)fp_{25}\}. \end{aligned} \tag{2.20}$$

We have made use of (2.19) to ensure that the terms after the first in the right-hand side of the relations in (2.20) are linear combinations of p_{15} and p_{25}.

Hence

$$\begin{aligned} \bar{p}_{12}\bar{p}_{25}&=e^{10}J^2\{p_{12}p_{25}+f(\lambda+\tfrac{1}{2}\mu f+\tfrac{1}{6}f^2)p_{15}p_{25}+f^2(\tfrac{1}{2}\lambda+\tfrac{1}{3}\mu f+\tfrac{1}{8}f^2)p_{25}^2\},\\ \bar{p}_{23}^2&=e^{10}J^2\{p_{23}^2+(\mu+\tfrac{1}{2}f)f(2\lambda+\mu f+\tfrac{1}{2}f^2)p_{25}^2\},\\ \bar{p}_{13}\bar{p}_{15}&=e^{10}J^2\{p_{13}p_{15}+(\mu+\tfrac{1}{2}f)fp_{15}^2+2(\lambda+\mu f+\tfrac{1}{2}f^2)fp_{15}p_{25}\\ &\qquad+(\lambda+\mu f+\tfrac{1}{2}f^2)f^2p_{25}^2\},\\ \bar{p}_{14}^2&=e^{10}J^2\{p_{14}^2+2(\mu+\tfrac{1}{2}f)fp_{15}^2+2f(\mu+f)^2p_{15}p_{25}+f^2(\mu+f)^2p_{25}^2\},\\ \bar{p}_{14}\bar{p}_{23}&=e^{10}J^2\{p_{14}p_{23}+f[\lambda+(\mu+f)(\mu+\tfrac{1}{2}f)]p_{15}p_{25}\\ &\qquad+(\lambda+\mu f+\tfrac{1}{2}f^2)(\mu+f)fp_{25}^2\}. \end{aligned}$$

Define

$$I=3p_{12}p_{25}+\tfrac{1}{2}p_{23}^2-p_{13}p_{15}+\tfrac{1}{2}p_{14}^2-p_{14}p_{23}, \tag{2.21}$$

and $\bar{I}$ similarly, we obtain

$$\bar{I} = e^{10} J^2 I. \tag{2.22}$$

Theorem *The quantity I defined by* (2.21) *is a relative affine invariant of the curve under nonsingular affine transformations and linear transformations of the parameter with weight* 2 *and* 10, *respectively.*

In the next section, we will give another proof for the theorem.

2.3 Singularities, Inflection Points and Three Related Relative Affine Invariants

The fact that the rational curve (2.1) is a quintic algebraic curve can be proved after simplifying the parametric expressions of the curve by suitable transformations (2.11) and (2.12).

Actually, we choose an affine transformation

$$\bar{x} = -\frac{2b_5}{p_{25}} x + \frac{2a_5}{p_{25}} y + \xi,$$

$$\bar{y} = \frac{120}{b_5} y + \eta$$

(ξ and η are appropriate constants) and a transformation of the parameter

$$t = \bar{t} - \frac{p_{15}}{p_{25}}.$$

Then we calculate the parametric expressions

$$\bar{x} = -\bar{t}^2, \qquad \bar{y} = g\bar{t} + c\bar{t}^2 + b\bar{t}^3 + a\bar{t}^4 + \bar{t}^5. \tag{2.23}$$

Certainly, all coefficients in (2.23) can be obtained directly by computation, but only a, b and g are involved while discussing singularities and inflection points and they can be found easily by the relations between $\bar{p}_{ij}$ and $\bar{p}_{ij}$. In this case

$$J = -\frac{240}{p_{25}}, \qquad e = 1, \qquad f = -\frac{p_{15}}{p_{25}};$$

$$\bar{p}_{12} = 2g, \qquad \bar{p}_{23} = -12b, \qquad \bar{p}_{25} = -240, \qquad \bar{p}_{24} = -48a,$$

otherwise $\bar{p}_{ij} = 0$.

So we have

$$a = 5\left(\mu - \frac{p_{15}}{p_{25}}\right), \tag{2.24}$$

$$b = 20\left[\frac{p_{23}}{p_{25}} - \mu\frac{p_{15}}{p_{25}} + \tfrac{1}{2}\left(\frac{p_{15}}{p_{25}}\right)^2\right], \tag{2.25}$$

$$g = -120\left[\frac{p_{12}}{p_{25}} - \tfrac{1}{2}\lambda\left(\frac{p_{15}}{p_{25}}\right)^2 + \tfrac{1}{6}\mu\left(\frac{p_{15}}{p_{25}}\right)^3 - \tfrac{1}{24}\left(\frac{p_{15}}{p_{25}}\right)^4\right]. \tag{2.26}$$

Eliminating $\bar{t}$ from (2.23), an implicit function of the quintic rational curve is

$$F(x, y) \equiv (y + cx - ax^2)^2 + x(x^2 - bx + g)^2 = 0. \tag{2.27}$$

We have written x, y instead of $\bar{x}$, $\bar{y}$, just for simplicity.

Now we can evaluate the number of real singularities and their coordinates without difficulty. We will consider three situations, corresponding to $g<0$, $g>0$ and $g=0$. Moreover, everything is still classified by $b<0$, $b>0$ and $b=0$. To show it clearly, we make a table here

	g	b	Real singularities	Coordinates
I	$g<0$	arbitrary	one loop	(x_{-1}, y_{-1})
II	$g>0$	$II_1: b>-2\sqrt{g}$	none	
		$II_2: b<-2\sqrt{g}$	two loops	$(x_\varepsilon, y_\varepsilon)\varepsilon=\pm 1$
III	$g=0$	$III_1: b\geqslant 0$	one cusp	$(0, 0)$
			one loop	(b, ab^2-bc)
		$II_2: b<0$	one cusp	$(0, 0)$

in which

$$x_\varepsilon = \tfrac{1}{2}(b + \varepsilon\sqrt{b^2 - 4g}), \qquad (\varepsilon = \pm 1).$$
$$y_\varepsilon = (ab - c)x_\varepsilon - ag,$$

The quantities a, b and g are involved in not only the determination of singularities, but the equations of inflection points. Actually, the inflection points of curve (2.23) are determined by

$$\frac{d\bar{x}}{d\bar{t}}\frac{d^2\bar{y}}{d\bar{t}^2} - \frac{d\bar{y}}{d\bar{t}}\frac{d^2\bar{x}}{d\bar{t}^2} = 0,$$

i.e.,

$$\bar{t}^4 + \tfrac{8}{15}a\bar{t}^3 + \tfrac{1}{5}b\bar{t}^2 - \frac{g}{15} = 0. \tag{2.28}$$

Let

$$A=\tfrac{8}{15}a, \qquad B=\tfrac{1}{5}b, \qquad G=-\tfrac{1}{15}g. \tag{2.29}$$

As we know, solving (2.28) for $\bar{t}$ is just to find the roots of the equation

$$(A\lambda)^2=(\lambda^2-G)(A^2+8\lambda-4B)$$

or, after setting $\tau=\lambda-\frac{2}{3}B$, to find the roots of standard equation

$$\tau^3+p\tau+q=0 \tag{2.30}$$

in which

$$\begin{aligned} p&=-(G+\tfrac{4}{3}B^2),\\ q&=-(\tfrac{1}{6}BG+\tfrac{1}{8}GA^2+\tfrac{16}{27}B^3). \end{aligned} \tag{2.31}$$

Its discriminant is

$$D=(15)^4(4p^3+27q^2). \tag{2.32}$$

By arrangement, D takes the form expressed by a, b and g

$$D=g(240g^2+\tfrac{192}{25}a^4g-\tfrac{549}{4}b^2g+\tfrac{72}{5}ga^2b+\tfrac{432}{5}b^4-\tfrac{768}{25}a^2b^3). \tag{2.33}$$

Using (2.24), (2.25) and (2.26), (2.33) becomes

$$D=\Phi\left(\frac{p_{12}}{p_{25}}, \frac{p_{15}}{p_{25}}, \frac{p_{23}}{p_{25}}, \lambda, \mu\right). \tag{2.34}$$

Thus, we have

Theorem *To make the numbers of real inflection points as small as possible, the discriminant of the quintic rational curve must be nonnegative.*

In fact, we have

1. *When $D>0$, the curve (2.30) has one real root and two imaginary roots.*
2. *When $D=0$, the curve (2.30) has two equal real roots.*
3. *When $D<0$, the curve (2.30) has three different real roots.*

Changing a quintic rational curve (2.1) into the curve represented by (2.13) by transformations (2.11) and (2.12), then by the transformation appearing at the beginning of this section, the new curve is similar to (2.23). What is the relationship between the coefficients $\bar{a}$, $\bar{b}$, $\bar{g}$ of the new curve and a, b, g of the previous curve?

From (2.24) to (2.26) and the corresponding expressions of $\bar{a}$, $\bar{b}$, $\bar{g}$, considering (2.18) and (2.20), we could verify

$$\bar{a} = \frac{1}{e} a, \qquad \bar{b} = \frac{1}{e^2} b, \qquad \bar{g} = \frac{1}{e^4} g. \tag{2.35}$$

This shows that a, b, g, and therefore Φ, are all relative affine invariants. In fact,

$$\Phi\left(\frac{\bar{p}_{12}}{\bar{p}_{25}}, \frac{\bar{p}_{15}}{\bar{p}_{25}}, \frac{\bar{p}_{23}}{\bar{p}_{25}}, \bar{\lambda}, \bar{\mu}\right) = e^{-12}\Phi\left(\frac{p_{12}}{p_{25}}, \frac{p_{15}}{p_{25}}, \frac{p_{23}}{p_{25}}, \lambda, \mu\right). \tag{2.36}$$

At last, we point out that (2.22) can be proved easily by using (2.35): By calculation, I in (2.21) has the expression

$$I = \tfrac{1}{800} p_{25}^2 (b^2 - 20g), \tag{2.37}$$

so that (2.22) follows immediately by using (2.20) and (2.35).

3 Some Relative Affine Invariants of Rational Integral Curves of Degree *n*

Suppose that the rational integral curve

$$\begin{aligned} x &= \sum_{i=0}^{n} \frac{1}{i!} a_i t^i, \\ y &= \sum_{i=0}^{n} \frac{1}{i!} b_i t^i \end{aligned} \tag{3.1}$$

satisfies h conditions

$$\begin{aligned} &p_{r,n} = 0 \qquad (r = n-h, n-h+1, \ldots, n-1), \\ &p_{n-h-1,n} \neq 0, \end{aligned} \tag{3.2}$$

in which $0 \leq h \leq n-3$ (when $h = n-3$, the curve takes the form $y = \sum_{i=0}^{n} c_i x^i$ and has $n-2$ inflection-points) and

$$p_{i,j} = a_i b_j - a_j b_i \qquad (i<j;\ i, j = 1, 2, \ldots, n). \tag{3.3}$$

Condition (3.2) shows that the coefficients of the last $h+1$ terms in the right-hand side of the two equalities in (3.1) are proportional. Such curves have $2n-h-4$ relative affine invariants (see Su Buchin [5], 1977).

3.1 Inflection Points of Rational Integral Curves

By an affine transformation in the xy-plane,

$$\begin{aligned}\bar{x} &= \alpha x + \beta y + \xi, \\ \bar{y} &= \gamma x + \delta y + \eta,\end{aligned} \tag{3.4}$$

(in which $J \equiv \alpha\delta - \beta\gamma \neq 0$) and a linear transformation

$$t = c\bar{t} + f \qquad (c \neq 0), \tag{3.5}$$

equations (3.1) become

$$\begin{aligned}\bar{x} &= \sum_{i=0}^{n} \frac{1}{i!} \bar{a}_i \bar{t}^i, \\ \bar{y} &= \sum_{j=0}^{n} \frac{1}{j!} \bar{b}_j \bar{t}^j.\end{aligned} \tag{3.6}$$

We have assumed

$$\begin{aligned}\bar{a}_i &= c^i \sum_{k=0}^{n-i} \frac{1}{k!} (\alpha a_{k+i}) f^k, \\ \bar{b}_j &= c^j \sum_{l=0}^{n-j} \frac{1}{l!} (\gamma a_{l+j} + \delta b_{l+j}) f^l.\end{aligned} \tag{3.7}$$

(When $i = j = 0$, we add ξ and η, respectively, to the right-hand side of the equations of (3.7).)

By definition $\bar{p}_{i,j} = \bar{a}_i \bar{b}_j - \bar{a}_j \bar{b}_i$, it is easy to show

$$\bar{p}_{i,j} = c^{i+j} J \sum_{k=0}^{n-i} \sum_{l=0}^{n-j} \frac{1}{k!\,l!} p_{k+i,l+j^*} f^{k+l} \qquad (i < j;\ i, j = 1, 2, \ldots, n). \tag{3.8}$$

Particularly, we have

$$\bar{p}_{i,n} = c^{n+i} J \sum_{k=0}^{n-i} \frac{1}{k!} p_{k+i,n^*} f^k.$$

Hence for $n - h \leq i \leq n - 1$, we obtain

$$\begin{aligned}\bar{p}_{i,n} &= 0, \\ \bar{p}_{n-h-1,n} &= c^{2n-h-1} J p_{n-h-1,n} \neq 0.\end{aligned} \tag{3.9}$$

This means that what we have discussed are rational integral curves having intrinsic affine invariant properties.

Here we mention an important equality,

$$\frac{\bar{p}_{n-h-2,n}}{\bar{p}_{n-h-1,n}}=\frac{1}{c}\left(\frac{p_{n-h-2,n}}{p_{n-h-1,n}}+f\right), \tag{3.10}$$

which can be derived from (3.8) and is useful in the sequel.

Furthermore, we should point out some relation from (3.2), that is

$$p_{r,s}=0, \qquad (r<s;\ r,s=n-h,\ n-h+1,\ldots,n-1). \tag{3.11}$$

Now, we turn our attention to the study of the inflection points of the curve (3.1). Denoting the first and second differentiations with respect to the parameter t by "$'$" and "$''$", the inflection-point equation $x'y''-x''y'$ can be written as

$$\sum_{i=1}^{n}\sum_{j=2}^{n}\frac{1}{(i-1)!(j-2)!}p_{i,j}t^{i+j-3}=0,$$

or

$$\sum_{k=0}^{2n-h-4}\frac{1}{k!}g_k t^k=0. \tag{3.12}$$

We have set

$$g_k=k!\sum_i\frac{1}{(i-1)!(k+1-i)!}p_{i,k+3-i} \qquad (k=0,1,\ldots,2n-h-4), \tag{3.13}$$

where, i in the summation satisfies $\max(1,k+3-n)\leqslant i\leqslant\min(n,k+2)$.

Using (3.9) and (3.11), we know that the curve (3.1) has $(2n-h-4)$ inflection points. This can also be seen in the next section.

3.2 Adjoint Transformation T^* and Relative Affine Invariants

The rational integral curve has such a character that its parametric equations will be simplified greatly under a so-called adjoint transformation T^* expressed by

$$\begin{aligned} x^* &= \frac{(n-h-1)!b_n}{p_{n-h-1,n}}x-\frac{(n-h-1)!a_n}{p_{n-h-1,n}}y+\xi^*,\\ y^* &= \frac{1}{b_n}y+\eta^*; \end{aligned} \tag{3.14}$$

and

$$t^*=t+\frac{p_{n-h-2,n}}{p_{n-h-1,n}}. \tag{3.15}$$

Hence we have

$$J^* = \frac{(n-h-1)!}{p_{n-h-1,n}},$$
$$c^* = 1, \qquad f^* = -\frac{p_{n-h-2,n}}{p_{n-h-1,n}}. \tag{3.16}$$

By T^*, the equations of the curve (3.1) become

$$x^* = t^{*n-h-1} + (*) + \frac{1}{(n-h-3)!} a^*_{n-h-3} t^{*n-h-3} + \cdots + a^*_1 t^*,$$
$$y^* = \frac{1}{n!} t^{*n} + \frac{1}{(n-1)!} b^*_{n-1} t^{*n-1} + \cdots + b^*_1 t^*, \tag{3.17}$$

in which, $(*)$ represents the missing terms, and

$$a^*_i = \sum_{k=0}^{n-i} \frac{(n-h-1)!}{k!} \frac{p_{k+i,n}}{p_{n-h-1,n}} \left(-\frac{p_{n-h-2,n}}{p_{n-h-1,n}}\right)^k \qquad (i = 1, 2, \ldots, n-h-3), \tag{3.18}$$

$$b^*_j = \sum_{l=0}^{n-j} \frac{1}{l!} \frac{b_{l+j}}{b_n} \left(-\frac{p_{n-h-2,n}}{p_{n-h-1,n}}\right)^l \qquad (j = 1, 2, \ldots, n-1). \tag{3.19}$$

(We simply let $b^*_n = 1$. When $a^*_{n-h-3} \neq 0$, we again apply an affine transformation and a transformation of the parameter to make (3.17) keep the same form, but after the transformation the corresponding coefficient a^*_{n-h-3} equals ± 1. Thus, the other coefficients are affine invariants of the curve. Conversely, when $a^*_{n-h-3} = 0$, we can turn another coefficient into ± 1 and obtain affine invariants similarly.)

We should point out that the right-hand sides in (3.17) have the following characteristics: (1) The coefficients of the terms of the highest degree are, respectively, 1 and $1/n!$; (2) The term of degree $(n-h-2)$ disappears in the first equation, which follows from (3.15). The fact that each equation does not contain a constant term follows from appropriate choices of ξ and η in (3.14).

From (3.18) and (3.19) we have

$$p^*_{i,j} = \sum_{k=0}^{n-i} \sum_{l=0}^{n-j} \frac{(n-h-1)!}{k!\,l!\,b_n p_{n-h-1,n}} (p_{k+i,n} b_{l+j} - p_{l+j,n} b_{k+i})$$
$$\times \left(-\frac{p_{n-h-2,n}}{p_{n-h-1,n}}\right)^{k+l} \qquad (i = 1, 2, \ldots, n-h-3; j > i; j = 1, 2, \ldots, n). \tag{3.20}$$

As in constructing g_k from $p_{i,j}$ in (3.13), we work out the corresponding quantities g_k^* in terms of $p_{i,j}^*$,

$$g_k^* = k!\sum_i \frac{1}{(i-1)!(k+1-i)!}\, p_{i,k+3-i}^* \qquad (0 \leqslant k \leqslant 2n-h-4). \quad (3.21)$$

The range of i is the same as in (3.13). Because the inflection point equation (3.12) is covariant with respect to T^*, after transformation, it takes the form

$$\sum_{k=0}^{2n-h-4} \frac{1}{k!}\, g_k^* t^{*k} = 0. \quad (3.22)$$

From (3.21) and $n \geqslant 3$, we see that

$$g_0^* = p_{12}^* \neq 0.$$

Note that $p_{12}^* \neq 0$ is a hypothesis. On the contrary, if $p_{12}^* = 0$, from (3.31), which appears later, we see that g_{2n-h-4}^* is a non-zero constant. Thus replacing G_r $(r = 1, 2, \ldots, 2n-h-4)$ in (3.23) by g_r^* $(r = 1, 2, \ldots, 2n-h-5)$, the number of invariants decreases to $2n-h-5$.

Letting

$$G_r = \frac{g_r^*}{g_0^*} \qquad (r = 1, 2, \ldots, 2n-h-4), \quad (3.23)$$

the equation (3.22) becomes

$$1 + \sum_{r=1}^{2n-h-4} \frac{1}{r!}\, G_r t^{*r} = 0. \quad (3.24)$$

We call (3.24) the *inflection-point equation* of the curve represented by (3.1).

Such quantities G_r $(r = 1, 2, \ldots, 2n-h-4)$ are relative affine invariants of rational integral curves.

To explain the facts just mentioned, we first change (3.1) into (3.6) by transformations (3.4) and (3.5), then write the inflection-point equation of the curve represented by (3.6) as

$$1 + \sum_{r=1}^{2n-h-4} \frac{1}{r!}\, \bar{G}_r \bar{t}^{*r} = 0, \quad (3.25)$$

in which

$$\bar{t}^* = \bar{t} + \frac{\bar{p}_{n-h-2,n}}{\bar{p}_{n-h-1,n}}. \quad (3.26)$$

We can easily prove that

$$\bar{G}_r = c^r G_r \qquad (r = 1, 2, \ldots, 2n-h-4). \quad (3.27)$$

Actually, from (3.5), (3.10) and (3.26) we get

$$\bar{t}^* = \frac{1}{c}\, t^*. \tag{3.28}$$

Substituting the last relation into (3.25), then comparing the resulting equation with (3.24), we obtain (3.27) immediately.

Concerning invariants G_r $(r = 1, 2, \ldots, 2n-h-4)$, we mention that when h takes its maximum value $n-3$, the number of inflection points is $n-1$. Meanwhile, only the first term of the right-hand side of the first equality in (3.17) remains, i.e., t^{*2}, so that $g_2^* = 0$, and furthermore $G_2 \equiv 0$. In particular, if $n = 3$, then $h = 0$ and the cubic parametric curve has but one non-zero relative affine invariant (see Chapter III).

On the other hand, if h assumes the minimal value 0, the number of inflection points is the biggest, i.e., $2n-4$, but among the invariants, there must be one which is identically zero. This is because from (3.17) we have the inflection-point equation

$$\frac{dx^*}{dt^*}\frac{d^2y^*}{dt^{*2}} - \frac{dy^*}{dt^*}\frac{d^2x^*}{dt^{*2}} = 0.$$

The coefficient from $t^{*2n-h-5}$ is

$$\frac{h(n-h-1)}{(n-2)!}\, b_{n-1}^*, \tag{3.29}$$

so that if $h = 0$ then

$$G_{2n-5} \equiv 0. \tag{3.30}$$

It remains to discuss the case $0 < h < n-3$. First of all, from (3.29) we have

$$g_{2n-h-5}^* = h(n-1)(n-h-1)b_{n-1}^*.$$

And from (3.21) or directly from (3.17) we get

$$g_{2n-h-4}^* = \frac{(h+1)(n-h-1)(2n-h-4)!}{(n-1)!}, \tag{3.31}$$

which is a non-zero constant.

We can derive $(2n-h-4)$ relative affine invariants G_r in which $G_{2n-h-5} \neq 0$. Functional relations may exist among the invariants. For example, when $n = 5$, $h = 1$, from (3.17) we have

$$g_0^* = a_1^* b_2^*, \qquad g_1^* = a_1^* b_3^* - 6b_1^*, \qquad g_2^* = a_1^* b_4^* - 6b_2^*,$$

$$g_3^* = a_1^*, \qquad g_4^* = 12 b_4^*, \qquad g_5^* = 30.$$

Then

$$72g_0^* = g_3^*(g_3^* g_4^* - 12g_2^*),$$

or

$$2G_5^2 = 5G_3(5G_3G_4 - 2G_2G_5). \tag{3.32}$$

But such relations may not always exist. For instance, if $n = 7$, $h = 2$, we compute

$$g_0^* = a_1^* b_2^* - a_2^* b_1^*, \qquad g_1^* = a_1^* b_3^*,$$

$$g_2^* = a_2^* b_3^* + a_1^* b_4^* - 24b_1^*,$$

$$g_3^* = a_2^* b_4^* + a_1^* b_5^* - 48b_2^*,$$

$$g_4^* = 3a_2^* b_5^* + a_1^* b_6^* - 48b_3^*,$$

$$g_5^* = 4a_2^* b_6^* + a_1^*,$$

$$g_6^* = 5(24b_5^* - a_2^*),$$

$$g_7^* = 336b_6^*, \qquad g_8^* = 672.$$

Thus, relations such as (3.32) do not occur. That is to say, for arbitrarily given G_r $(r = 1, 2, \ldots, 8)$, except for parametric displacement $(c = 1)$ and affine transformation, we could have some rational integral curves $(h = 2)$ of degree 7 whose relative affine invariants are just $G_1, G_2, \ldots, G_8$.

In summary, we conclude with the following

Theorem *Any rational integral curve of degree $n(\geqslant 3)$ which satisfies conditions* (3.2) *must have* $(2n - h - 4)$ *inflection points and the same number of relative affine invariants. When $h = 0$ or $h = n - 3$, there must be one zero invariant; when $0 < h < n - 3$, certain functional relations may exist among these invariants.*

3.3 Examples

The expressions of the invariants in the case $n = 3$ have been worked out in Chapter III. We now provide the expressions of the relative affine invariants of the rational integral curves $(h = 0)$ of degree four and five.

1. $n = 4$.

Let $\lambda = p_{2,4}/p_{3,4}$. The corresponding equations of (3.17) are

$$\begin{aligned} x' &= t^{*3} + (*) + a_1^* t^*, \\ y^* &= \frac{1}{4!} t^{*4} + \frac{1}{3!} b_3^* t^{*3} + \frac{1}{2} b_2^* t^{*2} + b_1^* t^*, \end{aligned} \tag{3.33}$$

in which

$$
\begin{aligned}
a_1^* &= 3\left(2\frac{p_{1,4}}{p_{3,4}} - \lambda^2\right),\\
b_1^* &= \frac{b_1}{b_4} - \frac{b_2}{b_4}\lambda + \frac{1}{2}\frac{b_3}{b_4}\lambda^2 - \frac{1}{6}\lambda^3,\\
b_2^* &= \frac{b_2}{b_4} - \frac{b_3}{b_4}\lambda + \frac{1}{2}\lambda^2,\\
b_3^* &= \frac{b_3}{b_4} - \lambda.
\end{aligned} \tag{3.34}
$$

Then we have

$$
\begin{aligned}
G_1 &= \frac{a_1^* b_3^* - 6b_1^*}{a_1^* b_2^*},\\
G_2 &= \frac{a_1^* - 6b_2^*}{a_1^* b_2^*},\\
G_3 &= 0,\\
G_4 &= \frac{12}{a_1^* b_2^*}.
\end{aligned} \tag{3.35}
$$

2. $n = 5$.

Let $\mu = p_{3,5}/p_{4,5}$. The corresponding equations of (3.17) are

$$
\begin{aligned}
x^* &= t^{*4} + (*) + \tfrac{1}{2}a_2^* t^{*2} + a_1^* t^*,\\
y^* &= \frac{1}{5!}t^{*5} + \frac{1}{4!}b_4^* t^{*4} + \frac{1}{3!}b_3^* t^{*3} + \frac{1}{2}b_2^* t^{*2} + b_1^* t^*,
\end{aligned} \tag{3.36}
$$

in which

$$
\begin{aligned}
a_1^* &= 8\left(3\frac{p_{1,5}}{p_{4,5}} - 3\frac{p_{2,5}}{p_{4,5}}\mu + \mu^3\right),\\
a_2^* &= 12\left(\frac{p_{2,5}}{p_{4,5}} - \mu^2\right);\\
b_1^* &= \frac{b_1}{b_5} - \frac{b_2}{b_5}\mu + \frac{1}{2}\frac{b_3}{b_5}\mu^2 - \frac{1}{3!}\frac{b_4}{b_5}\mu^3 + \frac{1}{4!}\mu^4,\\
b_2^* &= \frac{b_2}{b_5} - \frac{b_3}{b_5}\mu + \frac{1}{2}\frac{b_4}{b_5}\mu^2 - \frac{1}{12}\mu^3,\\
b_3^* &= \frac{b_3}{b_5} - \frac{b_4}{b_5}\mu + \frac{1}{2}\mu^2,\\
b_4^* &= \frac{b_4}{b_5} - \mu.
\end{aligned} \tag{3.37}
$$

Thus we get

$$
\begin{aligned}
G_1 &= \frac{a_1^* b_3^*}{a_1^* b_2^* - a_2^* b_1^*}, \\
G_2 &= \frac{a_2^* b_3^* + a_1^* b_4^* - 18 b_1^*}{a_1^* b_2^* - a_2^* b_1^*}, \\
G_3 &= \frac{2a_2^* b_4^* + a_1^* - 36 b_2^*}{a_1^* b_2^* - a_2^* b_1^*}, \\
G_4 &= \frac{3a_2^* - 36 b_3^*}{a_1^* b_2^* - a_2^* b_1^*}, \\
G_5 &= 0, \\
G_6 &= \frac{90}{a_1^* b_2^* - a_2^* b_1^*}.
\end{aligned} \tag{3.38}
$$

4 The Intrinsic Affine Invariants of Parametric Curves in an Affine Hyperspace

In m-dimensional space, we now consider the curves whose non-homogeneous coordinates x_p $(p = 1, 2, \ldots, m)$ are all polynomials of degree n in a certain parameter t, i.e. rational integral curves. In the case $m = 2$, when we choose $n = 3$ or $n = 5$, we get the cubic parametric curves discussed in Chapter III or the quintic parametric curves discussed in Section 2 of this chapter.

We will prove the following

Theorem *In m-dimensional space, a parametric curve of degree $n(> m > 2)$ generally has $m(n-m)-2$ intrinsic affine invariants.*

Proof By definition, the equation of C_n is

$$(E) \qquad \boldsymbol{x} = \sum_{i=0}^{n} \frac{1}{i!} \boldsymbol{a}_i t^i \qquad (n > m \geqslant 2),$$

in which $\boldsymbol{x} = (x_p)$, $\boldsymbol{a}_i = (a_{p_i})$ $p = 1, 2, \ldots, m$; $i = 0, 1, \ldots, n$.

Write the equation

$$(F) \qquad f(t) \equiv \det \left| \frac{d\boldsymbol{x}}{dt} \, \frac{d^2\boldsymbol{x}}{dt^2} \cdots \frac{d^m \boldsymbol{x}}{dt^m} \right| = 0.$$

Let

$$p_{i_1,i_2,\ldots,i_m}=\det|\boldsymbol{a}_{i_1}\boldsymbol{a}_{i_2}\cdots\boldsymbol{a}_{i_m}|,\qquad 0\leqslant i_1,i_2,\ldots,i_m\leqslant n,$$

and expand $f(t)$ to a polynomial in t as

$$f(t)=A_0+A_1t+\cdots\frac{1}{N!}A_Nt^N,$$

It is easy to see that $N=m(n-m)$.

Let

$$R=\frac{p_{n-m,n-m+2,\ldots,n}}{p_{n-m+1,n-m+2,\ldots,n}},$$

and assume $F(t^*)\equiv f(t^*-R)$. Rewrite (F) as

$$(F^*)\qquad \sum_{k=0}^{N}\frac{1}{k!}g_k^*t^{*k}=0,$$

where we have supposed $g_0^*=f(-R)\neq 0$. Then

$$1+\sum_{k=1}^{N}\frac{1}{k!}G_k^*t^{*k}=0,$$

in which

$$G_k^*=\frac{g_k^*}{g_0^*}\qquad (k=1,2,\ldots,N).$$

From now on, we will prove

$$g_N^*=\frac{n!N!}{(n-m)!}\prod_{p=1}^{m}(m-p)!,\qquad g_{N-1}^*\equiv 0.$$

Our final goal is to prove that, under the assumption $G_1^*\neq 0$,

$$I_r\equiv G_r^*/(G_1^*)^r,\qquad r=2,\ldots,N-2,N$$

and the desired $N-2$ intrinsic affine invariants.

To do so, we consider the normal affine transformation A:

$$\bar{x}_r=\sum_{S=1}^{m}\alpha_{rs}x_s+\alpha_{r0},\qquad r=1,2,\ldots,m,$$

in which

$$J\equiv\det|\alpha_{rs}|\neq 0.$$

Meanwhile, consider the linear transformation T of the parameter t,

$$t=c\bar{t}+f\qquad (c\neq 0).$$

By the above transformations, equation (E) turns into

$$(\bar{E}) \qquad \bar{\boldsymbol{x}} = \sum_{j=0}^{n} \frac{1}{j!} \bar{\boldsymbol{a}}_j \bar{t}^j.$$

Simple calculations show

$$\bar{a}_{rj} = c^j \sum_{s=1}^{m} a_{rs} \sum_{i=j}^{n} \frac{1}{(i-j)!} a_{si} f^{i-j} + \delta_{0j} a_{r0}, \qquad j = 0, 1, \ldots, n;\ r = 1, \ldots, m.$$

In what follows, we only evaluate such $\bar{a}_{rj}$, with $j \neq 0$, then we assume

$$i, j, l = 1, 2, \ldots, n,$$
$$p, r, s = 1, 2, \ldots, m.$$

Letting

$$A_{sj} = \sum_{i=j}^{n} \frac{1}{(i-j)!} a_{si} f^{i-j},$$

we have

$$\bar{a}_{rj} = c^j \sum_{s=1}^{m} \alpha_{rs} A_{sj}.$$

Let (a_{rs}) and (A_{sj}) denote the corresponding $m \times m$ and $m \times n$ matrices, respectively. Then

$$(\bar{a}_{rj}) = c^j (\alpha_{rs})(A_{sj}).$$

According to the definition and the above relations we see that

$$\bar{P}_{j_1, j_2, \ldots, j_m} = C^j \cdot J \cdot P_{j_1, j_2, \ldots, j_m} \qquad \left(j = \sum_{r=1}^{m} j_r\right),$$

where we define

$$P_{j_1, j_2, \ldots, j_m} \equiv \det |A_{s,j_1} A_{s,j_2} \cdots A_{s,j_m}|.$$

In particular, we now evaluate $\bar{P}_{n-m+1, n-m+2, \ldots, n}$ and $\bar{P}_{n-m, n-m+2, \ldots, n}$. From the definition of $A_{s,j}$, we get

$$A_{s,n} = a_{s,n},$$
$$A_{s,n-1} = a_{s,n-1} + a_{s,n} f,$$
$$A_{s,n-2} = a_{s,n-2} + a_{s,n-1} f + \frac{1}{2!} a_{s,n} f^2,$$
$$A_{s,n-m+2} = a_{s,n-m+2} + a_{s,n-m+3} f + \cdots + \frac{1}{(m-2)!} a_{s,n} f^{m-2},$$
$$A_{s,n-m+1} = a_{s,n-m+1} + a_{s,n-m+2} f + \cdots + \frac{1}{(m-1)!} a_{s,n} f^{m-1},$$
$$A_{s,n-m} = a_{s,n-m} + a_{s,m-n+1} f + \cdots + \frac{1}{m!} a_{s,n} f^m.$$

Hence

$$\bar{P}_{n-m+1,n-m+2,\ldots,n} = c^{\rho} \cdot J \cdot P_{n-m+1,n-m+2,\ldots,n},$$

$$\bar{P}_{n-m,n-m+2,\ldots,n} = c^{\rho-1} \cdot J \cdot [P_{n-m,n-m+2,\ldots,n} + fP_{n-m+1,n-m+2,\ldots,n}],$$

in which

$$\rho = \tfrac{1}{2}m(2n-m+1).$$

Defining $R = P_{n-m,n-m+2,\ldots,n}/P_{n-m+1,n-m+2,\ldots,n}$ and $\bar{R}$ similarly, the above relation turns into

$$\bar{R} = \frac{1}{c}(R+f).$$

Define $t^* = t + R$ as the normalized parameter of t, and similarly define $\bar{t}^* = \bar{t} + \bar{R}$ as that of $\bar{t}$. Then the above relation becomes

$$\bar{t}^* = \frac{1}{c}\, t^*.$$

If we can prove $A_{N-1}/A_N = R$, then, substituting $\frac{1}{c}t^*$ for t^* in

$$(\bar{F}^*) \qquad 1 + \sum_{r=1}^{N} \frac{1}{r!}\, \bar{G}_r^* \bar{t}^{*r} = 0,$$

and comparing the resulting equation with (F^*), we have

$$\bar{G}_r^* = c^r G_r^* \qquad (r = 1, 2, \ldots, N),$$

and we obtain the intrinsic affine invariants $I_r \equiv G_r^*/(G_1^*)^r, (r = 2, 3, \ldots, N)$.

To complete the proof, we assume that $P_{n-m+1,n-m+2,\ldots,n}$ and its principal minor determinants of order $1, 2, \ldots, m-1$ chosen from bottom to top are all non-zero. Then there exists only one affine transformation (i.e., the normalized transformation)

$$A^*: \boldsymbol{x} \to \boldsymbol{x}^*, \qquad \det|A^*| \neq 0$$

and normalized transformation of the parameter,

$$T^*: t = t^* - R,$$

to change (E) into its normalized system of equations

$$(E^*) \qquad x_p^* = \sum_{i=1}^{8n-m+p} \frac{1}{i!}\, a_{p,i}^* t^{*i},$$

in which

$$a^*_{p,n-m+p}=(n-m+p)!,\qquad a^*_{1,n-m}=0,\qquad p=1,2,\ldots,m.$$

Thus, (F) becomes

$$(F^*)\qquad \det\left|\frac{d\mathbf{x}^*}{dt^*}\ \frac{d^2\mathbf{x}^*}{dt^{*2}}\cdots\frac{d^m\mathbf{x}^*}{dt^{*m}}\right|=0,$$

or is expanded as

$$\sum_{k=0}^{N}\frac{1}{k!}g_k^*t^{*k}=0.$$

It now remains to calculate g_N^* and g_{N-1}^*.

Figure 8-1 symbolizes the m columns of the left-hand side in (F^*). In each column the circles of the same row represent a polynomial in t^*, in which the degree of each term decreases to zero from right to left. A full circle occurring at the last but one in the first row represents a missing term (for $a^*_{1,n-m}=0$).

Take column m as an example. The circles of row m express the terms of $d^m x^*_m/dt^{*m}$ of degree $n-m$, $n-m-1,\ldots,0$, respectively, from right to left. Terms represented by the circles of the same vertical line are of the same degree. For instance, the terms of line j_m numbered from the right are all of degree $n-m-j_m+1$ $(j_m=1,2,\ldots,m)$. Only the last j_m terms of

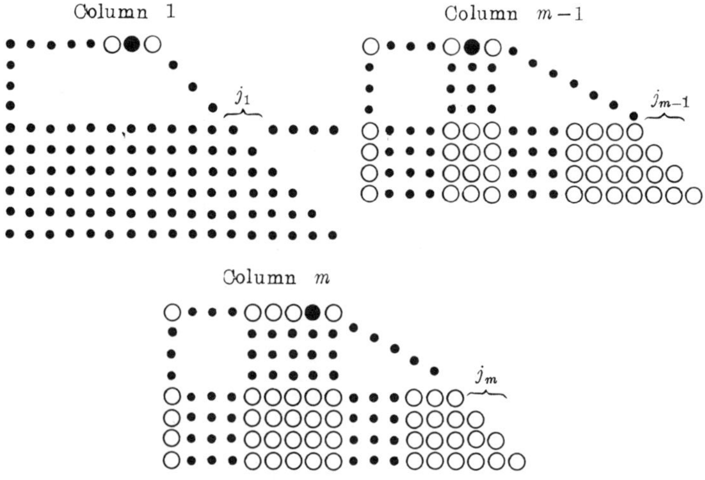

Figure 8-1

line j_m are not zero and the top non-zero term of it is

$$T_{m,j_m} = \frac{(n-j_m+1)!}{(n-m-j_m+1)!} t^{*n-m-j_m+1}.$$

As j_m in succession takes the values $1, 2, \ldots, m$, the non-zero terms form an isosceles triangle illustrated by Fig. 8-1.

The example adapts to any column. For column μ, consider the non-zero terms of line j_μ whose non-zero top term is

$$T_{\mu,j_\mu} = \frac{(n-j_\mu+1)!}{(n-\mu-j_\mu+1)!} t^{*n-\mu-j_\mu+1} \qquad (\mu = 1, 2, \ldots, m).$$

Note that if $j_\mu = j_\nu$ with $\mu \neq \nu$, then the terms in the rows of the same number of the two columns are proportional, and thus the determinant formed by the two columns and the other $m-2$ columns vanishes identically.

Now, it is not difficult to find g_N^* or $A = g_N^*/N!$.

In fact, in order to make the highest degree N of t^* occur, we should choose the vertical line in every related isosceles triangle, and $j_\mu \neq j_\nu$ must follow from $\mu \neq \nu$. Therefore $(j_1, j_2, \ldots, j_m)$ should be a permutation of $(1, 2, \ldots, m)$. Denote the parity of the permutation

$$\begin{pmatrix} j_1 & j_2 & \cdots & j_{m-1} & j_m \\ m+1-j_1 & m+1-j_2 & \cdots & m+1-j_{m-1} & m+1-j_m \end{pmatrix}$$

by $\sigma(j_1, j_2, \ldots, j_m)$ assuming $+1$ or -1 according as the permutation is even or odd. Then the determinant of order m formed by m vertical lines equals

$$\sigma(j_1, j_2, \ldots, j_m) T_{1,j_1} T_{2,j_2} \cdots T_{m,j_m}.$$

Since

$$\sum_{\mu=1}^{m} (n-\mu-j_\mu+1) = m(n-m) = N,$$

we know that the term of highest degree is At^{*N}, i.e.,

$$\sum \sigma(j_1, j_2, \ldots, j_m) T_{1,j_1} T_{2,j_2} \cdots T_{m,j_m} \qquad (j_1, j_2, \ldots, j_m) = (1, 2, \ldots, m).$$

Hence

$$A = \sum \sigma(j_1, j_2, \ldots, j_m) \frac{(n-j_1+1)!(n-j_2+1)! \cdots (n-j_m+1)!}{(n-j_1)!(n-j_2-1)! \cdots (n-m-j_m+1)!}$$

$$(j_1, j_2, \ldots, j_m) = (1, 2, \ldots, m).$$

We have

$$D_m^{m(n-m)} = \begin{vmatrix} \dfrac{(n-m+1)!}{(n-m)!} & \dfrac{(n-m+1)!}{(n-m-1)!} & \cdots & \dfrac{(n-m+1)!}{(n-2m+1)!} \\ \dfrac{(n-m+2)!}{(n-m+1)!} & \dfrac{(n-m+2)!}{(n-m)!} & \cdots & \dfrac{(n-m+2)!}{(n-2m+2)!} \\ \cdots & \cdots & \cdots & \cdots \\ \dfrac{n!}{(n-1)!} & \dfrac{n!}{(n-2)!} & \cdots & \dfrac{n!}{(n-m)!} \end{vmatrix}.$$

By direct computation or induction we can prove that

$$D_m^{m(n-m)} = \frac{n!}{(n-m)!} \prod_{\nu=1}^{m} (m-p)!.$$

Then we get

$$g_N^* = \frac{N!n!}{(n-m)!} \prod_{p=1}^{m} (m-p)!.$$

Secondly, we turn to calculate the higher degree term Bt^{*N-1} and obtain that $B=0$, i.e., $g_{N-1}^*=0$.

To explain this fact in detail, we need only study how Bt^{*N-1} is formed. From the procedure in finding A, we know clearly that among $j_1, j_2, \ldots, j_m$, there must be two equal elements. If they are less than m, then the determinant is zero as we have discussed; if $j_\mu = m$, then the line substituting for the vertical line m in the column μ is just the vertical line $j_\mu + 1$ in the same column, but the top term of the latter is the missing term represented by the full circle. Multiplying the missing term by its corresponding terms (except the term in line j_μ), we get zero. Thus, we have proved $B=0$.

Finally, we give a simple way to find invariants. Let

$$f(t) = \det \left| \frac{dx}{dt} \, \frac{d^2\mathbf{x}}{dt^2} \cdots \frac{d^m\mathbf{x}}{dt^m} \right|, \qquad F(t^*) = f(t^* - R).$$

Then, under the assumption $F(0) \neq 0$, the equation

$$\frac{1}{F(0)} F(t^*) = 0$$

coincides with

$$1 + \sum_{r=1}^{N} G_r t^{*r} = 0.$$

References

ADAMS, J. A.

[1] Geometric concepts for computer graphics, AD-750743, 1972.

[2] Cubic spline curve fitting with controlled end conditions, *CAD*[1] **6** (1974), 2–9.

[3] The intrinsic method for curve definition, *CAD* **7** (1975), 243–249.

AHLBERG, J. H.

[1] Spline approximation and computer-aided design, *Advances in Computers* **10** (1970), 275–290.

[2] The spline approximation as an engineering tool, *Computer Aided Engineering*, G. M. L. Gladwell, ed., 1971, 1–18.

[3] Cardinal splines on the real line, *J. Approx. Theory* **5** (1972), 428–437.

AHLBERG, J. H., AND NILSON, E. N.

Convergence properties of the spline fit, *J. Soc. Indust. Appl. Math.* **11** (1963), 95–104.

AHLBERG, J. H., NILSON, E. N., AND WALSH, J. L.

The Theory of Splines and Their Applications, Academic Press, 1967.

AHUJA, D. V.

An algorithm for generating spline-like curves, *IBM Systems J.* **7** (1968), 206–217.

AHUJA, D. V., AND COONS, S. A.

Interactive graphics in data processing, geometry for construction and display, *IBM Systems J.* **7** (1968), 188–205.

[1] *CAD* is an abbreviation of *Computer Aided Design.*

AKIMA, H.

[1] A new method of interpolation and smooth curve fitting based on local procedures, *J. ACM* **17** (1970), 589–602.

[2] A method of bivariate interpolation and smooth surface fitting based on local procedures, *Comm. ACM* **17** (1974), 18–20, 26–31.

[3] A method of bivariate interpolation and smooth surface fitting for irregularly distributed data points, *ACM Trans. Math. Software* **4** (1978), 148–159.

ALFT, W. E., AND COLLATZ, G.

Computer aided design of ship's lines by nonlinear distortion of parent forms, *Computer Applications in Automation of Shipyard Operation and Ship Design II*, 1976.

ANDERSON, W. L.

Application of bicubic spline functions to two-dimensional gridded data, U.S. Geological Survey Rpt. GD-71-022, 1971.

ARMIT, A. P.

[1] Computer systems for interactive design of three-dimensional shape, Cambridge University, Ph. D. Thesis, 1970.

[2] Curve and surface design using multipatch and multiobject design systems, *CAD* **3** (1971).

BALL, A. A.

[1] CONSURF Part 1: Introduction of the conic lofting tile, *CAD* **6** (1974), 243–249.

[2] CONSURF Part 2: Description of the algorithms, *CAD* **7** (1975), 237–242.

[3] CONSURF Part 3: How the program is used, *CAD* **9** (1977), 9–18.

[4] A simple specification of the parametric cubic segment, *CAD* **10** (1978), 181–182.

BARNHILL, R. E.

[1] Smooth interpolation over triangles, *CAGD*[2] 1974, 45–70.

[2] Representation and approximation of surfaces, *Mathematical Software III*, J. R. Rice ed., Academic Press, 1977, 69–120.

BARNHILL, R. E., BIRKHOFF, G., AND GORDON, W. J.

Smooth interpolation in triangles, *J. Approx. Theory* **8** (1973), 114–128.

BARNHILL, R. E., AND GREGORY, J. A.

Compatible smooth interpolation in triangles, *J. Approx. Theory* **15** (1975), 214–225.

BARNHILL, R. E., AND RIESENFELD, R. F. (eds)

Computer Aided Geometric Design, Academic Press, 1974.

BÉZIER, P. E.

[1] Numerical Control-Mathematics and Applications, John Wiley and Sons, 1972.

[2] Numerical control in automobile design and manufacture of curved

[2] CAGD is an abbreviation of *Computer Aided Geometric Design*.

surfaces, *Curved Surfaces in Engineering*, IPC Science and Technology Press, 1972.

[3] Mathematical and Practical Possibilities of UNISURF, *CAGD*, 1974, 127–152.

[4] Essai de definition numérique des courbes et des surfaces paramétriques, Thesis, University of Pierre et Marie Curie, Paris, 1977.

[5] General distortion of an ensemble of biparametric surfaces, *CAD* **10** (1978), 116–120.

BHATTACHARYYA, B. K.

Bicubic spline interpolation as a method for treatment of potential field data, *Geophysics* **34** (1969), 402–423.

BIRKHOFF, G., AND DEBOOR, C.

[1] Error bounds for cubic spline interpolation, *J. Math. Mech.* **13** (1964), 827–835.

[2] Piecewise polynomial interpolation and approximation. *In* Approximation of Functions (H. L. Garabedian, ed.), 1965, 164–190.

BIRKHOFF, G., BURCHARD, H., AND THOMAS, D.

Nonlinear interpolation by splines, pseudo-splines, and elastica. Res. Publ. General Motors Research, 468, 1965.

BIRKHOFF, G., AND GARABEDIAN, H. L.

Smooth surface interpolation, *J. Math. Phys.* **39** (1960), 258–268.

BOHM, W.

Über die Konstruktion von *B*-Spline Kurven, *Computing* **18** (1977), 161–166.

BOHMER, K., MEINARDUS, G., AND SCHEMPP, W. (eds)

Spline Functions, Lecture Notes 501, Springer-Verlag, 1976.

BOLTON, K. M.

Biarc curves, *CAD* **7** (1975), 89–92.

DEBOOR, C.

[1] Bicubic spline interpolation, *J. Math. and Phys.* **41** (1962), 212–218.

[2] On calculating with *B*-splines, *J. Approx. Theory* **6** (1972), 50–62.

[3] Package for calculating with *B*-splines, MRCTSR#1333 (1973); *SIAM J. Numer. Anal.* **14** (1977), 441–472.

[4] Splines as linear combinations of *B*-splines, a survey. *In* Approx. Theory II (G. G. Lorentz, ed.), Academic Press, 1976, 1–47.

[5] A Practical Guide to Splines, Springer-Verlag, 1978.

[6] On splines and their minimum properties, *J. Math. Mech.* **15** (1966), 953–969.

BURAU, P. W.

Algebraische Kurven und Flächen, Sammlung Göschen Bd., 435, I, 1962.

C. A. D. CENTRE

An Introduction to Numerical Master Geometry, Computer Aided Design Centre, Cambridge, 1972.

CADWELL, J. H., AND WILLIAMS, D. E.

Some orthogonal methods of curve and surface fitting, *Comput. J.* **4** (1961).

Carlson, R. E., and Hall, C. A.
Bicubic spline interpolation in rectangular polygons, *J. Approx. Theory* **6** (1972), 366–377.
Catmull, E., and Clark, J.
Recursively generated *B*-spline surface on arbitrary topological meshes, *CAD* **10** (1978), 350–355.
Catmull, E., and Rom, R.
A class of local interpolating splines, *CAGD*, 1974, 317–326.
Chang, G., and Wu, J.
On the mathematical foundations of the Bézier method, *Mathematica Numerica Sinica* **2** (1980), 41–49 (in Chinese).
Cheney, E., and Schurer, F.
Convergence of cubic spline interpolation, *J. Approx. Theory* **3** (1970), 114–116.
Clark, J. H.
[1] Some properties of *B*-splines, *Second USA-Japan Computer Conf. Proc.*, 1975, 542–545.
[2] Designing surfaces in 3-D, *Commun. ACM* **19** (1976), 454–460.
Clenshaw, C. W., and Hayes, J. G.
Curve and surface fitting, *J. Inst. Math. Appl.* **1** (1965), 164–183.
Cline A. K.
Scalar- and planar-valued curve fitting using splines under tension, *Commun. ACM* **17** (1974), 218–220.
Coons, S. A.
[1] Surfaces for computer-aided design of space figures, Mech. Eng. Dept., MIT, 1964.
[2] Surfaces for computer-aided design of space forms, AD-663504, 1967.
[3] Surface patches and *B*-spline curves, *CAGD*, 1974, 1–16.
[4] Modification of the shape of piecewise curves, *CAD* **9** (1977), 178–180.
Cox, M. G.
The numerical evaluation of *B*-splines, *J. Inst. Math. Appl.* **10** (1972), 134–149.
Curry, H. B., and Schoenberg, I. J.
On Pólya frequency functions IV. The fundamental spline functions and their limits, *J. d'Analyse Math.* **17** (1966), 71–107.
Davis, P. J.
Interpolation and Approximation, Ginn-Blaisdell Publ. Co., 1963.
Delvos, F. J.
On surface interpolation, *J. Approx. Theory* **15** (1975), 209–213.
Dimsdale, B.
[1] Bicubic patch bounds, *Comp. & Maths, with Appls.* **3** (1977), 95–104.
[2] Convex cubic splines, *IBM J. Res. Develop.* **22** (1978), 168–178.
Dimsdale, B., and Burkley, R. M.
Bicubic patch surfaces for high-speed numerical control processing, *IBM*

J. Res. Develop. **20** (1976), 358–367.

DIMSDALE, B., AND JOHNSON, K.
Multiconic surfaces, *IBM J. Res. Develop.* **19** (1975), 523–529.

DONG, GUANGCHANG *et al.*
Mathematical Lofting of Ship Hull—Bounce Method, Science Press, Beijing, 1978 (in Chinese).

DONG GUANGCHANG, LIANG YOUDONG, AND HE YUANJUN
Spline interpolation and approximation by biarc, *Acta Mathematicae Applicatae Sinica* **1** (1978), 330–340 (in Chinese).

EARNSHAW, J. L., AND YUILLE, I. M.
A method of fitting parametric equations for curves and surfaces to sets of points defining them approximately, *CAD* **3** (1971), 19–22.

ELLIS, T. M. R., AND MCLAIN, D. H.
Algorithm 514. A new method of cubic curve fitting using local data, *ACM Trans. Math. Software* **3** (1977), 175–179.

EPSTEIN, M. P.
On the influence of parametrisation in parametric interpolation, *SIAM J. Numer. Anal.* **13** (1976), 261–268.

FAUX, I. D.
Simple cross-sectional designs based on Bézier patch surfaces and a comparison with indirect Bézier methods and traditional proportional development methods, *Conference on Computer Aided Manufacture*, June 1978, 20–22.

FAUX, I. D., AND PRATT, M. J.
Computational Geometry for Design and Manufacture, Ellis Horwood Limited, Chichester, 1979.

FERGUSON, J.
Multivariable curve interpolation, *J. ACM* **11** (1964), 221–228.

FISHER, S. D.
Some nonlinear variational problems. *In* Approx. Theory II (G. G. Lorentz, ed.), Academic Press, 1976, 357–363.

FLUTTER, A. G., AND ROLPH, R. N.
POLYSURF: An interactive system for computer-aided design and manufacture of components, *CAD 76 Proceedings*, 150–158.

FORREST, A. R.
[1] Curves and surfaces for computer-aided design, Ph. D. Thesis, Cambridge University, 1968.
[2] Computational geometry, *Proc. Roy. Soc. London A* **321**, 1971, 187–195.
[3] Coons surfaces and multivariable functional interpolation, Cambridge University CAD Group Doc., December 1971.
[4] On Coons and other methods for the representation of curved surfaces, *Computer Graphics and Image Processing* **1** (1972), 341–359.
[5] Interactive interpolation and approximation by Bézier polynomials, *Computer J.* **15** (1972), 71–79.

[6] Computational geometry—achievements and problems, *CAGD*, 1974, 17–44.

[7] Recent trends in CAGD, *Proc. Conf. on Interactive Techniques in CAD*, Bologna, September 1978.

[8] Lecture Notes on Computer-Aided Geometric Design and Computational Geometry, University of East Anglia, 1978.

[9] The twisted cubic curve: A computer-aided geometric design approach, University of East Anglia, July 1979.

[10] On the rendering of surface, University of East Anglia, 1979.

FOWLER, A. H., AND WILSON, C. W.

Cubic spline, a curve fitting routine, Report Y-1400, Oak Ridge, 1963.

GLASS, J. M.

Smooth-curve interpolation: A generalized spline-fit procedure, *BIT* **6** (1966), 277–293.

GODWIN, A. N.

Family of cubic splines with one degree of freedom, *CAD* **11** (1979), 13–18.

GORDON, W. J.

[1] Spline-blended surface interpolation through curve networks, *J. Math. Mech.* **18** (1969), 931–952.

[2] Distributive lattices and the approximation of multivariate functions. *In* Approximations with Special Emphasis on Spline Functions (I. J. Schoenberg, ed.), Academic Press, 1969.

[3] Blending-function methods of bivariate and multivariate interpolation and approximation, *SIAM J. Numer. Anal.* **8** (1971), 158–177.

GORDON, W. J., AND RIESENFELD, R. F.

[1] Bernstein-Bézier methods for the computer aided design of free form curves and surfaces, *J. ACM* **21** (1974), 293–310.

[2] *B*-spline curves and surfaces, *CAGD*, 1974, 95–126.

GREGORY, J. A.

[1] Symmetric smooth interpolation on triangles, TR/34, Brunel Univ. Uxbridge, England, 1973.

[2] Smooth interpolation without twist constraints, *CAGD*, 1974, 71–87.

GREVILLE, T. N. E. (ed.)

Theory and Applications of Spline Functions, Academic Press, 1969.

GROSSMAN, M.

Parametric curve fitting, *Computer J.* **14** (1971), 169–172.

HALL, C. A.

[1] Bicubic interpolation over triangles, *J. Math. Mech.* **19** (1969), 1–11.

[2] Error bounds for bicubic spline interpolation, *J. Approx. Theory* **7** (1973), 41–47.

[3] Natural cubic and bicubic spline interpolation, *SIAM J. Numer. Anal.* **10** (1973), 1055–1060.

HALL, C. A., AND MEYER, W. W.
Optimal error bounds for cubic spline interpolation, *J. Approx. Theory* **16** (1976), 105–122.

HALLIDAY, J., WALL, J. F., AND JOYNER, W. D.
Report on multivariable curve fitting using fundamental splines, Report No. MSN. 167, British Aircraft, 1972.

HARTLEY, P. J., AND JUDD, C. J.
Parametrization of Bézier-type *B*-spline curves and surfaces, *CAD* **10** (1978), 130–134.

HAYES, J. G.
[1] Numerical methods for curve and surface fitting, *Bull. Inst. Math. Applic.* 1974.
[2] New shapes from bicubic splines, National Physical Laboratory, NSAC 58, 1974.

HAYES, J. G., AND HALLIDAY, J.
The least squares fitting of cubic spline surfaces to general data sets, *J. Inst. Maths. Applics.* **14** (1974), 89–103.

HOLLADAY, J. C.
Smoothest curve approximation, *Math. Tables Aids Computation* **11** (1957), 233–243.

HOSAKA, M.
[1] Fairing and elastica, *Proc. 8th Conf. of Information Processing Soc. of Japan*, 1967, 49–50.
[2] Theory and design of free-form surface, *Information Processing in Japan* **7** (1967), 54–61.
[3] Theory of curve and surface synthesis and their smooth fitting, *Information Processing in Japan* **9** (1969), 60–68.

HOSAKA, M., AND KUROTA, M.
On the decomposition of curves and surfaces in CAD, *Information Processing in Japan* **17** (1976), 1120–1127 (in Japanese).

HOSKINS, N. D., AND PENZO, P. J.
Some approximation properties of periodic parametric cubic splines, *BIT* **14** (1974), 152–156.

ICHIDA, K., YOSHIMOTO, F., AND KIYONO, T.
Curve fitting by a one pass method with a piecewise cubic polynomial, *ACM Trans. Math. Software* **3** (1977), 164–174.

INSELBERG, A.
Cubic splines with infinite derivatives at some knots, *IBM J. Res. Develop.* **20** (1976), 430–436.

ISHIMATSU, Y. *et al.*
Computer-aided generation of sculputured surfaces, *Jl. N. C.* April 74, 33–39, (1974).

KAMMERER, W. J., REDDIEN, G. W., AND VARGA, R. S.
Quadratic interpolatory splines, *Numer. Math.* **22** (1974), 241–259.

KERSHAW, D.
Inequality on the elements of the inverse of a certain tridiagonal matrix, *Math. of Computation* **24** (1970), 155–158.

KUO, C.
Computer methods for ship surface design, 1971.

LARKIN, F. M.
An interpolation procedure based on fitting elasticas to given data points, Culham Operating System-Note 5/66, Theory Division, Culham Laboratory, 1966.

LAWSON, C. L.
Software for C^1 surface interpolation, Math. Software III (J. R. Rice, ed.), Academic Press, 1977, 161–194.

LEE, E. H., AND FORSYTHE, G. E.
Variational study of nonlinear spline curves, *SIAM Rev.* **15** (1973), 120–133.

LEE, T. M. P.
Analysis of an efficient homogeneous tensor representation of surfaces for computer display, Advanced Computer Graphics, Plenum Press, 1971.

LEVIN, J.
A parametric algorithm for drawing pictures of solid objects composed of quadric surfaces, *Comm. AGM* **19** (1976), 555–563.

LI YUESHENG AND QI DONGXU
Splines Method, Science Press, Beijing, 1979 (in Chinese).

LIU DINGYUAN
[1] On equivalence for several kinds of spline curves, 1978 (in Chinese).
[2] Spline curves in tension and convexity preserving, 1979 (in Chinese).
[3] Fairness of cubic *B*-spline curves, 1979 (in Chinese).
[4] Shape control of a parametric cubic curve segment and a cubic Bézier curve, *Acta Mathematicae Applicatae Sinica*, **4** (1981), 158–165 (in Chinese).
[5] A theorem on the convexity of planar Bézier curves of degree n, *Chinese Annals of Mathematics*, **3** (1982), 45–55 (in Chinese).

LIU DINGYUAN AND SU WENRONG
[1] Local cubic curves and biarc splines, Hudong Technic Information, 1980, No. 2, 17–28 (in Chinese).
[2] Discrete curvature method for curves fairing, Shipbuilding Technology, 1980, No. 6, 12–16 (in Chinese).

LOVE, A. E. H.
The Mathematical Theory of Elasticity, 4th ed., Cambridge Univ. Press, 1934.

MACCALLUM, K. J.
Mathematical design of hull surfaces, *The Naval Architect*, July 1972, 359–373.

MacLaren, D. H.
Formulas for fitting a spline curve through a set of points, Boeing Appl. Math. Report 2, 1958.

Malcolm, M. A.
On the computation of nonlinear spline functions, *SIAM J. Numer. Anal.* **14** (1977), 254–282.

Manning, J. R.
Continuity conditions for spline curves, *Computer J.* **17** (1974), 181–186.

Mansfield, L.
Higher order compatible triangular finite elements, *Numer. Math.* **22** (1974), 89–97.

Marsden, M. J.
Quadratic spline interpolation, *Bull. Amer. Math. Soc.* **80** (1974), 903–906.

McAlister, D. F., Passow, E., and Roulier, J. A.
Algorithms for computing shape preserving spline interpolations to data, *Math. Computation* **139** (1977), 717–725.

McAllister, D. F., and Roulier, J. A.
Interpolation by convex quadratic splines, *Math. Comp.* **32**, 144 (1978), 1054–1062.

Mehlum, E.
[1] Curve and surface fitting based on variational criteriae for smoothness, Central Institute for Industrial Research, Oslo, Norway, 1969.
[2] Nonlinear splines, *CAGD*, 1974, 173–207.

Mehlum, E., and Sorensen, P. F.
Example of an existing system in the ship-building industry: the AUTOKON system, *Proc. Roy. Soc. London, A* **321** (1971), 219–233.

Minsky, M., and Papert, S.
An Introduction to Computational Geometry, MIT Press, 1969.

Munchmeyer, F. C., and Lau, G. K. H.
On the interactive design of smooth patched surfaces, *Proc. International Conf. Interactive Techniques in CAD*, 1978.

Munchmeyer, F. C., Schubert, C., and Nowaski, H.
Interactive design of fair hull surfaces using *B*-splines, *Computer Applications in the Automation of Shipyard Operation and Ship Design III*, 1979.

Nielson, G. M.
Some piecewise polynomial alternatives to splines under tension, *CAGD*, 1974, 209–235.

Nutbourne, A. W.
A cubic spline package: Part 2—the mathematics, *CAD* **5** (1973), 7–13.

Nutbourne, A. M., McLellan, and Kensit
Curvature profiles for plane curves, *CAD* **4** (1972), 176–184.

Nutbourne, A. W., Morus, R. B., and Hollins, C. M.
A cubic spline package: Part 1—the user's guide, *CAD* **4** (1972), 228–238.

Okada, Y.
A numerical experiment on the fairing free-form curves, *Information Processing in Japan* **9** (1969), 69–74.

Overhauser, A. W.
Analytic definition of curves and surfaces by parabolic blending, Technical Report No. SL 68-40, Ford Motor Company Scientific Laboratory, 1968.
Pal, T. K.
[1] Intrinsic spline curve with local control, *CAD* **10** (1978), 19-29.
[2] Mean tangent rotational angles and curvature integration, *CAD* **10** (1978), 30-34.
Pal, T. K., and Nutbourne, A. W.
Two-dimensional curve synthesis using linear curvature elements, *CAD* **9** (1977), 121-134.
Passow, E.
[1] Piecewise monotone spline interpolation, *J. Approx. Theory* **12** (1974), 240-241.
[2] Monotone quadratic spline interpolation, *J. Approx. Theory* **19** (1977), 123-134.
Passow, E., and Roulier, A.
Monotone and convex spline interpolation, *SIAM J. Numer. Anal.* **14** (1977).
Peters, G. J.
Interactive computer graphics application of the parametric bi-cubic surface to engineering design problems, *CAGD*, 1974, 259-302.
Pilcher, D. T.
Smooth parametric surfaces, *CAGD*, 1974, 237-253.
Podolsky, B., and Denman, H. H.
Conditions on minimization criteria for smoothing, *Math. Comp.* **18** (1964), 441-448.
Powell, M. J. D.
Piecewise quadratic surface fitting for contour plotting. *In* Software for Numerical Analysis (D. J. Evans, ed.), Academic Press, 1974, 253-271.
Prenter, P. M.
Splines and Variational Methods, Wiley-Interscience, 1975.
Pruess, S.
Properties of spline in tension, *J. Approx. Theory* **17** (1976), 86-96.
Qi Dongxu
Curve fitting by method of numerical smoothing, *Acta Mathematica Sinica* **18** (1975), 173-184 (in Chinese).
Riesenfeld, R. F.
[1] Applications of *B*-spline approximation to geometric problems of computer-aided design, Ph. D. Thesis at Syracuse University (1972). Published at University of Utah, UTEG-GSc-73-126 (1972).
[2] Nonuniform *B*-spline curves, *Proc. 2nd USA-Japan Computer Conference*, 1975, 551-555.

RIS, G.
Raccordement à l'ordre N entre carreaux de surfaces définis par des polynomes biparamétriques à coefficients vectoriels. Application aux surfaces UNISURF, These Université de Nancy (April 1975).

ROGERS, D. F., AND ADAMS, J. A.
Mathematical elements for computer graphics, McGraw-Hill, 1976.

SABIN, M. A.
[1] Spline surface, British Aircraft Corporation, 1969.
[2] Parametric splines in tension, British Aircraft Corporation, 1970.
[3] The British Aircraft Corporation Numerical Master Geometry System, *Proc. Roy. Soc. London A* **321** (1971), 197–205.
[4] A method for displaying the intersection curve of two quadric surfaces, *Comput. J.* **19** (1976), 336–338.
[5] The use of piecewise forms for the numerical representation of shape, Ph. D. Thesis, Hungarian Academy of Sciences, Budapest, Report 60/1977, 1977.

SABLONNIÈRE, P.
[1] Splines et base de Bernstein, Polygones associés à fonction-spline et applications, UER de Mathématiques, Université de Lille I Publications, No. 109, 112, 123 (1977).
[2] Spline and Bézier polygons associated with a polynomial spline curve, *CAD* **10** (1978), 257–261.

SADEGHL, M. M., AND GOULD, S. S.
A comparison of two parametric surface patch methods, *CAD* **6** (1974), 217–220.

SCHECHTER, A.
[1] Synthesis of 2D curves by blending piecewise linear curvature profiles, *CAD* **10** (1978), 8–18.
[2] Linear blending of curvature profiles, *CAD* **10** (1978), 101–109.

SCHOENBERG, I. J.
[1] Contributions to the problem of approximation of equidistant data by analytic functions, *Quart. Appl. Math.* **4** (1946), 45–99, 112–141.
[2] On variation diminishing approximation methods. *In* On Numerical Approximation (R. E. Langer, ed.), Univ. of Wisconsin Press, 1959, 249–274.
[3] On spline functions. *In* Inequalities (O. Shisha, ed.), Academic Press, 1967, 255–291.
[4] Cardinal Spline Interpolation, *CBMS* **12**, SIAM, 1973.

SCHOENBERG, I. J. (ed.)
Approximation Theory with Special Emphasis on Spline Functions, Academic Press, 1969.

SCHULTZ, M. H.
Spline Analysis, Prentice-Hall, 1973.

SCHUMAKER, L. L.
Fitting surfaces to scattered data. *In* Approximation Theory II (G. G. Lorentz, ed.), Academic Press, 1976, 203–268.

SCHWEIKERT, D. G.
An interpolation curve using a spline in tension, *J. Math. Phys.* **45** (1966), 312–317.

SHEPARD, D.
A two-dimensional interpolation function for irregularly spaced data, *Proc. 1964, ACM Nat. Conf.* 517–524.

SHU, H., HORI, S., MANN, W. R., AND LITTLE, R. N.
The synthesis of sculptured surfaces. *In* Numerical Control Programming Languages (W. H. P. Leslie, ed.), North Holland Publishing Co., Amsterdam, 1970.

SOUTH, N. E., AND KELLY, J. P.
Analytic surface methods, Ford Motor Company Report, December 1965.

SPÄTH, H.
[1] Two-dimensional smooth interpolation, *Computing* **4** (1969), 178–182.
[2] Exponential spline interpolation, *Computing* **4** (1969), 225–233.
[3] Two-dimensional exponential splines, *Computing* **7** (1971), 178–182.
[4] Spline Algorithms for Curves and Surfaces, Utilitas Mathematics Publishing Inc., Winnipeg, Canada, 1974.

SU BUCHIN
[1] Lectures on Higher Geometry, Shanghai Scientific and Technical Publishers, 1964 (in Chinese).
[2] Some notes on parametric cubic spline curves, *Acta Mathematicae Applicatae Sinica*, 1976, No. 1, 49–58 (in Chinese).
[3] A theorem on parametric cubic spline curves, *Acta Mathematicae Applicatae Sinica*, 1977, No. 1, 49–54 (in Chinese).
[4] A note on quintic rational curves, *Acta Mathematicae Applicatae Sinica*, 1977, No. 2, 80–89 (in Chinese).
[5] Some relative affine invariants of rational integral curves, *Fudan Journal*, 1977, No. 2, 22–29 (in Chinese).
[6] On affine invariants of a Bézier curve, *Mathematica Numerica Sinica*, **2** (1980), 289–298 (in Chinese).
[7] Some intrinsic invariants of a parametric curve in affine hyperspace, *Chinese Annals of Mathematics*, **1** (1980), 199–206 (English edition).
[8] Lectures on Differential Geometry, World Scientific Singapore, 1980.

SU BUCHIN *et al.*
Curves and Surfaces, Science Press, Beijing, 1977 (in Chinese).

SU BUCHIN AND HUA XUANJI
An extension of the biarc curve fitting, *Fudan Journal*, 1979, No. 4, 1–9 (in Chinese).

SUN JIACHANG

[1] The spline function in local coordinates and circular spline curve, *Acta Mathematica Sinica*, **20** (1977), 28–40 (in Chinese).

[2] Existence and uniqueness of interpolatory cubic splines on general end conditions, *Mathematica Numerica Sinica*, 1978, No. 2, 1-9 (in Chinese).

SUN JIACHANG AND ZHENG HUILIN

On arc and biarc curve approximation, *Mathematica Numerica Sinica*, **3** (1981), 97-112 (in Chinese).

THEILHEIMER, F., AND STARKWEATHER, W.

The fairing of ship line on a high-speed computer, *Math. Comp.* **15** (1961), 338–355.

THOMAS, D. H.

Pseudospline interpolation for space curves, *Math. Comp.* **30** (1976), 58–67.

VARAH, J. M.

On the condition number of local bases for piecewise cubic polynomials, *Math. Comp.* **31** (1977), 37–44.

VERON, M., RIS, G., AND MUSSE, J. P.

Continuity of biparametric surface patches, *CAD* **8** (1976), 267–273.

VERSPRILLE, K. J.

Computer aided design applications of the rational *B*-spline approximation form, Ph. D. Thesis, Syracuse University, 1975.

WALKER, L. F.

Curver surfaces in shipbuilding design and production. *In* Curved Surfaces in Engineering (proc. Conference at Churchill College, Cambridge, 1972), IPC Science and Technology Press, 1972.

WALKER, R. J.

Algebraic Curves, Princeton University Press, 1950.

WANG RISHUANG

The structural characterization and interpolation for multivariate splines, *Acta Mathematica Sinica*, **18** (1975), 91–106 (in Chinese).

WANG, RISHUANG

A series of convex conditions of cubic splines and some notes, *Mathematica Numerica Sinica* **1** (1979), 336-341 (in Chinese).

WANG J.

A spline interpolation with convexity, *Mathematica Numerica Sinica* **1** (1979), 233–243 (in Chinese).

WILSON, H. B., AND FARRIOR, D. S.

Computation of geometrical and inertial properties for general areas and volumes of revolution, *CAD* **8** (1976), 257–263.

WIELINGA, R. F.

Constrained interpolation using Bézier curves as a new tool in computer aided geometric design, *CAGD*, 1974, 153–172.

WIXOM, J. A.
Interpolation to networks of curves in E^3, *SIAM J. on Numer. Anal.* **15** (1978).

WOODFORD, C. H.
Smooth curve interpolation, *BIT* **9** (1969), 69–77.

WOODSFORD, P. A.
Mathematical methods in computer graphics—a survey, *Gesellschaft für Informatike, V., Symposium on Computer Graphics*, Berlin, 1971.

WU, S. C., ABEL, J. F., AND GREENBERG, D. P.
An interactive computer graphics approach to surface representation, *Comm. ACM* **10** (1977), 703–712.

XIN YUANLONG
[1] Curve fitting and fairing, *Fudan Journal*, 1975, No. 2, 103–110 (in Chinese).
[2] Bicubic spline functions and their applications in surface fairing, *Fudan Journal*, 1977, No. 1, 63–68 (in Chinese).

ZWART, P. B.
Multivariate splines with nondegenerate partitions, *SIAM J. Numer. Anal.* **10** (1973), 665–673.

Additional References

Published after 1979

ALFELD, P.

[1] A trivariate Clough-Tocher scheme for tetrahedral data, *Computer Aided Geometric Design* **1** (1984), 169–181.

[2] A bivariate C^2 Clough-Tocher scheme, *Computer Aided Geometric Design* **1** (1984), 257–267.

[3] Derivative generation from multivariate scattered data by functional minimization, *Computer Aided Geometric Design* **2** (1985), 281–296.

ALFELD, P., PIPER, B. R., AND SCHUMAKER, L. L.

Minimally supported bases for spaces of bivariate piecewise polynomials of smoothness r and degree $d \geq 4r+1$, *Computer Aided Geometric Design* **4** (1987), 105–124.

ALMGREN, F. J.

Applications of multiple-valued functions. *In* Geometric Modeling (G. Farin, ed.), SIAM, Philadelphia, 1986, 43–54.

BARNHILL, R. E.

[1] Coons' patches, *Computers in Industry* **3** (1982), 37–43.

[2] Computer aided surface representation and design. *In* Surfaces in Computer Aided Geometric Design (R. E. Barnhill and W. Boehm, eds.), North-Holland, Amsterdam, 1983, 1–24.

[3] A survey of the representation and design of surfaces, *IEEE Computer Graphics and Applications* **3** (1983), 9–16.

[4] Surfaces in computer aided geometric design: a survey with new results, *Computer Aided Geometric Design* **2** (1985), 1–17.

BARNHILL, R. E., AND BOEHM, W. (eds.)
Surfaces in Computer Aided Geometric Design, North-Holland, Amsterdam, 1983.

BARNHILL, R. E., AND FARIN, G.
C^1 quintic interpolation over triangles: two explicit representations, *Int. J. Num. Methods in Engineering* **17** (1981), 1763–1778.

BARNHILL, R. E., FARIN, G., JORDAN, M., AND PIPER, B. R.
Surface/surface intersection, *Computer Aided Geometric Design* **4** (1987), 3–16.

BARNHILL, R. E., PIPER, B. R., AND RESCORLA, K. L.
Interpolation to arbitrary data on a surface. *In* Geometric Modeling (G. Farin, ed.), SIAM, Philadelphia, 1986, 281–290.

BARNHILL, R. E., PIPER, B. R., AND STEAD, S. E.
A multidimensional surface problem: pressure on a wing, *Computer Aided Geometric Design* **2** (1985), 185–187.

BARNHILL, R. E., AND WHELAN, T.
A geometric interpretation of convexity conditions for surfaces, *Computer Aided Geometric Design* **1** (1984), 285–287.

BARSKY, B. A.
[1] The beta-spline: a local representation based on shape parameters and fundamental geometric measures, Dissertation, University of Utah, Salt Lake City, 1981.
[2] Computer aided geometric design, a bibliography with keywords and classified index, *IEEE Computer Graphics and Applications* **1** (1981), 67–109.
[3] End conditions and boundary conditions for uniform *B*-spline curve and surface representations, *Computers in Industry* **3** (1982), 17–29.

BARSKY, B. A., AND BEATTY, J. C.
Local control of bias and tension in beta-splines, *ACM Trans. on Graphics* **2** (1983), 109–134.

BARSKY, B. A., AND DEROSE, T. D.
An inutitive approach to geometric continuity for parametric curves and surfaces. *In* Computer Generated Images—The State of the Art (N. Magnenay and D. Thalmann, eds.), Springer, Berlin, 1985, 159–175.

BEZ, H. E.
On invariant curve forms, *Computer Aided Geometric Design* **3** (1986), 193–204.

BOEHM, W.
[1] Inserting new knots into *B*-spline curves, *Computer-Aided Design* **12** (1980), 199–201.
[2] Generating the Bézier points of *B*-spline curves and surfaces, *Computer-Aided Design* **13** (1981), 365–366.
[3] On cubics, a survey, *Computer Graphics and Image Processing* **19** (1982), 201–226.

[4] Generating the Bézier points of triangular splines. *In* Surfaces in Computer Aided Geometric Design (R. E. Barnhill and W. Boehm, eds.), North-Holland, Amsterdam, 1983, 77–92.

[5] Subdividing multivariate splines, *Computer-Aided Design* **15** (1983), 345–352.

[6] Calculating with box splines, *Computer Aided Geometric Design* **1** (1984), 149–162.

[7] Multivariate spline algorithms. *In* Mathematics of Surfaces (J. Gregory, ed.), Oxford University Press, 1985.

[8] Triangular spline algorithms, *Computer Aided Geometric Design* **2** (1985), 61–67.

[9] On the efficiency of knot insertion algorithms, *Computer Aided Geometric Design* **2** (1985), 141–143.

[10] Curvature continuous curves and surfaces, *Computer Aided Geometric Design* **2** (1985), 313–323.

[11] Smooth curves and surfaces. *In* Geometric Modeling (G. Farin, ed.), SIAM, Philadelphia, 1986, 175–184.

[12] Bézier presentation of airfoils, *Computer Aided Geometric Design* **4** (1987), 17–22.

[13] Rational geometric splines, *Computer Aided Geometric Design* **4** (1987), 67–78.

BOEHM, W., FARIN, G., AND KAHMANN, J.

A survey of curve and surface methods in CAGD, *Computer Aided Geometric Design* **1** (1984), 1–60.

BOSWORTH, K.

Shape constrained curve and surface fitting. *In* Geometric Modeling (G. Farin, ed.), SIAM, Philadelphia, 1986, 247–264.

BRUNET, P.

Increasing the smoothness of bicubic spline surfaces, *Computer Aided Geometric Design* **2** (1985), 157–164.

BRUNET, P., AND AYALA, D.

Extended octtree representation of free form surfaces, *Computer Aided Geometric Design* **4** (1987), 141–154.

DEBOOR, C.

[1] *B*-form basics. *In* Geometric Modeling (G. Farin, ed.), SIAM, Philadelphia, 1986, 131–148.

[2] Cutting corners always works, *Computer Aided Geometric Design* **4** (1987), 125–132.

DEBOOR, C., AND HÖLLIG, K.

B-splines without divided differences. *In* Geometric Modeling (G. Farin, ed.), SIAM, Philadelphia, 1986, 21–28.

BRUECKNER, I.

Construction of Bézier points of quadrilaterals from those of triangles, *Computer-Aided Design* **12** (1980), 21–24.

CHANG, G., AND DAVIS, P. J.

A new proof for the convexity of the Bernstein–Bézier surfaces over triangles, *J. Approx. Theory* **40** (1984), 11–28.

CHANG, G., AND FENG, Y.

An improved condition for the convexity of Bernstein–Bézier polynomials over triangles, *Computer Aided Geometric Design* **2** (1985), 279–283.

GHANG, G., AND HOSCHEK, J.

Convexity and variation diminishing property of Bernstein polynomials over triangles. *In* Multivariate Approximation Theory III, Birkhäuser, Basel, 1985.

CHANG, G., AND SU, B.

Families of adjoint patches for a Bézier triangular surface, *Computer Aided Geometric Design* **2** (1985), 37–42.

CHARROT, P., AND GREGORY, J. A.

A pentagonal surface patch for computer aided geometric design, *Computer Aided Geometric Design* **1** (1984), 87–94.

COHEN, E., AND SCHUMAKER, L. L.

Rates of convergence of control polygons, *Computer Aided Geometric Design* **2** (1985), 229–235.

COHEN, E., LYCHE, T., AND RIESENFELD, R.

Discrete box splines and refinement algorithms, *Computer Aided Geometric Design* **1** (1984), 131–148.

DAHMEN, W., AND MICCHELLI, C. A.

[1] Subdivision algorithms for the generation of box spline surfaces, *Computer Aided Geometric Design* **1** (1984), 115–129.

[2] Line average algorithm: a method for the computer generation of smooth surfaces, *Computer Aided Geometric Design* **2** (1985), 77–85.

[3] On the piecewise structure of discrete box splines, *Computer Aided Geometric Design* **3** (1986), 185–191.

DANNENBERG, L., AND NOWACKI, H.

Approximate conversion of surface representations with polynomial bases, *Computer Aided Geometric Design* **2** (1985), 123–131.

DEVORE, R. A., AND YAN, Z.

Error analysis for piecewise quadratic curve fitting algorithms, *Computer Aided Geometric Design* **3** (1986), 205–215.

DOKKEN, T.

Finding intersections of B-spline represented geometries using recursive subdivision techniques, *Computer Aided Geometric Design* **2** (1985), 189–195.

FARIN, G. E.

[1] Visually C^2 cubic splines, *Computer-Aided Design* **14** (1982), 137–139.

[2] Designing C^1 surfaces consisting of triangular cubic patches, *Computer-Aided Design* **14** (1982), 253–256.

[3] A construction for the visual C^1 continuity of polynomial surface patches, *Computer Graphics and Image Processing* **20** (1982), 272–282.

[4] Smooth interpolation to scattered 3D data. *In* Surfaces in Computer Aided Geometric Design (R. E. Barnhill and W. Boehm, eds.), North-Holland, Amsterdam, 1983, 43–64.

[5] Algorithms for rational Bézier curves, *Computer-Aided Design* **15** (1983), 73–77.

[6] A modified Clough-Tocher interpolant, *Computer Aided Geometric Design* **2** (1985), 19–27.

[7] Piecewise triangular C^1 surface strips, *Computer-Aided Design* **18** (1985), 45–47.

[8] Some remarks on V^2-splines, *Computer Aided Geometric Design* **2** (1985), 325–328.

[9] Triangular Bernstein–Bézier patches, *Computer Aided Geometric Design* **3** (1986), 83–127.

FARIN, G. (ed.)
Geometric Modeling, SIAM, Philadelphia, 1986.

FARIN, G., REIN, G., SAPIDIS, N., AND WORSEY, A. J.
Fairing cubic *B*-spline curves, *Computer Aided Geometric Design* **4** (1987), 91–104.

FAROUKI, R. T.
The approximation of non-degenerate offset surfaces, *Computer Aided Geometric Design* **3** (1986), 15–43.

FAROUKI, R. T., AND RAJAN, V. T.
On the numerical condition of polynomials in Bernstein form, *Computer Aided Geometric Design* **4** (1987), 191–216.

FENG, Y.-Y.
Rates of convergence of Bézier net over triangles, *Computer Aided Geometric Design* **4** (1987), 245–250.

FILIP, D., MAGEDSON, R., AND MARKOT, R.
Surface algorithms using bounds on derivatives, *Computer Aided Geometric Design* **3** (1986), 295–311.

FOLEY, T. A.
[1] Scattered data interpolation and approximation with error bounds, *Computer Aided Geometric Design* **3** (1986), 163–177.

[2] Local control of interval tension using weighted splines, *Computer Aided Geometric Design* **3** (1986), 281–294.

FORREST, A. R.
The twisted cubic curve: a computer aided geometric design approach, *Computer-Aided Design* **12** (1980), 165–172.

FRANKE, R.
Thin plate splines with tension, *Computer Aided Geometric Design* **2** (1985), 87–95.

FRITSCH, F. N.
[1] Energy comparisons of Wilson–Fowler splines with other interpolating splines. *In* Geometric Modeling (G. Farin, ed.), SIAM, Philadelphia, 1986, 185–202.

[2] The Wilson-Fowler spline is a ν-spline, *Computer Aided Geometric Design* **3** (1986), 155-162.

FRITSCH, F. N., AND CARLSON, R. E.

Monotonicity preserving bicubic interpolation: a progress report, *Computer Aided Geometric Design* **2** (1985), 117-121.

GOLDMAN, R. N.

[1] Using degenerate Bézier triangles and tetrahedra to subdivide Bézier curves, *Computer-Aided Design* **14** (1982), 307-311.

[2] Subdivision algorithms for Bézier triangles, *Computer-Aided Design* **15** (1983), 159-166.

[3] The method of resolvents: a technique for the implicitization, inversion, and intersection of non-planar, parametric, rational cubic curves, *Computer Aided Geometric Design* **2** (1985), 237-255.

GOLDMAN, R. N., AND DEROSE, T. D.

Recursive subdivision without the convex hull property, *Computer Aided Geometric Design* **3** (1986), 247-265.

GOLDMAN, R. N., SEDERBERG, T. W., AND ANDERSON, D. C.

Vector elimination: a technique for the implicitization, inversion, and intersection of planar parametric rational polynomial curves, *Computer Aided Geometric Design* **1** (1984), 327-356.

GOODMAN, T. N. T.

Properties of β-splines, *J. Approx. Theory* **44** (1985), 132-153.

GORDON, W.

An operator calculus for surface and volume modeling, *IEEE Computer Graphics and Applications* **3** (1983), 18-22.

GREGORY, J. A.

[1] A C^1 triangular interpolation patch for Computer Aided Geometric Design, *Computer Graphics and Image Processing* **13** (1980), 80-87.

[2] C^1 rectangular and non-rectangular surface patches, *Surfaces in CAGD* (R. E. Barnhill and W. Boehm, eds.), North-Holland, Amsterdam, 1983, 25-34.

[3] N-sided surface patches, *The Mathematics of Surfaces* (J. A. Gregory, ed.), Oxford, 1986, 217-232.

GREGORY, J. A., AND HAHN, J.

Geometric continuity and convex combination patches, *Computer Aided Geometric Design* **4** (1987), 79-90.

GRIEGER, I.

Geometry cells and surface definition by finite elements, *Computer Aided Geometric Design* **2** (1985), 213-222.

HAGEN, H.

[1] Geometric spline curves, *Computer Aided Geometric Design* **2** (1985), 223-227.

[2] Geometric surface patches without twist constraints, *Computer Aided Geometric Design* **3** (1986), 179-184.

HAGEN, H., AND SCHULZE, G.
Automatic smoothing with geometric surface patches, *Computer Aided Geometric Design* **4** (1987), 231–236.

HARTLEY, P. J., AND JUDD, C. J.
Parametrization and shape of *B*-spline curves and surfaces for CAD, *Computer-Aided Design* **12** (1980), 226–236.

HERRON, G.
[1] Smooth closed surfaces with discrete triangular interpolants, *Computer Aided Geometric Design* **2** (1985), 297–306.
[2] Techniques for visual continuity. *In* Geometric Modeling (G. Farin, ed.), SIAM, Philadelphia, 1986, 163–174.

HÖLLIG, K.
Geometric continuity of spline curves and surfaces, Computer Sciences Technical Report 645, University of Wisconsin, Madison, 1986.

HOLMSTRÖM, L.
Piecewise quadric blending of implicitly defined surfaces, *Computer Aided Geometric Design* **4** (1987), 171–190.

HOSAKA, M., AND KIMURA, F.
[1] Synthesis methods of curves and surfaces in interactive Computer Aided Design, *Proceedings: Interactive Techniques in Computer Aided Design*, Bologna, 1978, 151–156.
[2] Non-four-sided patch expressions with control points, *Computer Aided Geometric Design* **1** (1984), 75–86.

HOSCHEK, J.
[1] Detecting regions with undesirable curvature, *Computer Aided Geometric Design* **1** (1984), 183–192.
[2] Smoothing of curves and surfaces, *Computer Aided Geometric Design* **2** (1985), 97–105.
[3] Approximate conversion of spline curves, *Computer Aided Geometric Design* **4** (1987), 59–66.

HOUGHTON, E. G., EMNETT, R. F., FACTOR, J. D., AND SABHARWAL, C. L.
Implementation of a divide-and-conquer method for intersection of parametric surfaces, *Computer Aided Geometric Design* **2** (1985), 173–183.

JENSEN, T.
Assembling triangular and rectangular patches and multivariate splines. *In* Geometric Modeling (G. Farin, ed.), SIAM, Philadelphia, 1986, 203–220.

JONES, A.
Shape control of curves and surfaces through constrained optimization. *In* Geometric Modeling (G. Farin, ed.), SIAM, Philadelphia, 1986, 265–280.

JORDAN, M. C., AND SCHINDLER, F.
Curves under tension, *Computer Aided Geometric Design* **1** (1984), 291–300.

KAHMANN, J.
Continuity of curvature between adjacent Bézier patches, *Surfaces in Computer Aided Geometric Design* (R. E. Barnhill and W. Boehm, eds.), North-Holland, Amsterdam, 1983.

LANE, J. M., AND RIESENFELD, R. F.
[1] A theoretical development for the computer generation of piecewise polynomial surfaces, *IEEE Trans. on Pattern Analysis and Machine Intelligence* **2** (1980), 35–46.
[2] A geometric proof for the variation diminishing property of *B*-spline approximation, *J. Approx. Theory* **37** (1983), 1–4.

LASSER, D.
Bernstein–Bézier representation of volumes, *Computer Aided Geometric Design* **2** (1985), 145–149.

LEE, E.
A simplified *B*-spline computation routine, *Computing* **29** (1982), 365–373.

LEE, E. T. Y.
[1] Some remarks concerning *B*-splines, *Computer Aided Geometric Design* **2** (1985), 307–311.
[2] The rational Bézier representation for conics. *In* Geometric Modeling (G. Farin, ed.), SIAM, Philadelphia, 1986, 3–20.

LITTLE, F. F.
Convex combination surfaces. *In* Surfaces in Computer Aided Geometric Design (R. E. Barnhill and W. Boehm, eds.), North-Holland, Amsterdam, 1983, 99–108.

LIU, D.
[1] A relative projective invariant of cubic parametric curve in projective plane and its applications, *Chinese Annals of Mathematics. Ser. A* **5** (1984), 543–549 (in Chinese).
[2] Rational Bézier curves, *Acta Mathematicae Applicatae Sinica* **8** (1985), 70–83 (in Chinese).
[3] A geometric condition for smoothness between adjacent rectangular Bézier patches, *Acta Mathematicae Applicatae Sinica* **9** (1986), 432–442 (in Chinese).
[4] Algorithms for computing area and volume bounded by Bézier curves and surfaces, *Mathematica Numerica Sinica* **9** (1987), 327–336 (in Chinese).
[5] Inflection points and singular points of planar rational cubic Bézier curves, *Sino-German CAD/CAM Conference*, Xian, China, 1987.

LIU, D., AND HU, K.
Fitting of Bézier surfaces, *Acta Mathematicae Applicatae Sinica* **7** (1984), 250–256 (in Chinese).

LIU, D., ZHAO, Y., ZHAN, T., AND XIAO, H.
Fair fitting methods using Bézier curves and *B*-spline curves, *Mathematica Numerica Sinica* **6** (1984), 360–365 (in Chinese).

LYCHE, T., AND MORKEN, K.
Knot removal for parametric *B*-spline curves and surfaces, *Computer Aided Geometric Design* **4** (1987), 217–230.

LYCHE, T., COHEN, E., AND MORKEN, K.
Knot line refinement algorithms for tensor product *B*-spline surfaces, *Computer Aided Geometric Design* **2** (1985), 133–139.
[1] A locally controllable spline with tension for interactive curve design, *Computer Aided Geometric Design* **1** (1984), 199–205.
[2] Rectangular *v*-splines, *IEEE Computer Graphics and Applications* **6** (1986), 35–40.
[3] A visually continuous transfinite triangular interpolant. *In* Geometric Modeling (G. Farin, ed.), SIAM, Philadelphia, 1986, 235–246.
[4] Knot line refinement algorithms for tensor product *B*-spline surfaces, *Computer Aided Geometric Design* **2** (1985), 133–139.

NIELSON, G. M., AND FRANKE, R.
Surface construction based upon triangularizations. *In* Surfaces in Computer Aided Geometric Design (R. E. Barnhill and W. Boehm, eds.), North-Holland, Amsterdam, 1983.

NIELSON, G. M., AND RAMARAJ, R.
Interpolation over a sphere based upon a minimum norm network, *Computer Aided Geometric Design* **4** (1987), 41–58.

PIEGL, L.
[1] Representation of quadric primitives by rational polynomials, *Computer Aided Geometric Design* **2** (1985), 151–155.
[2] The sphere as a rational Bézier surface, *Computer Aided Geometric Design* **3** (1986), 45–52.
[3] Representation of rational Bézier curves and surfaces by recursive algorithms, *Computer-Aided Design* **18** (1986), 361–366.
[4] On the use of infinite control points in computer aided geometric design, *Computer Aided Geometric Design* **4** (1987), 155–166.

PIPER, B.
Visually smooth interpolation wth triangular Bézier patches. *In* Geometric Modeling (G. Farin, ed.), SIAM, Philadelphia, 1986, 221–233.

PRATT, M. J.
Smooth parametric surface approximations to discrete data, *Computer Aided Geometric Design* **2** (1985), 165–171.

PRAUTZSCH, H.
[1] A short proof of the Oslo algorithm, *Computer Aided Geometric Design* **1** (1984), 95–96.
[2] Degree elevation of *B*-spline curves, *Computer Aided Geometric Design* **1** (1984), 193–198.
[3] Generalized subdivision and convergence, *Computer Aided Geometric Design* **2** (1985), 69–75.

PRAUTZSCH, H., AND MICCHELLI, C. A.
Computing curves invariant under halving, *Computer Aided Geometric Design* **4** (1987), 133–140.

DeRose, T.
Geometric continuity: a parametrization independent measure of continuity for CAGD, Report No. UCB/CSD 86/255, University of California, Berkeley, 1985.

Rescorla, K. L.
[1] Cardinal interpolation: a bivariate polynomial example, *Computer Aided Geometric Design* **3** (1986), 313-321.
[2] C^1 trivariate polynomial interpolation, *Computer Aided Geometric Design* **4** (1987), 237-244.

Rosenfeld, A.
Survey picture processing 1982, *Computer Vision, Graphics, and Image Processing* **22** (1983), 339-387.

Sabin, M. A.
[1] A review of methods for scattered data. *In* Mathematical Methods in Computer Graphics and Design (K. W. Brodlie, ed.), Academic Press, New York, 1980.
[2] Non-rectangular surface patches suitable for inclusion in a *B*-spline surface. *In* Eurographics '83 (P. J. W. Ten Hagen, ed.), North-Holland, Amsterdam, 1983, 57-69.

Sablonnière, P.
Bernstein-Bézier methods for the construction of bivariate spline approximants, *Computer Aided Geometric Design* **2** (1985), 29-36.

Sarraga, R. F.
G^1 interpolation of generally unrestricted cubic Bézier curves, *Computer Aided Geometric Design* **4** (1987), 23-40.

Schmidt, R.
Fitting scattered surface data with large gaps. *In* Surfaces in Computer Aided Geometric Design (R. E. Barnhill and W. Boehm, eds.), North-Holland, Amsterdam, 1983, 185-190.

Schrack, G. F.
[1] Survey, computer graphics: a keyword-indexed bibliography for the year 1979, *Computer Graphics and Image Processing* **15** (1981), 45-78.
[2] Survey, computer graphics: a keyword-indexed bibliography for the year 1980, *Computer Graphics and Image Processing* **18** (1982) 145-187.

Schumaker, L. L.
Spline Functions: Basic Theory, Wiley, New York, 1981.

Schumaker, L. L., and Volk, W.
Efficient evaluation of multivariate polynomials, *Computer Aided Geometric Design* **3** (1986), 149-154.

Schwartz, Z.
Subdividing Bézier curves and surfaces. *In* Geometric Modeling (G. Farin, ed.), SIAM, Philadelphia, 1986, 55-66.

SEDERBERG, T. W.

[1] Planar piecewise algebraic curves, *Computer Aided Geometric Design* **1** (1984), 241–255.

[2] Degenerate parametric curves, *Computer Aided Geometric Design* **1** (1984), 301–307.

[3] Piecewise algebraic surface patches, *Computer Aided Geometric Design* **2** (1985), 53–59.

[4] Improperly parametrized rational curves, *Computer Aided Geometric Design* **3** (1986), 67–75.

[5] Algebraic geometry for surface and solid modeling. *In* Geometric Modeling (G. Farin, ed.), SIAM, Philadelphia, 1986, 29–42.

SEDERBERG, T. W., AND PARRY, S.

A comparison of three curve intersection algorithms. *In* Computer-Aided Design **18** (1986), 58–64.

SU, B., AND LIU, D.

An affine invariant theory and its application in computational geometry, *Scientia Sinica* **26** (1983), 259–272.

SU, B., HUA, X., AND XIN, Y.

Practical Differential Geometry, Science Press, Beijing, 1986 (in Chinese).

TILLER, W.

Rational B-splines for curve and surface representation, *IEEE Computer Graphics and Applications* **3** (1983), 61–69.

VAN WIJK, J. J.

Bicubic patches for approximating non-rectangular control-point meshes, *Computer Aided Geometric Design* **3** (1986), 1–13.

WHELAN, T.

A representation of a C^2 interpolant over triangles, *Computer Aided Geometric Design* **3** (1986), 53–66.

WORSEY, A. J.

A modified C^2 Coons' patch, *Computer Aided Geometric Design* **1** (1984), 357–360.

ZHOU, C., AND LIU, D.

The use of Bézier surface in design of ship hull surface, *Proc. ICCAS*, Italy, 1985, 379–386.

Index